Contents in Brief

Focal Points and Connections

About the Cover

Shapes, position, and patterns are featured topics in Kindergarten. Have students identify all of the shapes on the cover. Ask students to use words such as near/far to describe the position of the crab or the trees. Then have students describe the patterns they see on the cover.

Three Horizontally Aligned Programs

- Common vocabulary
- Common manipulatives
- Common technology
- Common Professional Development
- Aligned to NCTM Focal Points

Grade K
NSF-funded, integrated performance assessment aligned with investigative instruction

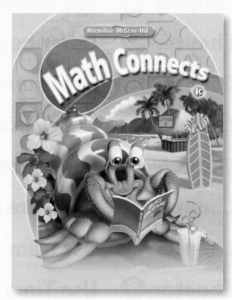

Grade K
Intensive Intervention for students two or more years below grade level (Tier 3 RTI)

The McGraw·Hill Companies

 Macmillan/McGraw-Hill

Send all inquiries to:
Macmillan/McGraw-Hill
8787 Orion Place
Columbus, OH 43240-4027

Volume 2
ISBN: 978-0-02-105736-8 *(Teacher Edition)*
MHID: 0-02-105736-2 *(Teacher Edition)*
ISBN: 978-0-02-105724-5 *(Student Edition)*
MHID: 0-02-105724-9 *(Student Edition)*

Printed in the United States of America.
5 6 7 8 9 10 RJE/LEH 16 15 14 13 12 11 10

Math Connects, Grade K

Benefits of Student Edition Organization

Math Connects, kindergarten Student Edition, has a 3-part organization.

1. **Start Smart** gets students ready for kindergarten with a review of key math standards that are prerequisites for kindergarten.

2. **Chapters 1–12** Each chapter has coherent groups of lessons focused on related kindergarten math standards and the NCTM Focal Points.

3. **Looking Ahead** prepares students for success with lessons on several key math standards.

The organization and pacing of *Math Connects* helps ensure in-depth coverage of all kindergarten standards and a good start for grade 1.

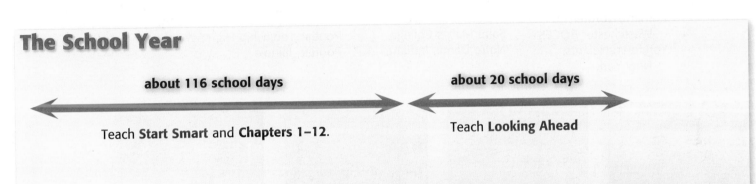

The School Year

about 116 school days

about 20 school days

Teach **Start Smart** and **Chapters 1–12**.

Teach **Looking Ahead**

Pacing Guide
Each chapter includes days for review and assessment.

Start Smart	12 days
Chapter 1	9 days
Chapter 2	10 days
Chapter 3	8 days
Chapter 4	10 days
Chapter 5	7 days
Chapter 6	9 days
Chapter 7	8 days
Chapter 8	8 days
Chapter 9	9 days
Chapter 10	10 days
Chapter 11	8 days
Chapter 12	8 days
Total	116 days
Looking Ahead	20 days

Mary Behr Altieri
Putnam/Northern
 Westchester BOCES
Yorktown Heights,
 New York

Don S. Balka
Professor Emeritus
Saint Mary's College
Notre Dame, Indiana

Roger Day, Ph.D.
Mathematics Department Chair
Pontiac Township High School
Pontiac, Illinois

Philip D. Gonsalves
Mathematics Coordinator
Alameda County Office
 of Education and
 California State
 University East Bay
Hayward, California

Ellen C. Grace
Mathematics Consultant
Albuquerque,
 New Mexico

Stephen Krulik
Professor Emeritus
 Mathematics Education
Temple University
Cherry Hill, New Jersey

Carol E. Malloy, Ph.D
Associate Professor of
 Mathematics Education
University of North
 Carolina at Chapel Hill
Chapel Hill, North
 Carolina

Rhonda J. Molix-Bailey
Mathematics Consultant
Mathematics by Design
Desoto, Texas

Lois Gordon Moseley
Staff Developer
NUMBERS: Mathematics
 Professional
 Development
Houston, Texas

Brian Mowry
Independent Math Educational
 Consultant/Part-Time Pre-K
 Instructional Specialist
Austin Independent School District
Austin, Texas

Christina L. Myren
Consultant Teacher
Conejo Valley Unified
    School District
Thousand Oaks, California

Jack Price
Professor Emeritus
California State
    Polytechnic University
Pomona, California

Mary Esther Reynosa
Instructional Specialist for
    Elementary Mathematics
Northside Independent
    School District
San Antonio, Texas

Rafaela M. Santa Cruz
SDSU/CGU Doctoral
    Program in Education
San Diego State University
San Diego, California

Robyn Silbey
Math Content Coach
Montgomery County
    Public Schools
Gaithersburg, Maryland

Kathleen Vielhaber
Mathematics Consultant
St. Louis, Missouri

Contributing Authors

Donna J. Long
Mathematics Consultant
Indianapolis, Indiana

FOLDABLES Dinah Zike
Educational Consultant
Dinah-Might Activities, Inc.
San Antonio, Texas

Consultants

Macmillan/McGraw-Hill wishes to thank the following professionals for their feedback. They were instrumental in providing valuable input toward the development of this program in these specific areas.

Mathematical Content

Viken Hovsepian
Professor of Mathematics
Rio Hondo College
Whittier, California

Grant A. Fraser, Ph.D.
Professor of Mathematics
California State University, Los Angeles
Los Angeles, California

Arthur K. Wayman, Ph.D.
Professor of Mathematics Emeritus
California State University, Long Beach
Long Beach, California

Assessment

Jane D. Gawronski, Ph.D.
Director of Assessment and Outreach
San Diego State University
San Diego, California

Cognitive Guided Instruction

Susan B. Empson, Ph.D.
Associate Professor of Mathematics
   and Science Education
University of Texas at Austin
Austin, Texas

English Learners

Cheryl Avalos
Mathematics Consultant
Los Angeles County Office of Education, Retired
Hacienda Heights, California

Kathryn Heinze
Graduate School of Education
Hamline University
St. Paul, Minnesota

Family Involvement

Paul Giganti, Jr.
Mathematics Education Consultant
Albany, California

Literature

David M. Schwartz
Children's Author, Speaker, Storyteller
Oakland, California

Vertical Alignment

Berchie Holliday
National Educational Consultant
Silver Spring, Maryland

Deborah A. Hutchens, Ed.D.
Principal
Norfolk Highlands Elementary
Chesapeake, Virginia

Reviewers

Each reviewer reviewed at least two chapters of the Student Edition, giving feedback and suggestions for improving the effectiveness of the mathematics instruction.

Ernestine D. Austin
Facilitating Teacher/Basic Skills Teacher
LORE School
Ewing, NJ

Susie Bellah
Kindergarten Teacher
Lakeland Elementary
Humble, TX

Megan Bennett
Elementary Math Coordinator
Hartford Public Schools
Hartford, CT

Susan T. Blankenship
5th Grade Teacher – Math
Stanford Elementary School
Stanford, KY

Wendy Buchanan
3rd Grade Teacher
The Classical Center at Vial
Garland, TX

Sandra Signorelli Coelho
Associate Director for Mathematics
PIMMS at Wesleyan University
Middletown, CT

Joanne DeMizio
Asst. Supt., Math and Science Curriculum
Archdiocese of New York
New York, NY

Anthony Dentino
Supervisor of Mathematics
Brick Township Schools
Brick, NJ

Lorrie L. Drennon
Math Teacher
Collins Middle School
Corsicana, TX

Ethel A. Edwards
Director of Curriculum and Instruction
Topeka Public Schools
Topeka, KS

Carolyn Elender
District Elementary Math Instructional
Specialist
Pasadena ISD
Pasadena, TX

Monica Engel
Educator Second Grade
Pioneer Elementary School
Bolingbrook, IL

Anna Dahinden Flynn
Math Teacher
Coulson Tough K-6 Elementary
The Woodlands, TX

Brenda M. Foxx
Principal
University Park Elementary
University Park, MD

Katherine A. Frontier
Elementary Teacher
Laidlaw
Western Springs, IL

Susan J. Furphy
5th Grade Teacher
Nisley Elementary
Grand Jct., CO

Peter Gatz
Student Services Coordinator
Brooks Elementary
Aurora, IL

Amber Gregersen
Teacher – 2nd Grade
Nisley Elementary
Grand Junction, Colorado

Roberta Grindle
Math and Language Arts Academic
Intervention Service Provider
Cumberland Head Elementary School
Plattsburgh, NY

Sr. Helen Lucille Habig, RSM
Assistant Superintendent/Mathematics
Archdiocese of Cincinnati
Cincinnati, Ohio

Holly L. Hepp
Math Facilitator
Barringer Academic Center
Charlotte, NC

Martha J. Hickman
2nd Grade Teacher
Dr. James Craik Elementary School
Pomfret, MD

Margie Hill
District Coordinating Teacher for
Mathematics, K-12
Blue Valley USD 229
Overland Park, KS

Carol H. Joyce
5th Grade Teacher
Nathanael Greene Elementary
Liberty, NC

Stella K. Kostante
Curriculum Coach
Roosevelt Elementary
Pittsburgh, PA

Pamela Fleming Lowe
Fourth Grade eMINTS Teacher
O'Neal Elementary
Poplar Bluff, MO

Lauren May, NBCT
4th Grade Teacher
May Watts Elementary School
Naperville, IL

Lorraine Moore
Grade 3 Math Teacher
Cowpens Elementary School
Cowpens, SC

Shannon L. Moorehead
4th Grade Teacher
Centervile Elementary
Anderson, SC

Gina M. Musselman, M.Ed
Kindergarten Teacher
Padeo Verde Elementary
Peoria, AZ

Jen Neufeld
3rd Grade Teacher
Kendall
Naperville, IL

Cathie Osiecki
K-5 Mathematics Coordinator
Middletown Public Schools
Middletown, CT

Phyllis L. Pacilli
Elementary Education Teacher
Fullerton Elementary
Addison, IL

Cindy Pearson
4th/5th Grade Teacher
John D. Spicer Elementary
Haltom City, TX 76137

Herminio M. Planas
Mathematics Curriculum Specialist
Administrative Offices-Bridgeport Public
Schools
Bridgeport, CT

Jo J. Puree
Educator
Lackamas Elementary
Yelm, WA

Teresa M. Reynolds
Third Grade Teacher
Forrest View Elementary
Everett, WA

Dr. John A. Rhodes
Director of Mathematics
Indian Prairie SD #204
Aurora, IL

Amy Romm
First Grade Teacher
Starline Elementary
Lake Havasu, AZ

Delores M. Rushing
Numeracy Coach
Dept. of Academic Services-Mathematics
Department
Washington, DC

Daniel L. Scudder
Mathematics/Technology Specialist
Boone Elementary
Houston, TX

Laura Seymour
Resource Teacher Leader –Elementary
Math & Science, Retired
Dearborn Public Schools
Dearborn, MI

Petra Siprian
Teacher
Army Trail Elementary School
Addison, IL

Sandra Stein
K-5 Mathematics Consultant
St. Clair County Regional Educational
Service Agency
Marysville, MI

Barb Stoflet
Curriculum Specialist
Roseville Area Schools
Roseville, MN

Kim Summers
Principal
Dynard Elementary
Chaptico, MD

Ann C. Teater
4th Grade Teacher
Lancaster Elementary
Lancaster, KY

Anne E. Tunney
Teacher
City of Erie School District
Erie, PA

Joylien Weathers
1st Grade Teacher
Mesa View Elementary
Grand Junction, CO

Christine F. Weiss
Third Grade Teacher
Robert C. Hill Elementary School
Romeoville, IL

Teacher Handbook

Mathematics Teacher Handbook

Table of Contents
PreK–12 Mathematics: Focus on Kindergarten

Welcome to
Math Connects

Concepts • Skills • Problem Solving

The only true vertically aligned PreK–12 Mathematics Curriculum

Math Connects offers three dimensions of vertical alignment.

❶ Content Design

Vertical content alignment is a process that ensures you and your students experience an articulated, coherent sequence of content from grade level to grade level. This provides you with the assurance that content is introduced, reinforced, and assessed at appropriate times in the series, eliminating gaps and unnecessary duplication. You are able to target your instruction to student needs because you are not teaching content intended to be covered later or that students have previously mastered.

❷ Instructional Design

Our strong vertical alignment in instructional approach from PreKindergarten through Algebra 2 provides a smooth transition for students from elementary to middle school to high school. Our common vocabulary, technology, manipulatives, lesson planning, and Data-Driven Decision Making reduces the confusion students often encounter when transitioning between grade levels without this built-in articulation.

❸ Visual Design

The student pages of *Math Connects* have a consistent visual design from grade to grade. This aids students' transition from elementary school to middle school and from middle school to Algebra 1. Students are more likely to succeed when they are already familiar with how to navigate student pages.

PreK-2

3–5

5 Keys to Success

① Backmapping

According to College Board research, about 80% of students who successfully complete Algebra 1 and Geometry by 10th grade attend and succeed in college. (Changing the Odds: Factors Increasing Access to College, 1990) *Math Connects* was conceived and developed by backmapping with the final result in mind—student success in Algebra 1 and beyond.

② Balanced, In-Depth Content

Math Connects was developed to specifically target the skills and topics that give students the most difficulty, such as Problem Solving, in each grade span.

Grades K–2	Grades 3–5
1. Problem Solving	1. Problem Solving
2. Money	2. Fractions
3. Time	3. Measurement
4. Measurement	4. Decimals
5. Fractions	5. Time
6. Computation	6. Algebra
Grades 6–8	**Grades 9–12**
1. Fractions	1. Problem Solving
2. Problem Solving	2. Fractions
3. Measurement	3. Algebra
4. Algebra	4. Geometry
5. Computation	5. Computation
	6. Probability

– *K–12 Math Market Analysis Survey,* Open Book Publishing, 2006

③ Ongoing Assessment

Math Connects includes diagnostic, formative, and summative assessment; data-driven instruction; intervention options; and performance tracking, as well as remediation, acceleration, and enrichment tools throughout the program.

④ Intervention and Differentiated Instruction

A three-tiered Response To Intervention (RTI) is provided.

TIER 1 **Daily Intervention** Reteach masters and Alternative Strategy suggestions address concepts from a different modality or learning style.

TIER 2 **Strategic Intervention** Teachers can use the myriad of intervention tips and ancillary materials, such as the Strategic Intervention Guide (1–5) and Study Guide and Intervention (6–8).

TIER 3 **Intensive Intervention** For students who are two or more years below grade level, *Math Triumphs* provides step-by-step instruction, vocabulary support, and data-driven decision making to help students succeed.

⑤ Professional Development

Math Connects includes many opportunities for teacher professional development. Additional learning opportunities in various formats—video, online, and on-site instruction—are fully aligned and articulated from Kindergarten through Algebra 2.

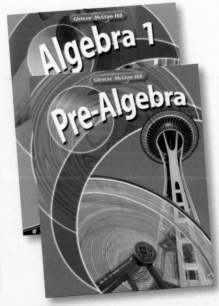

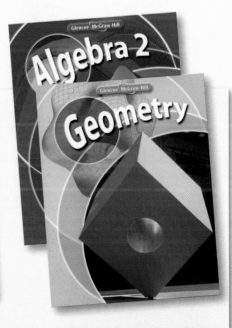

6–8　　　　　Pre-Algebra and Algebra 1　　　　　Geometry and Algebra 2

The Research Base

Continuous research with teachers, students, academician, and leading experts helps to build a solid foundation for *Math Connects.*

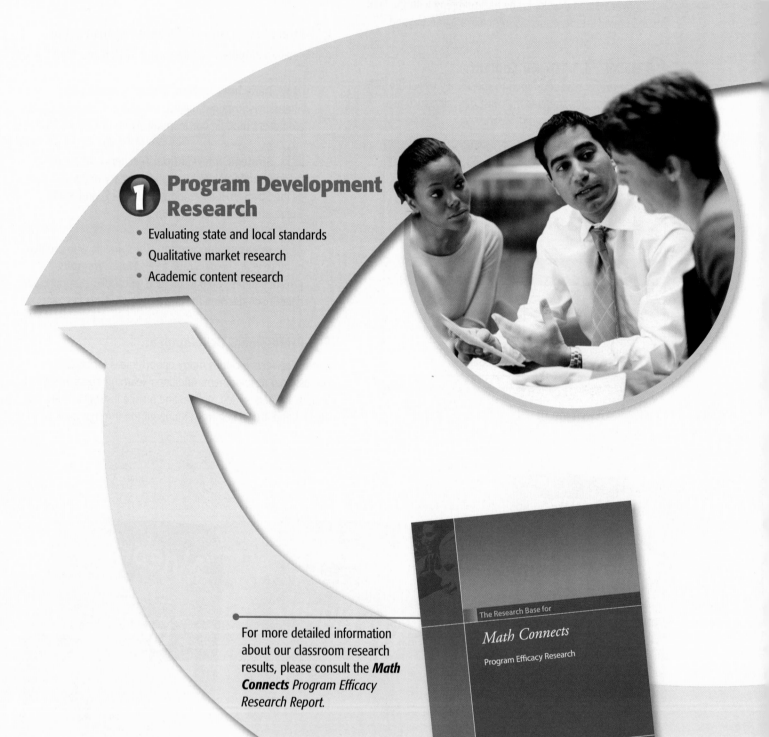

1 Program Development Research

- Evaluating state and local standards
- Qualitative market research
- Academic content research

For more detailed information about our classroom research results, please consult the *Math Connects* Program Efficacy Research Report.

The Research Base for

Math Connects

Program Efficacy Research

McGraw Hill Glencoe   McGraw Hill Macmillan McGraw-Hill

for *Math Connects*

2 Formative Research

- Pedagogical research base
- Classroom field tests
- Teacher advisory boards
- Academic consultants and reviewers

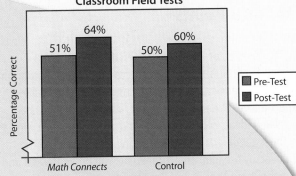

Student Data from 2006–2007 Classroom Field Tests

Percentage Correct

| Math Connects | | Control | |
| 51% | 64% | 50% | 60% |

■ Pre-Test
■ Post-Test

Classroom Type

Students using a field test of the *Math Connects* program (**experimental group**) had *higher* pre-test to post-test gains than students using other textbook programs (**control group**).

3 Summative Research

- Evidence of increased test scores
- Quasi-experimental program efficacy research
- Longitudinal studies
- Qualitative program evaluations

Access all *Math Connects* research at macmillanmh.com.

NCTM Focal Points

The NCTM Focal Points

In 2006, the National Council of Teachers of Mathematics (NCTM) released the Curriculum Focal Points for Pre-Kindergarten through Grade 8 Mathematics. These Curriculum Focal Points focus on the most important mathematical topics for each grade level. The concepts are vertically-aligned and expect a level of depth, complexity, and rigor at each level. They comprise related ideas, concepts, skills, and procedures that form the foundation for understanding and lasting learning. The Focal Points emphasize depth versus breadth. The Focal Points will be addressed and highlighted throughout our PreK-8 and Pre-Algebra series.

What is the benefit to you in your classroom?

These Focal Points identify content for each grade level that should be mastered in order for your students to have true mathematical understanding—being able to not only calculate the answer, but to explain the answer and how to apply the calculation. The NCTM Focal Points were used as the basis in the development of *Math Connects.* The authors have incorporated the Focal Points into the content to assist you in building depth of understanding.

NCTM Focal Points for Grade K	Supporting Chapters in *Math Connects*
Number and Operations	Chapters 1, 2, 4, 6, 8, 11, 12
Geometry	Chapter 10
Measurement	Chapters 7, 9
Connections to the Focal Points	
Data Analysis	Chapters 1, 5
Geometry	Chapter 10
Algebra	Chapter 3

KEY

GK-FP1 Grade K Focal Point 1	**GK-FP5C** Grade K Focal Point 5 Connection
GK-FP2 Grade K Focal Point 2	**GK-FP6C** Grade K Focal Point 6 Connection
GK-FP3 Grade K Focal Point 3	
GK-FP4C Grade K Focal Point 4 Connection	

The Curriculum Focal Points identify key mathematical ideas for this grade. They are not discrete topics or a checklist to be mastered; rather, they provide a framework for the majority of instruction at a particular grade level and the foundation for future mathematics study. The complete document may be viewed at www.nctm.org/focalpoints.

GK-FP1 *Number and Operations:* **Representing, comparing, and ordering whole numbers and joining and separating sets**

Children use numbers, including written numerals, to represent quantities and to solve quantitative problems, such as counting objects in a set, creating a set with a given number of objects, comparing and ordering sets or numerals by using both cardinal and ordinal meanings, and modeling simple joining and separating situations with objects. They choose, combine, and apply effective strategies for answering quantitative questions, including quickly recognizing the number in a small set, counting and producing sets of given sizes, counting the number in combined sets, and counting backward.

GK-FP2 *Geometry:* **Describing shapes and space**

Children interpret the physical world with geometric ideas (e.g., shape, orientation, spatial relations) and describe it with corresponding vocabulary. They identify, name, and describe a variety of shapes, such as squares, triangles, circles, rectangles, (regular) hexagons, and (isosceles) trapezoids presented in a variety of ways (e.g., with different sizes or orientations), as well as such three-dimensional shapes as spheres, cubes, and cylinders. They use basic shapes and spatial reasoning to model objects in their environment and to construct more complex shapes.

GK-FP3 *Measurement:* **Ordering objects by measurable attributes**

Children use measurable attributes, such as length or weight, to solve problems by comparing and ordering objects. They compare the lengths of two objects both directly (by comparing them with each other) and indirectly (by comparing both with a third object), and they order several objects according to length.

Connections to the Focal Points

GK-FP4C *Data Analysis:* Children sort objects and use one or more attributes to solve problems. For example, they might sort solids that roll easily from those that do not. Or they might collect data and use counting to answer such questions as, "What is our favorite snack?" They re-sort objects by using new attributes (e.g., after sorting solids according to which ones roll, they might re-sort the solids according to which ones stack easily).

GK-FP5C *Geometry:* Children integrate their understandings of geometry, measurement, and number. For example, they understand, discuss, and create simple navigational directions (e.g., "Walk forward 10 steps, turn right, and walk forward 5 steps").

GK-FP6C *Algebra:* Children identify, duplicate, and extend simple number patterns and sequential and growing patterns (e.g., patterns made with shapes) as preparation for creating rules that describe relationships.

Program Philosophy

Balanced Instruction, Vertically-Aligned from Grades PreK through Algebra 1

The vertical alignment of *Math Connects* PreK-8 and *Algebra 1* incorporates a balance of instruction throughout. These programs provide students a balanced approach to mathematics by:

- investigating concepts and building conceptual understanding.
- developing, reinforcing, and mastering computational and procedural skills.
- applying mathematics to problem-solving situations.

This sequence of Student Edition pages illustrates the vertically-aligned development of the conceptual understanding and corresponding computational and procedural skills for an important algebra topic.

Primary Students use two-color counters to model addition sentences. This activity forms a basis for future understanding of and success in solving algebraic equations.

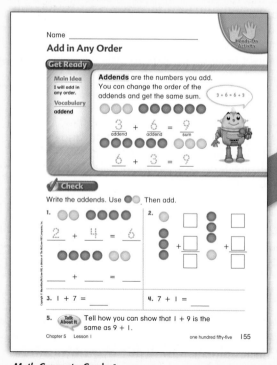

Math Connects, Grade 1,
Student Edition, page 155

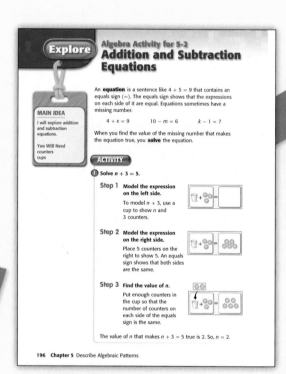

Math Connects, Grade 4,
Student Edition, page 196

Intermediate Students build on their experience with counters to using cups and counters to model and solve addition and subtraction equations. The exercises are designed to help students bridge the gap from using cups and counters to solving equations symbolically.

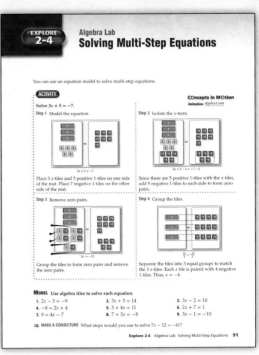

Glencoe Algebra 1,
Student Edition, page 91

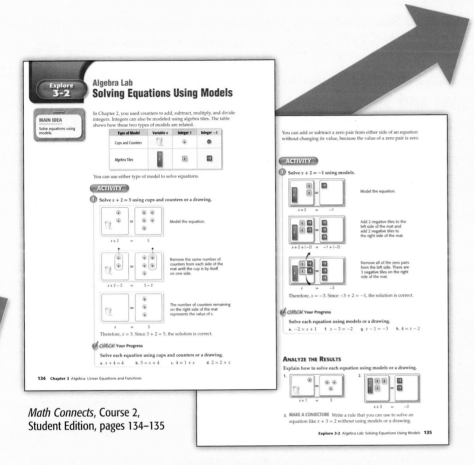

Math Connects, Course 2,
Student Edition, pages 134–135

Algebra 1 Students continue the use of algebra tiles to investigate solving multi-step equations. In the next lesson, students apply the procedure developed in the Algebra Lab to a symbolic approach.

Middle School Students represent the variable *x* as a cup, as a counter, or as a written *x*. In this Algebra Lab, students make the transition from cups and counters to the more abstract algebra tiles. In the next lesson, students solve simple equations symbolically.

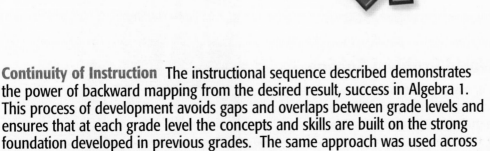

Continuity of Instruction The instructional sequence described demonstrates the power of backward mapping from the desired result, success in Algebra 1. This process of development avoids gaps and overlaps between grade levels and ensures that at each grade level the concepts and skills are built on the strong foundation developed in previous grades. The same approach was used across all strands throughout the entire PreK-12 series.

Program Philosophy
Balance of Instruction

Relevant Problem Solving

Math Connects provides students with the appropriate development of problem-solving strategies, skills, and applications from PreK through grade 5. In grades 6–8, students continue to learn and apply problem-solving skills and strategies. Students are provided with ongoing opportunities to apply their math skills and solve problems using visual thinking, logical reasoning, number sense, and algebra.

Problem-Solving Strategies and Skills

Problem-Solving Strategy or **Skill** lessons introduce students to multiples methods for solving problems all using the *four-step* plan.

- **U**nderstand
- **P**lan
- **S**olve
- **C**heck

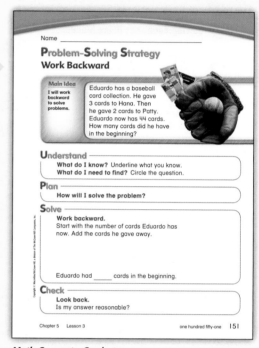

Math Connects, Grade 2
Student Edition, page 151

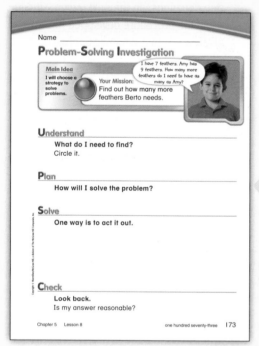

Math Connects, Grade 1
Student Edition, page 173

Problem-Solving Investigations

Problem-Solving Investigation lessons help students learn to choose appropriate strategies and apply them in problem-solving situations.

Real-World Problem Solving

Each chapter has a Problem Solving lesson that makes a tie to another discipline. These lessons encourage students to see problem solving in real-world applications.

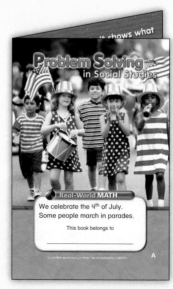

Math Connects, Kindergarten
Student Edition, pages 143–144

Real-World Problem Solving Readers

Fiction and nonfiction leveled readers extend problem-solving skills and strategies and make real-world applications. The books are provided for On Level, Sheltered English, and Spanish readers.

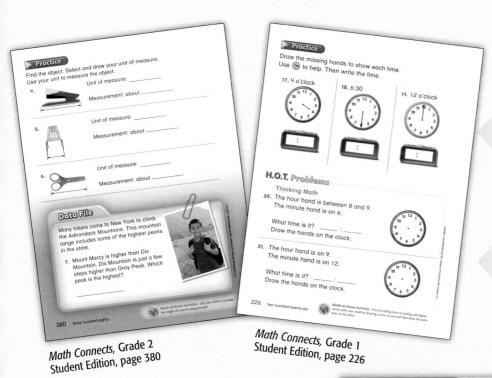

Math Connects, Grade 2
Student Edition, page 380

Math Connects, Grade 1
Student Edition, page 226

Data File Problems

The Data File features present math in real-world settings. Students are asked to use data to solve problems.

H.O.T. Problems

H.O.T. Problems require students to use **Higher Order Thinking** skills to solve problems.

Looking Ahead

Looking Ahead lessons introduce important concepts and skills that students can use.

Math Connects, Kindergarten
Student Edition, pages LA1–LA2

Comprehensive Assessment System

PRINT SOLUTIONS

Data-Driven Decision Making

Math Connects offers frequent and meaningful assessment of student progress within the curriculum structure and printed teacher support materials. See pages T22 and T23 for digital assessment solutions.

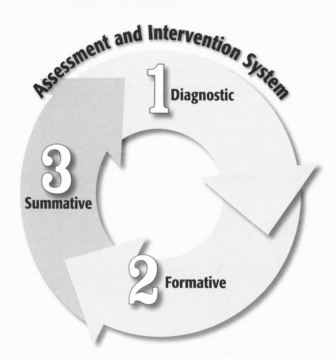

Assessment and Intervention System

1 Diagnostic

2 Formative

3 Summative

1 Diagnostic

Initial Assessment Assess students' knowledge **at the beginning of the year** with the *Diagnostic and Placement Tests*. This booklet will help you determine whether your students need additional materials and resources to meet grade-level standards.

Entry–Level Assessment Assess students' prior knowledge **at the beginning of a chapter or lesson** with one of the following options.

Student Edition
• Are You Ready?

Teacher Edition
• Intervention Options
• 5-Minute Check

Additional Resources
• Chapter Resource Masters, Chapter Diagnostic Test

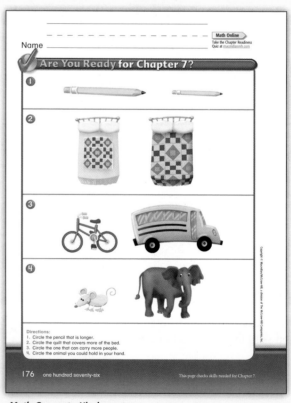

Name _____

Math Online
Take the Chapter Readiness Quiz at macmillanmh.com

Are You Ready for Chapter 7?

①
②
③
④

Directions:
1. Circle the pencil that is longer.
2. Circle the quilt that covers more of the bed.
3. Circle the one that can carry more people.
4. Circle the animal you could hold in your hand.

176 one hundred seventy-six   This page checks skills needed for Chapter 7.

Math Connects, Kindergarten
Student Edition, page 176

Formative

Progress Monitoring Determine if students are progressing adequately as you teach each lesson. Use the assessments to differentiate lesson instruction and practice.

Student Edition
- Mid-Chapter Check
- Find the Error
- Check What You Know
- Talk About It
- Writing in Math
- Study Guide and Review
- Foldables™

Teacher Edition
- Alternate Teaching Strategy
- Step 4 (Assess) of the Teaching Plan
- Quick Check
- Data-Driven Decision Making

Additional Resources

Chapter Resource Masters
- Mid-Chapter Test
- 3 Quizzes

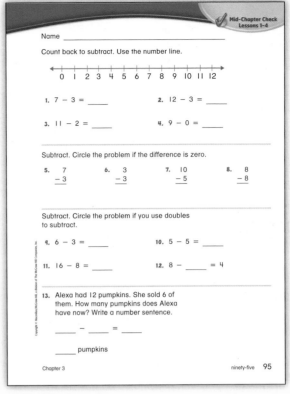

Math Connects, Grade 2
Student Edition, page 95

Summative

Summative Evaluation Assess student success in learning the concepts in each chapter.

Student Edition
- Chapter Test
- Test Practice
- Foldables™

Teacher Edition
- Data-Driven Decision Making

Additional Resources

Chapter Resource Masters
- Oral Assessment
- Listening Assessment
- 4 Leveled Chapter Tests
- Cumulative Test

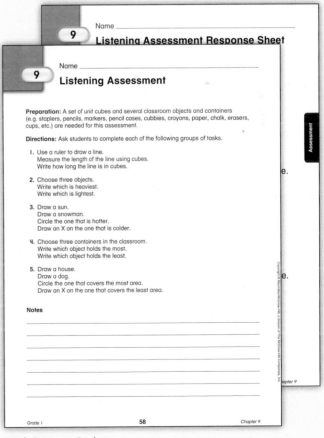

Math Connects, Grade 1
Chapter 9 Resource Masters, pages 58–59

 # Comprehensive Assessment System

Data-Driven Decision Making

Math Connects provides digital assessment options to create, customize, administer, and instantly score a variety of assessments. These digital solutions offer the same quality assessments and reporting as the print resources in easy-to-use technology tools.

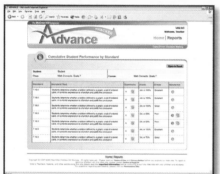

Math Connects, Grade 4

Math Connects, Grade 1

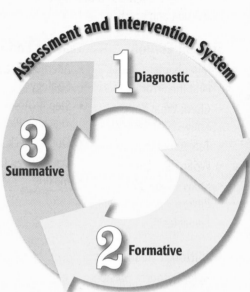

Advance Tracker helps teachers administer online tests, diagnose student achievement, and create prescriptive reports for a student or class.

ExamView Assessment Suite allows teachers to create and customize their own assessment and assignments. Print in one or two columns to match state test.

1 Diagnostic

Initial Assessment Assess students' knowledge **at the beginning of the year** with the *Diagnostic and Placement Tests.* These assessments will help you determine whether your students need additional materials and resources to meet grade-level standards.

ExamView Assessment Suite
- Diagnostic and Placement Tests

- Diagnostic and Placement Tests

Entry–Level Assessment Assess students' prior knowledge **at the beginning of a chapter or lesson.**

Math Online macmillanmh.com Students can complete online tests and the results are emailed to the teacher.
- Chapter Readiness

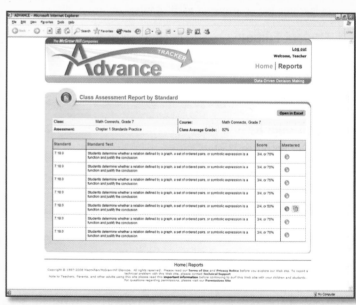

Math Connects Grade 2 Advance Tracker

Formative

Progress Monitoring Determine if students are progressing adequately as you teach each lesson. Use the assessments to differentiate lesson instruction and practice.

- Mid-Chapter Test
- Study Guide and Review

Math Online macmillanmh.com

- Self-Check Quizzes

Math Connects, Kindergarten, Advance Tracker

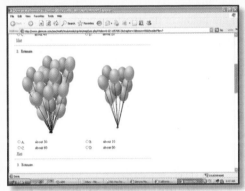
Math Connects, Grade 1, Self-Check Quiz

Summative

Summative Evaluation Assess students' success in learning the concepts in each chapter.

- Chapter Tests
- Cumulative Standardized Test Practice

- Chapter Tests
- Cumulative Standardized Test Practice

Math Online macmillanmh.com

- Chapter Tests

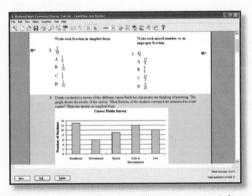
Math Connects, Grade 2, ExamView Assessment Suite

Math Connects, Grade 1, Advance Tracker

Differentiated Instruction

Reaching All Learners

Math Connects, provides extensive support for reaching all learners.

Every chapter and lesson includes suggestions for identifying and meeting your students' needs. Strategies include differentiation in pacing and student grouping, alternate approaches, ways to enhance instruction with manipulatives, questions to promote higher-order thinking, and language hints.

Personalize instruction for:

BL Students who are below or approaching grade level

ELL English language learners

AL Students who are above or beyond grade level

Leveled Exercise Sets

The assignments for each lesson are leveled for students.

BL Below or Approaching Grade Level

OL On Grade Level

AL Above or Beyond Grade Level

Leveled Resources

All of the blackline masters and transparencies that accompany the program, as well as all of the Teacher Edition pages, are available on the **TeacherWorks Plus™ CD-ROM.** Resources and assignments are leveled for students who are:

BL Below or Approaching Grade Level

OL On Grade Level

AL Above or Beyond Grade Level

ELL English Language Learners

Learning Stations

Cross-curricular learning centers offer students guided opportunities to explore chapter concepts as individuals or in small groups. Content areas include:

- Science
- Health
- Social Studies
- Writing
- Reading
- Music
- Art

Learning Station cards are English on one side and Spanish on the other.

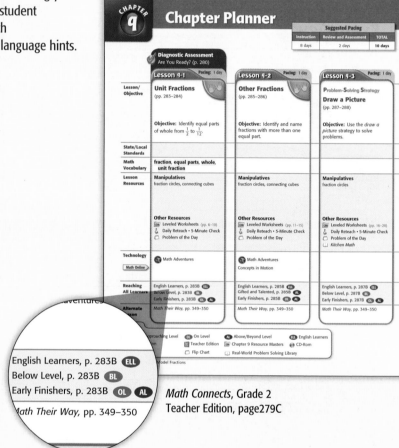

Math Connects, Grade 2
Teacher Edition, page279C

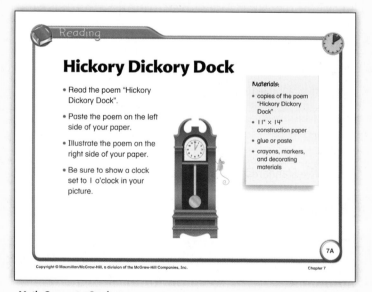

Math Connects, Grade 1
Learning Station Card 7A

Advanced Learners

Acceleration and Enrichment Resources and assignments for students who are above level may be used with advanced learners. In particular, the **Enrich Masters** provide students with valuable opportunities for extending your lessons.

ELL English Language Learners

Our authors have identified seven keys for effective instruction with English language learner students and used them throughout the program.

1. Simplify language, not concepts.
2. Activate background knowledge.
3. Teach in multiple modalities.
4. Use core vocabulary and common use verbs.
5. Express mathematical understanding in different ways.
6. Incorporate higher-level problem-solving skills.
7. Provide a mathematics-rich classroom environment.

The English Language Learners Guide provides additional support for English language learner students that can be used alone or with core instruction in the Student Edition and Teacher Edition.

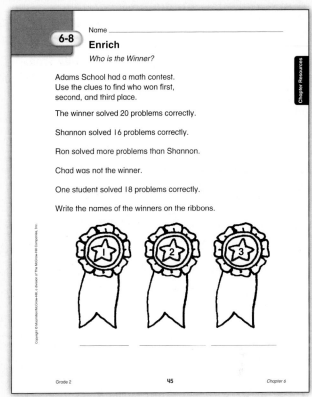

Math Connects, Grade 2,
Chapter 6 Resource Masters, page 45

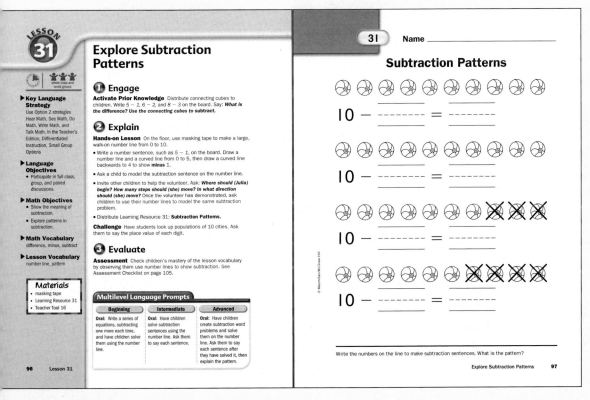

Math Connects, Kindergarten
ELL Guide, pages 96–97

Blending Your Instruction
Basal – NSF-Funded – Tier 3 Intervention

Math Connects, IMPACT Mathematics, and *Math Triumphs* provide a three-pronged approach to mathematics instruction. This unique combination provides built-in strategies to easily tip the balance of instruction to a more conceptual approach or to a more skills-based approach, depending on the needs of your students.

These programs are horizontally aligned in the following ways.

- Common vocabulary
- Common manipulatives
- Common teacher planning guides
- Common technology
- Common authors
- Common professional development

Basal Program–Focused on Comprehensive Instruction

NSF Program–Focused on Investigations

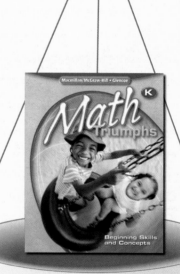

Intensive Intervention (Tier 3 RTI)–Focused on Skills

RTI (Response to Intervention)

In the *Math Connects* Teacher Editions, the Data-Driven Decision Making chart provides a comprehensive RTI (Response to Intervention) beginning with diagnostic review and continuing with prescriptions at all three RTI tiers.

Tier 1 – Leveled exercise sets and leveled resources

Tier 2 – Strategic Intervention Guide (1–5), Study Guide and Intervention (6–8)

Tier 3 – Intensive Intervention, *Math Triumphs*

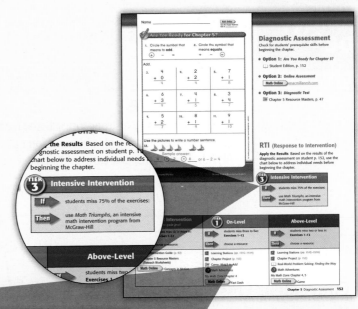

Math Connects, Grade 1
Teacher Edition, page 152

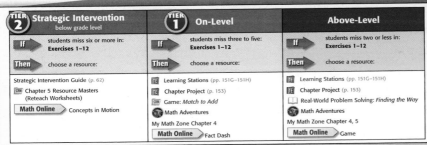

The Chapter Planner, also in the Teacher Edition of *Math Connects,* references alternative lessons found in *IMPACT Mathematics.* These lessons provide opportunities for investigative instruction with hands-on explorations.

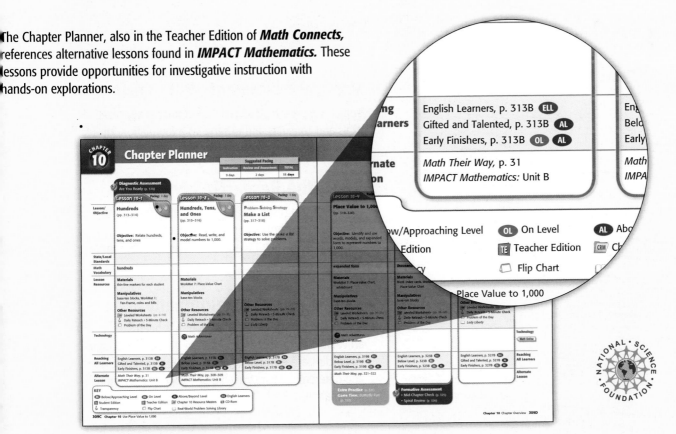

Math Connects, Grade 2
Teacher Edition, pages 309C–309D

Planning for Success

Ease of Use

Math Connects has a strong instructional model that includes differentiated instructional options, reteaching, reinforcement, and extension options, Teacher Tips to help address various learners, Pre-AP/Advanced items, and assessment linked with instruction.

Convenient Lesson Planning at Your Fingertips

The **Chapter Overview** helps you plan your instruction by showing the objectives to be covered, suggested pacing, and coverage of Focal Points.

TeacherWorks™ Plus

This electronic lesson planner contains multi-purpose management software including the Teacher Edition pages, program blackline masters, and daily calendars that make planning a snap.

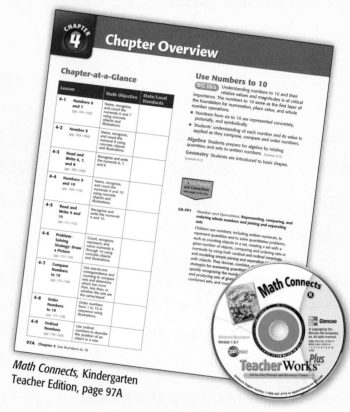

Math Connects, Kindergarten Teacher Edition, page 97A

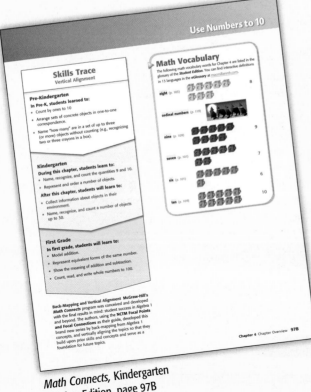

Math Connects, Kindergarten Teacher Edition, page 97B

Vertical Alignment Skills Trace

Topics are presented to build upon prior grade level skills and concepts and to serve as a foundation for future topics.

What the Research Says

Citations from research help to validate *Math Connects* program. An additional Research Bibliography can be found in the **Teacher Reference Handbook.**

Professional Development

Targeted professional development has been articulated throughout the program. Actual classroom video clips are especially helpful when planning lessons and differentiating instruction. See page T32 for more information.

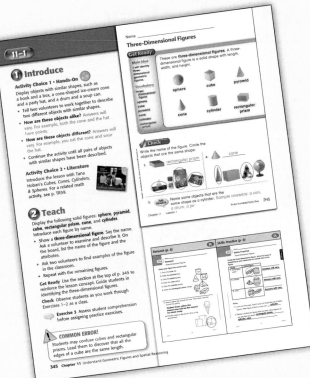

Math Connects, Grade 2
Teacher Edition, page 345

Four-Step Teaching Plan

Organizes your instruction as you **Focus** and **Teach** and help your students **Practice** and **Assess** what they've learned.

Scaffolding Questions

Each lesson contains **Scaffolding Questions** for you to use to help students investigate and understand the main ideas of the lesson.

Vertical Alignment

Vertical Alignment at the beginning of each chapter shows the objectives that lead into and follow the current lesson's content for a coherent PreK–12 scope and sequence.

Differentiated Practice

Because most classrooms include students at a wide range of ability levels, **Differentiated Practice** allows you to customize your assignments.

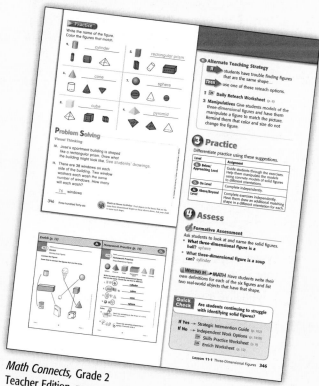

Math Connects, Grade 2
Teacher Edition, page 346

Planning for Success
State-of-the-Art Technology

Math Connects provides fully integrated technology resources for teachers, students, and parents.

For Teachers

 TeacherWorks™ Plus is your all-in-one planner and resource center.
- entire Teacher Edition
- all print ancillaries
- electronic lesson planner

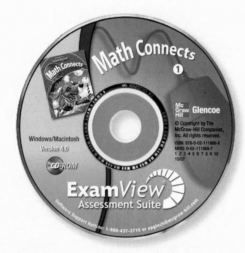

 ExamView® Assessment Suite allows teachers to create and customize their own assessment and assignments.

New features:
- correlated to state standards
- online content update
- one- or two-column formatting

Advance Learner Management System helps you track progress and differentiate your instruction.
- formative assessments aligned to standards
- links to intervention help

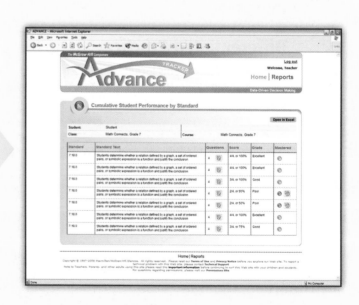

Other Technology: My Math Zone (CD-ROM)
Math Songs (English and Spanish, CD-ROM)

For Students

 StudentWorks™ Plus is your students' backpack solution.
- entire Student Edition
- all student worksheets
- links to **Math Online**

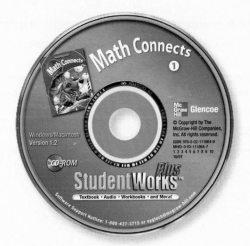

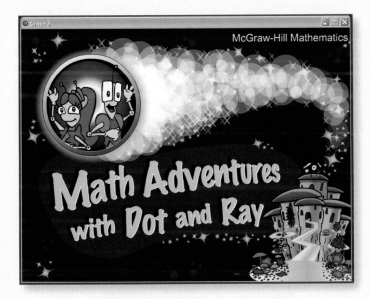

Math Online provides a wealth of resources – convenient for students and parents!

- Self-Check Quizzes
- Personal Tutor
- Concepts in Motion
- Math Adventures with Dot and Ray
- eGlossary (14 languages)
- Math Tool Chest
- And much, much more!

Math Online *Math Connect's* **eBook** is easy to use, easy to read, and packed with features.

- links to online study tools and resources right from the page
- includes audio

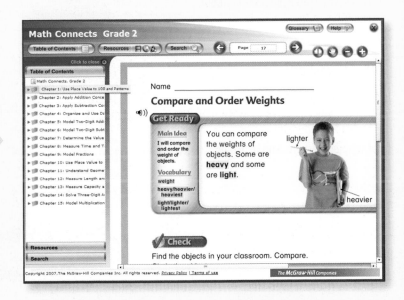

Other Technology: Math Adventures with Dot and Ray (CD-ROM)
Math Tool Chest (CD-ROM)

PreK-12 Data-Driven Professional Development

McGraw-Hill Professional Development (MHPD) provides a comprehensive plan for mathematics that is fully aligned and articulated with **Math Connects K–8** and the **Glencoe Mathematics** high school series.

Professional Development Needs	Online Courses	DVD Workshops	Video Library	Teach-Use-Succeed	Ready-Access Math
Has immediate classroom application	✓	✓	✓	✓	✓
Builds content knowledge	✓	✓			✓
Promotes best teaching practices		✓	✓		
Supports new and experienced teachers	✓	✓	✓	✓	✓
Allows customization of courses	✓	✓			✓
Can be self-paced	✓	✓		✓	✓
Adaptable for various timeframes	✓	✓	✓	✓	✓
Is grade-level specific			✓	✓	✓
Promotes a learning community	✓	✓			✓
Provides vertically-aligned content	✓	✓	✓		✓
Helps with RTI (Response to Intervention), Tiers 1–3	✓	✓	✓		✓

Use students' mathematics achievement data to help develop a targeted Professional Development Plan.

Accredited Online Courses
(available for purchase)
- Watch video clips of math classrooms
  Complete interactive exercises
  Develop electronic portfolios.
- Complete each 3- to 5-hour online module one segment at a time.
- University credit (additional tuition charge)

DVD Workshops
- Watch video clips of classroom mathematics lessons and commentaries by leading educators.
- Complete lessons and activities.

MHPD Online
- Access this online Professional Development resource for K–12 educators.
- Link to relevant Web sites.
- Download grade-level student resources.

McGraw-Hill Professional

- Professional Development Web sites
- McGraw-Hill's Experienced Consultants
- Ready Access Math Training Materials
- Textbook Implementation Modules
- Mini Clip Video Library
- Video Workshops Mentor-led or Self-Study
- Accredited Online Courses

Development Portfolio

Video Library | Math Online
- Access hundreds of K–12 video clips.
- See clips that illustrate mathematics content and instructional strategies.
- Watch demonstrations or commentaries by math specialists

Teach-Use-Succeed Textbook Implementation Modules
- Watch an experienced teacher demonstrate the *Math Connects* K–8 Student Editions, Teacher Editions, and program ancillaries
- Online or DVD

Ready-Access Math, Personalized Professional Development
- Access training materials for nearly 300 mathematics professional development lessons.
- Create a customized sequence of professional development sessions.
- Deliver 45–60 minute after-school professional development sessions.

Teacher Edition

Macmillan McGraw-Hill

Math Connects

k

Lemonade
5¢

BEACH VACATIONS

Volume 2

Authors

**Altieri • Balka • Day • Gonsalves • Grace • Krulik
Malloy • Molix-Bailey • Moseley • Mowry • Myren
Price • Reynosa • Santa Cruz • Silbey • Vielhaber**

Macmillan/McGraw-Hill

T60217

Contents

Start Smart

Contents

Focal Points and Connections

GK-FP4C

Contents

CHAPTER
2

Use Numbers 0 to 5

CHAPTER 3

Describe Position and Patterns

v

Contents

CHAPTER 4

Use Numbers to 10

Contents

Focal Points and Connections

GK-FP4C

Contents

CHAPTER 6

Use Numbers to 20

Contents

Focal Points
and Connections

GK-FP3

CHAPTER
7

Compare Measurements

Contents

Focal Points and Connections

GK-FP1

Contents

Focal Points and Connections

GK-FP3

Contents

Focal Points
and Connections

GK-FP2

CHAPTER
10

Describe Geometric Figures

Contents

Focal Points and Connections

GK-FP1

CHAPTER 11

Model Addition

Contents

CHAPTER 12 **Model Subtraction**

Looking Ahead

Problem-Solving Projects

Contents

Student Handbook

Photo Credits

WorkMat 1: Story Mat

WorkMat 2: Two-Part Mat

WorkMat 3: Graphing Mat

WorkMat 4: Sorting Mat/T-CHART

WorkMat 5: Ten-Frame

WorkMat 6: Ten-Frames

WorkMat 7: Part-Part-Whole

WorkMat 8: Number Lines

Chapter Overview

Chapter-at-a-Glance

In Chapter 8, students learn to name, recognize, and count the quantities from 21 to 30. They also learn to compare numbers and to estimate.

Lesson	Math Objective	State/Local Standards
8-1 **Numbers 21–25** (pp. 205–206)	Count, recognize, and write the numerals 21 through 25.	
8-2 **Numbers 26–30** (pp. 207–208)	Count, recognize, and write the numerals 26 through 30.	
8-3 **Problem-Solving Strategy: Make a Model** (pp. 209–210)	Count, recognize, and write the numerals 21 though 30.	
8-4 **Compare Numbers to 30** (pp. 213–214)	Count to compare groups and numbers to determine which has more, which has less or which is the same or equal.	
8-5 **Order Numbers to 30** (pp. 215–216)	Order numbers from 0 to 30 in sequence.	
8-6 **Estimate** (pp. 217–218)	Estimate a group of objects and then count them.	

Use Numbers Beyond 20

BIG Idea As students increase their number sense, it is important that they also begin to recognize and use numbers larger than 20. Kindergarten students should be able to count, recognize, represent, name, and order numbers up to 30. In preparation for first grade, students will work on some basic estimation skills as well.

Algebra Students prepare for algebra by beginning to use manipulatives to compare numbers. *Lessons 8-3 and 8-4*

Focal Points and Connections

GK-FP1 *Number and Operations:* **Representing, comparing, and ordering whole numbers and joining and separating sets**

Children use numbers, including written numerals, to represent quantities and to solve quantitative problems, such as counting objects in a set, creating a set with a given number of objects, comparing and ordering sets or numerals by using both cardinal and ordinal meanings, and modeling simple joining and separating situations with objects. They choose, combine, and apply effective strategies for answering quantitative questions, including quickly recognizing the number in a small set, counting and producing sets of given sizes, counting the number in combined sets, and counting backward.

Skills Trace
Vertical Alignment

PreKindergarten

In PreK, students learn to:
- Understand that number represents quantity.
- Enumerate small sets by subitizing (nonverbal counting of sets of five or fewer).
- Practice addition, subtraction, and division by using manipulatives and other concrete objects.

Kindergarten

During this chapter, students learn to:
- Count, recognize, represent, name, and order a number of objects up to 30.
- Know that the larger numbers describe sets with more objects in them than the smaller numbers have.
- Recognize when an estimate is reasonable.

After this chapter, students will learn to:
- Understand and describe simple additions and subtractions.
- Use concrete objects to determine the answers to addition and subtraction problems (for two numbers that are each less than 10).

First Grade

In first grade, students will learn to:
- Count, read, and write whole numbers up to 100.
- Make precise calculations and check the validity of the results from the context of the problem.
- Make reasonable estimation when comparing larger or smaller numbers.

Backmapping and Vertical Alignment McGraw-Hill's *Math Connects* program was conceived and developed with the final results in mind: student success in Algebra 1 and beyond. The authors, using the **NCTM Focal Points and Focal Connections** as their guide, developed this brand new series by backmapping from Algebra 1 concepts, and vertically aligning the topics so that they build upon prior skills and concepts and serve as a foundation for future topics.

Math Vocabulary

The following math vocabulary words for Chapter 8 are listed in the glossary of the **Student Edition**. You can find interactive definitions in 13 languages in the **eGlossary** at macmillanmh.com.

about How many? (p. 217)

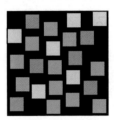

estimate (p. 217)

Visual Vocabulary Cards Use Visual Vocabulary Cards 2, 4, 13, 14, 20, and 25 to introduce the vocabulary in this chapter. (The Define/Example/Ask routine is printed on the back of each card.)

estimate

Chapter Planner

Suggested Pacing		
Instruction	**Review and Assessment**	**TOTAL**
6 days	2 days	**8 days**

Diagnostic Assessment
Are You Ready? (p. 192)

	Lesson 8-1 Pacing: 1 day	**Lesson 8-2** Pacing: 1 day	**Lesson 8-3** Pacing: 1 day
Lesson/ Objective	**Numbers 21–25** (pp. 205–206) **Objective:** Count, recognize, and write the numerals 21 through 25.	**Numbers 26–30** (pp. 207–208) **Objective:** Count, recognize, and write the numerals 26 through 30.	**Problem-Solving Strategy** **Make a Model** (pp. 209–210) **Objective:** Count, recognize, and write the numerals 21 through 30.
State/Local Standards			
Math Vocabulary			
Lesson Resources	**Materials** drawing paper, crayons, WorkMat 5: Ten-Frames **Manipulatives** two-colored counters **Other Resources** CRM Leveled Worksheets (pp.6–9) Daily Reteach Problem of the Day	**Materials** writing paper, pencils, paper ten-frames, glue, small paper squares **Manipulatives** two-colored counters **Other Resources** CRM Leveled Worksheets (pp. 10–13) Daily Reteach Problem of the Day	**Materials** poster board, sticky notes, pictures of flowers **Manipulatives** two-colored counters, connecting cubes **Other Resources** CRM Leveled Worksheets (pp. 14–18) Daily Reteach Problem of the Day *What are Seasons?*
Technology Math Online	Math Adventures	Math Adventures Concepts in Motion	
Reaching All Learners	Below Level, p. 205B **BL** English Learners, p. 205B **ELL** Early Finishers, p. 205B **OL** **AL**	Gifted and Talented, p. 207B **AL** English Learners, p. 207B **ELL** Early Finishers, p. 207B **OL** **AL**	Gifted and Talented, p. 209B **AL** English Learners, p. 209B **ELL** Early Finishers, p. 209B **OL** **AL**
Alternate Lesson	*Math Their Way*, p. 47	*Math Their Way*, pp. 44–45	

Formative Assessment
Mid-Chapter Check (p. 211)

Game Time: Peanut Roundup! (p. 212)

KEY

BL Below/ Approaching Level	**OL** On Level	**AL** Above/Beyond Level	**ELL** English Learners
SE Student Edition	**TE** Teacher Edition	**CRM** Chapter 8 Resource Masters	CD-Rom
Transparency	Flip Chart	Real-World Problem Solving Library	

Lesson 8-4 Pacing: 1 day	**Lesson 8-5** Pacing: 1 day	**Lesson 8-6** Pacing: 1 day	**Lesson/ Objective**
Compare Numbers to 30 (pp. 213–214) **Objective:** Count to compare groups and numbers to determine which has more, which has less, or which is the same or equal.	**Order Numbers to 30** (pp. 215–216) **Objective:** Order numbers from 0 to 30 in sequence.	**Estimate** (pp. 217–218) **Objective:** Estimate a group of objects and then count them.	
			State/Local Standards
		about estimate	**Math Vocabulary**
Materials pencils, construction paper, dry cereal, 1–30 number cards, glue, index cards, yarn, markers **Manipulatives** 2-colored counters, color tiles, connecting cubes **Other Resources** CRM Leveled Worksheets (pp. 19–22) Daily Reteach Problem of the Day	**Materials** number lines, masking tape, number cards, paper, pencils **Other Resources** CRM Leveled Worksheets (pp. 23–26) Daily Reteach Problem of the Day	**Materials** paper plates, pencils, white board **Manipulatives** 2-colored counters, color tiles **Other Resources** CRM Leveled Worksheets (pp. 27–30) Daily Reteach Problem of the Day	**Lesson Resources**
Math Adventures	Math Adventures Concepts in Motion		**Technology** Math Online
Below Level, p. 213B BL English Learners, p. 213B ELL Early Finishers, p. 213B OL AL	Gifted and Talented, p. 215B AL English Learners, p. 215B ELL Early Finishers, p. 215B OL AL	Below Level, p. 217B BL English Learners, p. 217B ELL Early Finishers, p. 217B OL AL	**Reaching All Learners**
Math Their Way, p. 125	*Math Their Way,* p. 104	*Math Their Way,* pp. 308–309	**Alternate Lesson**

Problem Solving in Social Studies (p. 219)

Summative Assessment
- Chapter Review/Test (p. 221)
- Test Practice (p. 223)

Assessment Options

✓ Diagnostic Assessment

SE *Option 1:* Are You Ready? (p. 202)
Option 2: Online Quiz (macmillanmh.com)
CRM *Option 3:* Diagnostic Test (p. 40)

✓ Formative Assessment

TE Alternate Teaching Strategies (every lesson)
TE Writing in Math (every lesson)
TE Line Up (every lesson)
SE Mid-Chapter Check (p. 211)
CRM Mid-Chapter Test (p. 41)

✓ Summative Assessment

SE Chapter Review/Test (p. 221)
SE Test Practice (p. 223)
CRM Leveled Chapter Tests (pp. 46–52)
CRM Cumulative Test Practice (pp. 54–55)
CRM Listening Assessment (pp. 44–45)
CRM Oral assessment (pp. 42–43)
ExamView® Assessment Suite

Assessment Tips

Counting, ordering, and comparing are important prerequisite skills that are necessary for learning addition and subtraction concepts.

- Use a clipboard that has a list of the students' names and the concepts you want to assess.
- As students count, order, and compare numbers, write down your observations on the clipboard.
- These observations should help you plan next steps with the students.
- Make sure you record the date of the observation so you can begin to see progress over time.

McGraw Hill Professional Development

Targeted professional development has been articulated throughout **McGraw-Hill's *Math Connects*** program. The **McGraw-Hill Professional Development Video Library** provides short videos that support the **NCTM Focal Points and Focal Connections.** For more information, visit macmillanmh.com.

| Model Lessons | Instructional Strategies |

Teacher Notes

Learning Stations
Cross-Curricular Links

 Art

Make a Number Quilt

- Choose a square.
- Write a number from 21 to 25 on it.
- Draw a shape on the square.

Teacher Note: Tell the class they will make a number quilt. Have students choose a paper square. Have them draw a design on the square, such as a sun, square, triangle, smile, apple, or star. Have them write their name on their square along with a number from 21 to 25. Hang all squares together to make a number quilt.

Materials:
- colored paper squares
- crayons
- colored pencils
- markers

  Reading

Make a Counting Book

- Choose one or more objects to draw.
- Tell about what you drew.
- Write and say the numbers.

Teacher Note: Show students blank art number books. Have them brainstorm objects to draw to make a 26 to 30 counting book. List all. Have them draw 26 of one object on a page, 27 of the same or another object on another page, and so on. Have them write the number of objects at the bottom of the page. Have them describe their objects and say the numbers.

Materials:
- blank books
- crayons
- colored pencils

 Science

Tell a Nature Number Story

- Choose a nature object. Collect 20 or more.
- Draw a picture or choose a picture.
- Tell a nature story about your objects and show your picture to your partner.

Teacher Note: Have pairs collect two large sets of one or two types of nature objects, then draw a nature picture or choose one magazine picture. Tell pairs to think of and tell a nature story to compare the number of their objects, such as a story about two squirrels collecting nuts. Have partners take turns grouping the objects and telling part of the story. Encourage using comparing words, such as more than, less than, and the same as or equal to.

Materials:
- drawing paper
- crayons
- nature pictures from magazines
- nature objects: twigs, shells, feathers, leaves, stones, nuts

Social Studies

How Many, How Much?

- Set up a store with things to sell.
- Buy an item with counters.
- How many counters are left?
- Buy an item with those counters.

Teacher Note: Set up a store to display classroom objects on a table or shelves. Make price signs for the objects. Give students 30 counters each. Tell students that prices are for single objects and are between numbers one and 30. Tell students to use their counters to buy an item. Have them count how many counters they have left. Challenge students to find an item that costs the same amount as the number of counters they have left after their first purchase.

Materials:
- table or shelves
- various classroom objects
- paper
- pencils

Social Studies

Build by Numbers

- Take 30 blocks.
- Build an object with the blocks.
- Add each block in order.

Teacher Note: Write one number, from one to 30, on sticky notes. Tape the numbers to blocks. Number different size and shape blocks. Have students work in pairs to build a block structure. Instruct pairs to build the structure one block at a time, placing each block in numerical order. Tell pairs to use all 30 blocks in their structure.

Materials:
- sticky notes or paper slips
- markers or pencil
- tape
- blocks of various sizes and shapes

Calendar Time

Estimate the Number

- Guess how many Xs.
- Write your guess on paper.
- Tell how you came up with your guess.

Teacher Note: Draw Xs in 30 consecutive boxes on a blank calendar page. Give each student a slip of paper and a pencil. Have students look at the calendar page. After ten seconds, cover the calendar page, and ask students to estimate and write the number of boxes that have Xs. Have students discuss how they arrived at their estimates and if their estimate is reasonable. Count the boxes aloud with students to check estimates. Ask how many estimated the exact number. Show how they might have counted the Xs vertically and horizontally to reach an estimate.

Sunday	Monday	Tuesday	Wednesday	Thursday	Friday	Saturday
X	X	X	X	X	X	X
X	X	X	X	X	X	X
X	X	X	X	X	X	X
X	X	X	X	X	X	X
X	X					

Introduce the Chapter

 Real World: Counting Raisins

Materials: beads, bowl

- Gather students into a circle. Put a large number of beads near a bowl in the center of the circle.

- Tell students to pretend they are making a cake, and that they will put 25 raisins in the cake. Tell them the beads represent raisins. Invite students to count with you as you put the beads, one-by-one, into the bowl.

- Invite students to talk about why it is important to use numbers in recipes when baking cakes.

- **What could happen if we added more or less raisins in a cake recipe?** Sample answer: The cake may not bake correctly.

Use the Student Page

Have students turn to p. 201. Guide students to discuss the images on the page and answer the Explore questions.

Key Vocabulary

Introduce the key vocabulary in the chapter using the routine below.

Define: To **estimate** means to find a number close to an exact amount.

Example: Telling how many pennies are in a jar before counting them is one way to estimate.

Ask: What classroom objects can you estimate the number of?

Diagnostic Assessment

Check for students' prerequisite skills before beginning the chapter.

- **Option 1:** *Are You Ready for Chapter 8?*

  SE Student Edition, p. 202

- **Option 2:** *Online Quiz*

  Math Online > macmillanmh.com

- **Option 3:** *Diagnostic Test*

  CRM Chapter 8 Resource Masters, p. 40

RTI (Response to Intervention)

Apply the Results Based on the results of the diagnostic assessment on student p. 192, use the chart on the next page to address individual needs before and during the chapter.

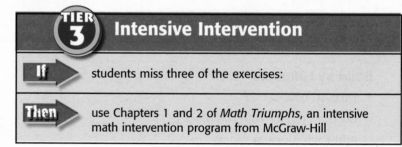

TIER 3 **Intensive Intervention**

If students miss three of the exercises:

Then use Chapters 1 and 2 of *Math Triumphs*, an intensive math intervention program from McGraw-Hill

---

 **Dinah Zike's Foldables**

Guide students to create an Accordion Book Foldable graphic organizer to continue a number line with numbers 21–30.

NOTE: Steps 1 and 2 should be done only if paper is too large to begin with.

 1 Fold four pieces of paper into hamburgers. Fold one side one half inch shorter than the other side.

 2 Fold this tab forward over the shorter side, and then fold it back away from the shorter piece of paper.

3 Glue together to form an accordion by gluing a straight edge of one section into the valley of another section.

4 Write one number on the top left side of each section. Have students find and place pictures on the appropriate sections to illustrate each number.

When to Use It Lessons 8-1, 8-2, and 8-5 (Additional instructions for using the Foldable with these lessons are found on pp. 211 and 221).

Key Vocabulary
about
estimate

Explore
Do you think there are more blueberries or more red raspberries? Count to see.
Check students' answers.

Math Online
Take the Chapter Readiness Quiz at macmillanmh.com

Name _____

Are You Ready for Chapter 8?

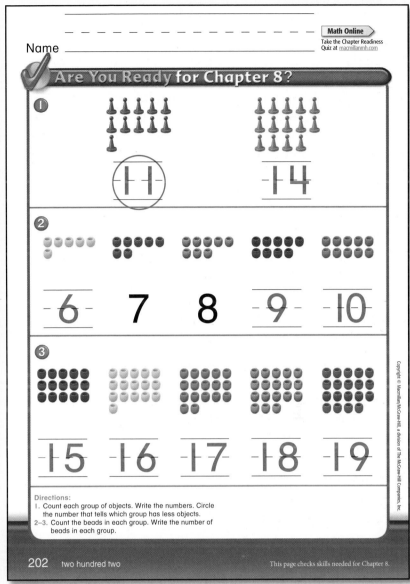

Directions:
1. Count each group of objects. Write the numbers. Circle the number that tells which group has less objects.
2–3. Count the beads in each group. Write the number of beads in each group.

RTI (Response to Intervention)

TIER 2 Strategic Intervention below/approaching grade level	TIER 1 On-Level	Above/Beyond Level
If students miss two in: **Exercises 1–3**	**If** students miss one in: **Exercises 1–3**	**If** students miss none in: **Exercises 1–3**
Then choose a resource:	**Then** choose a resource:	**Then** choose a resource:
CRM Chapter 6 Resource Masters (Reteach Worksheets) Math Online Concepts in Motion	TE Learning Stations (pp. 201G–201H) TE Chapter Project (p. 203) CRM Game: Can You Make This Number? Math Adventures My Math Zone Chapter 7	TE Learning Stations (pp. 201G–201H) TE Chapter Project (p. 203) Real-World Problem Solving: *What are Seasons?* My Math Zone Chapters 7 and 8 Math Online Game

WRITING IN ►MATH

Starting the Chapter

Ask students to use connecting cubes to make a set of 20 cubes. Have students write the number that represents this set. Then have students add one cube to the set. Help them determine how many cubes are in the set now. Write 21 on the chalkboard and have students use it as a model as they write the number.

✓ Chapter 8 Project

Number Posters

- Have students work together in small groups to make posters for the numbers 20 to 30.

- Assign each group a number (20–30) and provide them with a sheet of butcher paper and craft materials to create their poster.

- Each poster should include the number, word for the number (you may have to help students write this), and ways to represent the number using drawings, craft materials, or pictures from old magazines.

- Ask each group to share their posters (out of number order). Have students help you arrange the posters in order from 20–30 so you can hang them up in the classroom to make a number line for students to use.

Chapter 8 Literature List

Lesson	Book Title	Author
8-1	Reese's Pieces Count by Fives	Jerry Pallotta
8-2	Naughty Little Monkeys	Jim Aylesworth
8-3	Frogs Jump	Steven Kellogg
8-4	Crayon Counting Book	Pam Munoz Ryan Jerry Pallota
8-5	Anno's Counting Book	Mitsumasa Anno
8-6	How Many Snails? A Counting Book	Paul Giganti, Jr.
Any	City by Numbers	Stephen T. Johnson
Any	More Than One	Miriam Schlein

ELL National ESL Standards Alignment for Chapter 8			
Lesson, Page	ESL Standard	Modality	Level
8-1, p. 205B	Goal 1, Standard 3, b	Auditory	Intermediate
8-2, p. 207B	Goal 1, Standard 3, f	Spatial	Beginning
8-3, p. 209B	Goal 2, Standard 1, g	Intrapersonal	Advanced
8-4, p. 213B	Goal 2, Standard 1, a	Spatial	Intermediate
8-5, p. 215B	Goal 1, Standard 3, e	Linguistic	Intermediate
8-5, p. 217B	Goal 3, Standard 3, b	Auditory	Intermediate

The National ESL Standards can be found in the Teacher Reference Handbook.

English

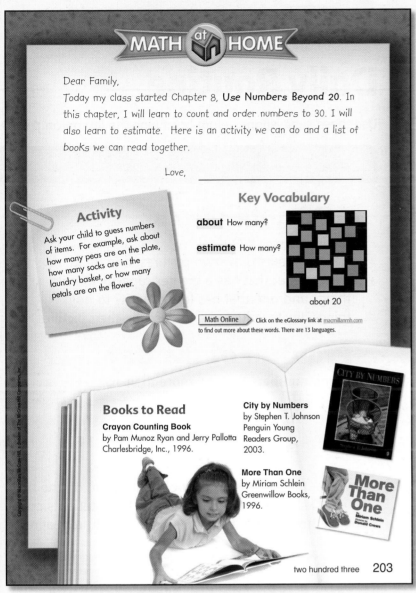

MATH at HOME

Dear Family,

Today my class started Chapter 8, **Use Numbers Beyond 20**. In this chapter, I will learn to count and order numbers to 30. I will also learn to estimate. Here is an activity we can do and a list of books we can read together.

Love, _____

Activity
Ask your child to guess numbers of items. For example, ask about how many peas are on the plate, how many socks are in the laundry basket, or how many petals are on the flower.

Key Vocabulary
about How many?

estimate How many?

about 20

Math Online ▶ Click on the eGlossary link at macmillanmh.com to find out more about these words. There are 13 languages.

Books to Read
Crayon Counting Book
by Pam Munoz Ryan and Jerry Pallotta
Charlesbridge, Inc., 1996.

City by Numbers
by Stephen T. Johnson
Penguin Young Readers Group, 2003.

More Than One
by Miriam Schlein
Greenwillow Books, 1996.

two hundred three **203**

Español

MATEMÁTICAS en CASA

Estimada familia:

Hoy mi clase comenzó el Capítulo 8, **Usar los números más allá del 20**. En este capítulo, aprenderé a contar y a ordenar los números hasta el 30. También aprenderé a estimar. A continuación, hay una actividad que podemos realizar y una lista de libros que podemos leer juntos.

Cariños, _____

Actividad
Pídanle a su hijo(a) que adivine el número de varios artículos. Por ejemplo, pregunten cuántas arvejas hay en el plato, cuántas medias hay en la cesta de la ropa o cuántos pétalos tiene la flor.

Vocabulario clave
alrededor de ¿Cuántos?

estimar ¿Cuántos?

alrededor de 20

Math Online ▶ Visiten el enlace eGlossary en macmillanmh.com para averiguar más sobre estas palabras, las cuales se muestran en 13 idiomas.

Libros recomendados
Mejor Libro para Contar
de Richard Scary
Turtleback Books, 2004.

Cuenta los insectos
de Jerry Pallota
Charlesbridge Publishing, 1993.

204 two hundred four

MATH at HOME

- Read the Math at Home letter on p. 203 with the class and have each student sign it.

- Send home copies of the Math at Home letter with each student.

- Use the Spanish letter on p. 204 for students with Spanish-speaking parents or guardians.

Read-Aloud Anthology

For an optional reading activity to introduce this chapter's math concepts, see the Read-Aloud Anthology on p. TR31.

Lesson Planner

Objective
Count, recognize, and write the numerals 21 through 25.

Review Vocabulary
twenty, more

Resources
Materials: drawing paper, crayons, WorkMat 5: Ten-Frames
Manipulatives: two-colored counters
Literature Connection: *Reese's Pieces Count by Fives* by Jerry Pallotta
Alternate Lesson: Adapt *Numeral Sequence Cards* on page 47 of *Math Their Way* for practice in recognizing, counting, and writing numbers 21 through 25.
Teacher Technology
  ◉ TeacherWorks

Focus on Math Background
In this lesson, students work with numbers beyond 20, concentrating on 21–25. Amounts above 20 look like big numbers to typical kindergartners. They often count each object one-by-one instead of decomposing the whole into parts. Visualizing the parts of whole quantities helps students quickly determine how many total objects are in a set.

Daily Routine

Use these suggestions before beginning the lesson on p. 205.

5-Minute Check
(Reviews Lesson 7-6)
Have students draw two pictures: one of an object or container that has a greater capacity to hold things and one that has less capacity to hold things. Invite volunteers to describe their pictures.

Problem of the Day
Name numbers that are more than 15.

| 16 | 19 | 12 | 20 | 29 | 17 | 21 |

16, 19, 20, 17

LINE UP Put a measuring tape number line on the floor showing numbers 21–25. Have students count aloud as they line up, beginning with 21, and repeating.

Review Math Vocabulary
Divide students into five groups. Give each group a number/name card between 21 and 25.

- Write numbers one to 20 on the chalkboard. Have students read the numbers aloud. Write 21.
- **What is this number? How do you know?** 21; It is **twenty** and 1 **more**.
- Ask the 21 group to come to the front of the room. Have a student hold up the card and the other students in the group clap, snap, stamp, or pat their knees 21 times as the rest of the class counts.
- Repeat the activity for numbers 22 through 25.

Visual Vocabulary Cards
Use Visual Vocabulary Card 25 to reinforce the vocabulary reviewed in this lesson. (The Define/Example/Ask routine is printed on the back of each card.)

more

Differentiated Instruction

Small Group Options

Option 1
Below/Approaching Level (BL)   KINESTHETIC

Materials: poster board, tiles, markers

- Draw five lines on a poster board to make six equal sections. Divide students into five groups, and give each group 25 color tiles and a marker.
- For the first group, assign each member a task: write "20" in the first section, draw 20 tally marks, or place 20 color tiles. Have the class count aloud.
- Have other groups repeat for 21–25.

Option 2
English Language Learners (ELL)   AUDITORY

Materials: magnetic numbers, connecting cubes
Core Vocabulary: twenty, together, when
Common Use Verb: means

Hear Math This strategy teaches combining number vocabulary.

- Give students magnetic numbers 0-5.
- Have two students hold up 2 and 0.
- Say: "When you put two numbers **together**, you make a new number." Have two students stand together while you model 20. Say: "Two and zero **together mean 20.**"

Independent Work Options

Option 1
Early Finishers (OL) (AL)   VISUAL

Materials: number cards 21–25, two-colored counters

- Have students mix up the number cards.
- Have each student pick a number card and show that quantity using counters.
- Repeat the activity.

Option 2
Student Technology

Math Online macmillanmh.com

Math Adventures

Option 3
Learning Station: Art (p. 191G)

Direct students to the Art Learning Station for opportunities to explore and extend the lesson concept.

Leveled Lesson Resources

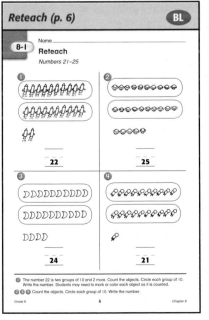

Reteach (p. 6) (BL)

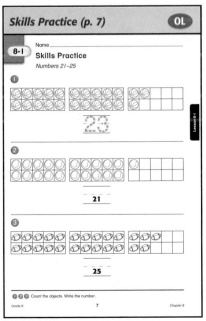

Skills Practice (p. 7) (OL)

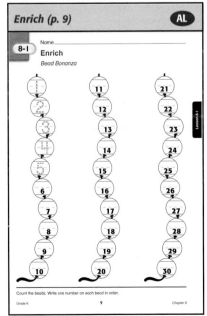

Enrich (p. 9) (AL)

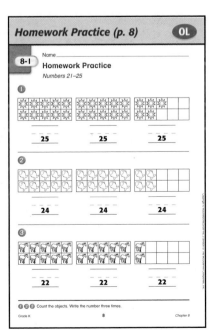

Homework Practice (p. 8) (OL)

① Introduce

Circle Time

Activity Choice 1 • Literature

Reese's Pieces Count by Fives by Jerry Pallotta

Materials: drawing paper, crayons

- Read and discuss the book aloud.
- Lead students in a discussion of numbers **twenty** to 25, referring to the book page showing those numbers.
- Divide students into six groups. Have each group illustrate one number from 20 to 25 and write the matching numeral.
- Put the illustrations in numerical order.

Activity Choice 2 • Hands-On

- Divide the class into six groups. Assign each group a number from 20 to 25. Give each group three ten-frames and 25 counters.
- Have students count out the number of counters that matches their group's number.
- Have students place the counters in the ten-frames one at a time while they count aloud.
- Ask each group to gather their counters from the ten-frames and bring them to the front of the room. Have groups put their counters in a single stack on a table or desk, beginning with 20 and ending with 25.
- Have students describe the differences in the stacks of counters, noting that each stack has one **more** counter than the stack before it.

② Teach

- Direct students to the top of p. 205.
- **How many counters are there in the filled ten-frames?** 20
- **How many more counters need to be filled in for the number 21? How do you know?** One; 21 is one more than 20.
- Have students fill in one more counter on the third ten-frame.
- Have them trace the number 21 below the ten-frames to show the number of counters they have modeled.
- Repeat the activity for numbers 22 to 25.

ⒷⓁ Alternate Teaching Strategy

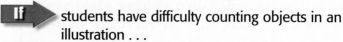

If students have difficulty counting objects in an illustration . . .

Then use one of these reteach options.

1. ⒸⓇⓂ **Daily Reteach Worksheet** (p. 6)
2. **Counting with Counters** Write the numbers zero to 20 on the chalkboard, leaving space to add five more numbers.
   - Distribute ten-frames and counters to students. Have them use the manipulatives to model 20.
   - **What do you notice about the ten-frames?** Sample answers: They are both full; they each have 10 counters; there are 20 counters in all.
   - **What number would show if you added one more counter beneath the ten-frames?** 21; 21 is one more than 20.
   - Have students add the counter. Write 21 next to 20. Have students read from zero to 21 aloud. Emphasize that 21 is two filled ten-frames and one more, or 20, and one more.

> ⚠ **COMMON ERROR!**
> Students may have difficulty keeping track of numbers as they count to 25. Have them use ten-frames and counters, dragging one counter at a time to the ten-frame.

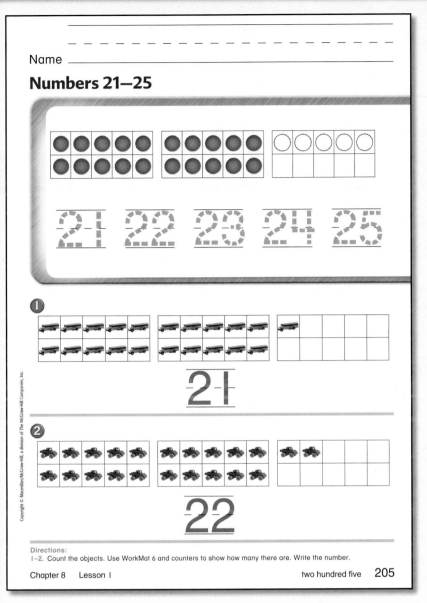

Name _____

Numbers 21–25

21 22 23 24 25

1

21

2

22

Directions:
1–2. Count the objects. Use WorkMat 6 and counters to show how many there are. Write the number.

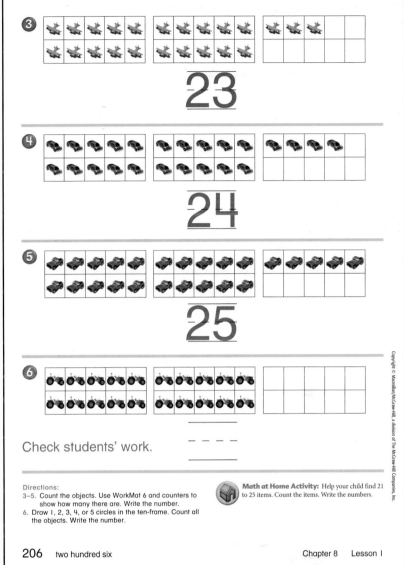

3

23

4

24

5

25

6

Check students' work.

Directions:
3–5. Count the objects. Use WorkMat 6 and counters to show how many there are. Write the number.
6. Draw 1, 2, 3, 4, or 5 circles in the ten-frame. Count all the objects. Write the number.

Math at Home Activity: Help your child find 21 to 25 items. Count the items. Write the numbers.

③ Practice

Guided Practice

- Direct students to the bottom of p. 205.
- In Exercise 1, have students touch and count aloud the buses in the ten-frames. Ask how many buses there are. Have students use counters and WorkMat 6 to show how many. Have students write the number 21.
- In Exercise 2, have students touch and count aloud each truck. Ask how many trucks there are. Have students use counters and WorkMat 6 to show how many. Have students write the number 22.

Independent Practice

Have students turn to p. 206. Explain the directions and have students work independently on the exercises.

④ Assess

Formative Assessment

Ask students to use ten-frames and counters to model the numbers 21 through 25.

Quick Check	**Are students still struggling with counting numbers to 25?**

If Yes → Small Group Options (p. 205B)

If No → Independent Work Options (p. 205B)

CRM Skills Practice Worksheet (p. 7)

CRM Enrich Worksheet (p. 9)

Lesson Planner _____

Objective
Count, recognize, and write the numerals 26 through 30.

Review Vocabulary
twenty, more

Resources
Materials: writing paper, pencils, construction paper, paper ten-frames, glue, small paper squares
Manipulatives: two-colored counters
Literature Connection: *Naughty Little Monkeys* by Jim Aylesworth
Alternate Lesson: Adapt Large Numeral Cards on pages 44–45 of *Math Their Way* for practice in recognizing, counting, and writing numbers 26 through 30.
Teacher Technology
TeacherWorks • Concepts in Motion

Focus on Math Background

This lesson focuses on quantifying and representing numbers 26 to 30 with their corresponding numerals and words, as well as with pictures, concrete objects, and models. To encourage kindergarteners to visualize these larger numbers as two sets of tens and some leftovers, 26 through 30 are represented with ten-frames. A ten frame is a powerful model to help students understand place value concepts.

Daily Routine _____

Use these suggestions before beginning the lesson on p. 207.

5-Minute Check
(Reviews Lesson 8-1)
Have students arrange 25 counters on a sheet of paper and then count them aloud.

Problem of the Day
Look at a calendar for April, June, September, or November. Count each day's number until you reach day number 30.

LINE UP Have students line up, counting the number of feet in line. When one line reaches 30, have remaining students begin a new line, counting from zero.

Review Math Vocabulary
Divide students into five groups. Give each group a number/name card from 26 to 30.

- Write numbers one to 25 on the chalkboard and have students read them aloud. Write number 26.
- **What is the number? How do you know?** 26; It is **twenty** and six **more**.
- Have the group holding the 26 number/name card come to the front. Have a student hold up the card, and the others draw an illustration representing 26 on the chalkboard. Suggest the use of two ten-frames or two ten-frames and 6 more.
- Have a student in the group put the 26 number/name card on the chalkboard ledge.
- Repeat the activity for 27 to 30.

Differentiated Instruction

Small Group Options

Option 1 Gifted and Talented (AL)

Materials: paper with letters of the alphabet

- Make an alphabet grid with the letters in alphabetical order and a blank line next to each letter.
- Have students write the number next to each letter to show each letter's order in the alphabet. (A = 1; Z = 26)
- **How many letters are in the alphabet? How do you know?** 26 letters; The boxes are numbered one to 26.

SPATIAL

Option 2 English Language Learners (ELL)

Materials: 10" × 50" picture, scissors, bag, tape
Core Vocabulary: pull, a piece, if
Common Use Verb: put together
See Math This strategy helps students understand numbers 26-30.

- Number the backs of the pictures from one to 30. Cut each number out and put the pieces in a bag.
- Have students pull a piece and put it together as a number puzzle with tape.
- Collect and tape the pieces; showing only the numbered side. Say: "**If** we **put** the **pieces together** correctly, there will be a picture."
- Flip to reveal the picture.

Independent Work Options

VISUAL

Option 1 Early Finishers (OL) (AL)

Materials: paper, pencil

- Write a number from 26 to 30 on the chalkboard.
- Have students draw lines on their paper that corresponds to the number on the board.
- Have them write the number beneath their pencil lines.

Option 2 Student Technology

Math Online ▸ macmillanmh.com

 Math Adventures

Option 3 Learning Station: Reading (p. 201G)

Direct students to the Reading Learning Station for opportunities to explore and extend the lesson concept.

Leveled Lesson Resources

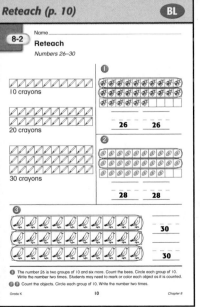

Reteach (p. 10) **BL**

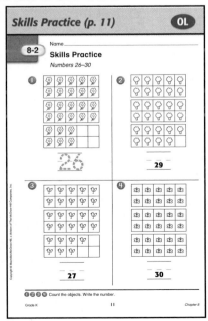

Skills Practice (p. 11) **OL**

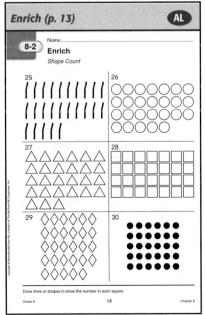

Enrich (p. 13) **AL**

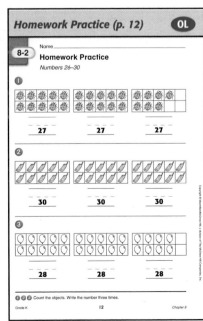

Homework Practice (p. 12) **OL**

❶ Introduce

ⒸircleTime

Activity Choice 1 • Literature

Naughty Little Monkeys
by Jim Aylesworth
Materials: writing paper, pencils

- Read and discuss the book aloud, counting as the 26 monkeys are introduced.

- Review numbers to 25. Then lead students in a discussion of numbers 26 to 30.

- Have each student think of a new book ending by creating four more naughty monkeys, for a total of 30. Have students count and write the numbers 26 to 30 as they share their new endings to the book.

Activity Choice 2 • Hands-On

- Divide the class into six groups. Give each group three paper ten-frames and glue.

- Assign each group a number from 25 to 30, and give each group the number of small paper squares that matches their group's number.

- Have each group count out **twenty** paper squares, and glue them one at a time to fill two ten-frames.

- Have each group count how many **more** squares they have left (unglued), and say the number aloud.

- Have groups glue each remaining square into the third ten-frame, counting each one aloud from 20.

- When all squares are glued, ask students how many squares they have in all.

❷ Teach

- Direct students to the top of p. 207.
- **How many counters are on the ten-frames?** 25
- **How many more counters need to be filled in for the number 26? How do you know?** one; 26 is one more than 25.
- Have students fill in one more counter on the third ten-frame.
- Have them trace the number 26 to show the number of counters they have modeled with their ten-frames.
- Repeat the activity for numbers 27 to 30.

ⒷⓁ Alternate Teaching Strategy

If ▶ students have difficulty counting to numbers greater than 20 . . .

Then ▶ use one of these reteach options.

1 [CRM] **Daily Reteach Worksheet** (p. 10)

2 **Counting with Counters** Write numbers zero to 25 on the chalkboard, leaving space to add five more numbers.

- Distribute three ten-frames and counters to students. Have them use the materials to model 25.

- **What do you notice about the ten-frames?** Sample answer: Two ten-frames are full with 10 counters each, and five more counters are in the third ten-frame.

- **What would the number be if you added one more counter beneath the ten-frames? How do you know?** 26; 26 is one more than 25.

- Have students add the counter. Write 26 next to 25. Have students count from zero to 26 aloud. Emphasize that 26 is two filled ten-frames and six more.

- Repeat the activity with numbers 27 to 30.

 COMMON ERROR!

Students may make a counting error when transitioning from 29 to 30. Use ten-frames and counters to count from one to 30 aloud. Point out transitions: from ones to tens, to twenties, and to thirty.

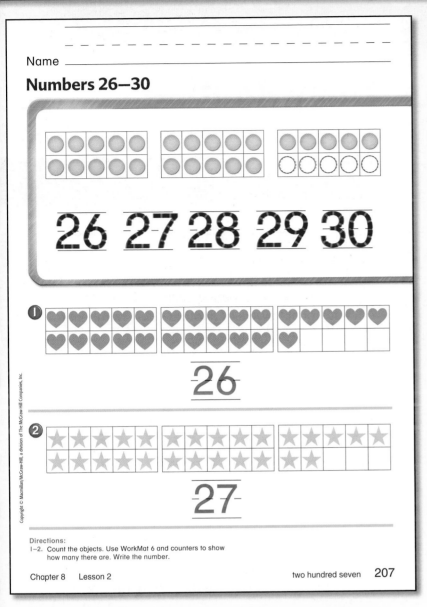

Name

Numbers 26–30

26 27 28 29 30

1

26

2

27

Copyright © Macmillan/McGraw-Hill, a division of The McGraw-Hill Companies, Inc.

Directions:
1–2. Count the objects. Use WorkMat 6 and counters to show how many there are. Write the number.

3

28

4

29

5

30

6

Check students' work.

Copyright © Macmillan/McGraw-Hill, a division of The McGraw-Hill Companies, Inc.

Directions:
3–5. Count the objects. Use WorkMat 6 and counters to show how many there are. Write the number.
6. Draw 1, 2, 3, 4, or 5 circles in the ten-frame. Count all the objects. Write the number.

Math at Home Activity: Using dry cereal or macaroni, count groups of 26 to 30 pieces. Write the number.

③ Practice

Guided Practice

- Direct students to the bottom of p. 207.
- In Exercise 1, have students touch and count aloud the hearts in the ten-frames. Ask how many hearts there are. Have students use counters and WorkMat 6 to show how many. Have students write the number 26.
- In Exercise 2, have students touch and count aloud the stars in the ten-frames. Ask how many stars there are. Have students use counters and WorkMat 6 to show how many. Have students write the number 27.

Independent Practice

Have students turn to p. 208. Explain the directions and have students work independently on the exercises.

④ Assess

✔ Formative Assessment

- Assign each student a number from 26 to 30.
- Have students use counters and ten-frames to show their number.

Quick Check

Are students still struggling to count and write numbers 26 to 30?

If Yes → Small Group Options (p. 207B)

If No → Independent Work Options (p. 207B)

  CRM Skills Practice Worksheet (p. 11)

  CRM Enrich Worksheet (p. 13)

Lesson 8-2 Numbers 26–30   **208**

Lesson Planner _____

Objective

Count, recognize, and write the numerals 21 through 30.

Resources

Materials: poster board, sticky notes, pictures of flowers
Manipulatives: two-colored counters, connecting cubes
Literature Connection: *Frogs Jump* by Steven Kellogg
Teacher Technology

💿 TeacherWorks

📖 **Real-World Problem Solving Library**
Math and Social Studies: *What are Seasons?*
Use these leveled books to reinforce and extend problem-solving skills and strategies.

Leveled for:

OL On Level
ELL Sheltered English
SP Spanish

For additional support, see the Real-World Problem Solving Teacher Guide.

On-level title is available in classroom Big Book.

Daily Routine _____

Use these suggestions before beginning the lesson on p. 209.

5-Minute Check

(Reviews Lesson 8-2)
Have students work in pairs to draw 26 flowers of one color, numbering each, and then four additional flowers of another color, numbering each from 27 to 30.

Problem of the Day 📖

How many flowers are in each jar? How many flowers are there altogether? How do you know? 10; 30; counted all flowers in the three jars

LINE UP Have students line up with one hand in the air, counting the number of thumbs and fingers. When one line reaches 30, have remaining students begin a new line, counting from zero.

Differentiated Instruction

Small Group Options

Option 1
Gifted and Talented (AL)   LOGICAL

Materials: paper, pencil, cubes

- Pair students. Tell the first student in each pair to write a number from 20 to 30 on paper.
- Have the partner use cubes to make groups of ten plus how many more needed to make the number. Have the first student count to check if the number of cubes is correct. Have partners switch roles and repeat.

Option 2
English Language Learners (ELL)   INTRAPERSONAL

Materials: pairs of animals (stuffed, plastic, or pictures)
Core Vocabulary: Which animal is missing, model sets, explain
Common Use Verb: remember

See Math This strategy helps students visualize and improve memory using models.

- Cover the first **set** of animals. Then display a second set with one missing. Ask: "**Which animal is missing?**"
- Have students explain how they remembered the missing animals. Restate their answer to the group.
- Allow students to repeat the memory activity in pairs.

Independent Work Options

Option 1
Early Finishers (OL) (AL)   KINESTHETIC

Materials: blocks

- Have students make block towers, with the first tower made of two blocks, the next tower made of three blocks, and so on through seven blocks.
- Have students line up the block towers one behind the other, from shortest to tallest.
- Have students count the total number of blocks used.

Option 2
Student Technology

Math Online ⟩ macmillanmh.com

Option 3
Learning Station: Science (p. 201G)

Direct students to the Science Learning Station for opportunities to explore and extend the lesson concept.

Leveled Lesson Resources

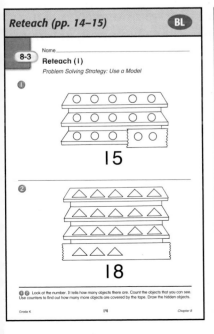

Reteach (pp. 14–15) (BL)

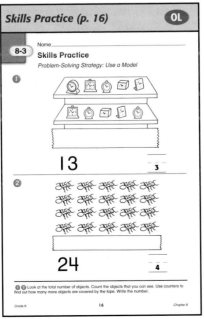

Skills Practice (p. 16) (OL)

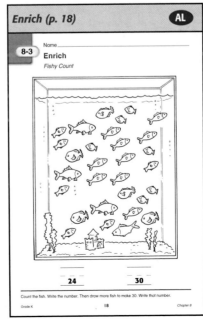

Enrich (p. 18) (AL)

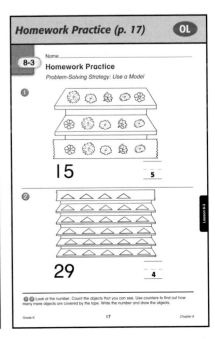

Homework Practice (p. 17) (OL)

① Introduce

Circle Time

Activity Choice 1 • Literature

Frogs Jump by Steven Kellogg

Materials: counters

- Designate a table near the center of the room to be "the pond."

- Divide the class into six small groups, giving each group a different color set of five counters. Read *Frogs Jump* aloud.

- Tell students they are going "pond jumping," and that each counter respresents a frog. Have each group jump their frogs to the pond, then count all frogs in the water at that time. Repeat the process until all 30 have jumped. Count the 30 frogs again aloud.

- **How many groups of ten frogs did it take to make 30 frogs?** three

Activity Choice 2 • Hands-On

- Display a picture of 30 flowers on a poster board, with five flowers partially covered with five different sticky notes.

- Write the number 30 below the flowers.

- Have students count out 30 cubes to show the written number 30.

- Have students count each visible flower. **How many flowers do you see?** 25

- Using the 30 cubes, have each student place a cube on one of the flowers until all flowers are covered. Have students count aloud as they place each cube.

- **How many cubes are left over?** 5

- Ask five students to remove a different sticky note one at a time.

- As each flower is revealed, have another student place a cube on the new flower.

- Have the class count the flowers aloud from one each time a new flower is uncovered.

- When all flowers are visible, ask students how many flowers there are in all.

② Teach

Making a model can help students by using manipulatives as a reference to solve the problem. The model can serve to provide hands on counting to ensure that students are counting accurately to solve the problem. For example, When needing to know how many objects are hidden in a picture, the student can count out the total by using objects and refer to the total to find the number of hidden objects.

- Direct students to the top of p. 209.

- Have them identify the number. Have them use counters to show the number.

- Have them use counters to count the number of bears that are seen. Have them use the remaining counters to show the number of bears that are covered by the tape.

- **How many bears are hidden? How do you know?** five; five counters were left over

- Count aloud with students both the visible bears and the counters to get the total number of bears.

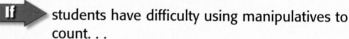

BL Alternate Teaching Strategy

If students have difficulty using manipulatives to count. . .

Then use one of these reteach options.

1 **CRM** **Daily Reteach Worksheet** (pp. 14–15)

2 **Compare Numbers** Give each student two connecting cube trains of different lengths. Each train should have between 21 and 30 cubes.

- Have students line up the ends of their trains to see the difference in length.

- **How can you tell which train has more cubes?** The train with more cubes is longer.

- Have students take apart their trains one cube at a time, counting each cube as they remove it, in order to check their answer.

 COMMON ERROR!

Students may forget that the number of counters is the same as the number of objects. Help them count one counter for each object shown and remind them that the remaining counters represent the hidden objects.

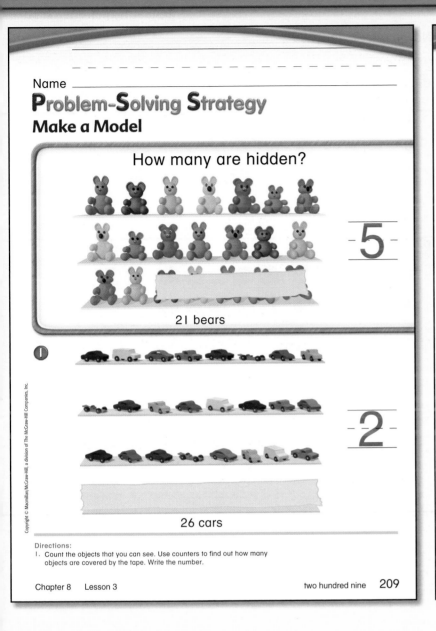

Name _____

Problem-Solving Strategy
Make a Model

How many are hidden?

-5-

21 bears

❶

-2-

26 cars

Directions:
1. Count the objects that you can see. Use counters to find out how many objects are covered by the tape. Write the number.

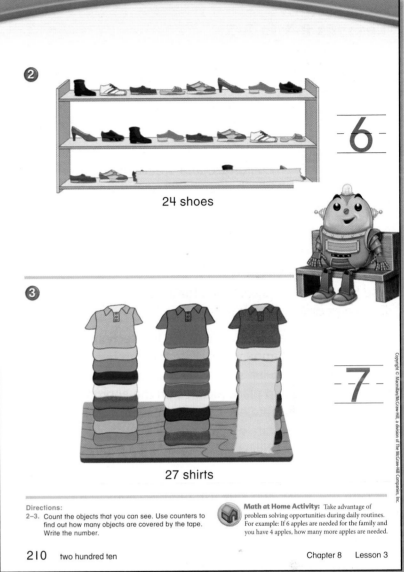

❷

-6-

24 shoes

❸

-7-

27 shirts

Directions:
2–3. Count the objects that you can see. Use counters to find out how many objects are covered by the tape. Write the number.

Math at Home Activity: Take advantage of problem solving opportunities during daily routines. For example: If 6 apples are needed for the family and you have 4 apples, how many more apples are needed.

---

❸ Practice

Guided Practice

- Direct students to the bottom of p. 209.
- Have students use counters to show the number.
- **How many cars are covered by the tape?** two
- **How do you know?** sample answer: I used 26 counters, placed one counter on each car and had 2 left over
- **How many cars are there in all? How do you know?** 26; counted 24 cars and two counters

Independent Practice

Have students turn to p. 210. Explain the directions and have students work independently on the exercises.

- Have students determine another approach, strategy and materials to solve these problems.

❹ Assess

✓ Formative Assessment

- Show students a poster board with 25 balloons drawn in it and with four of the balloons partially covered by a ruler. Write the number 25 below the balloons.
- Ask students to identify the number and to count out enough cubes to show that number.
- **How many balloons are hidden under the ruler?** 4 balloons

Quick Check	Are students still struggling with making a model?

If Yes → Small Group Options (p. 209B)

If No → Independent Work Options (p. 209B)

  CRM Skills Practice Worksheet (p. 16)

  CRM Enrich Worksheet (p. 18)

Lesson 8-3 Problem-Solving Strategy   **210**

Lessons 8-1 to 8-3

✓ Formative Assessment

Use the Mid-Chapter Check to assess student's progress in the first half of the chapter.

ExamView Assessment Suite Customize and create multiple versions of your Mid-Chapter Check and the test answer keys.

FOLDABLES® Dinah Zike's Foldables

Use these lesson suggestions for incorporating the Foldables during the chapter.

Lesson 8-1 Make and glue together five sections of the Foldable Number Line. Write the numbers 21 to 25 on the top left side of each section. Have students find and place pictures on the appropriate sections to illustrate each number. Students can use magazines, catalogs, advertisements, worksheets, or original artwork to find pictures or illustrations.

Lesson 8-2 Make and glue five more sections to the number line. Write the numbers 26 to 30 on the top left side of each section. Have students find and place pictures on the appropriate sections to illustrate each number. Students can use magazines, catalogs, advertisements, worksheets, or original artwork to find pictures or illustrations.

Name _____

①

23

②

Check students' work. _ _ _ _

③

Check students' work. _ _ _ _

Directions:
1. Count the objects. Write the number.
2–3. Draw 1, 2, 3, 4, or 5 circles in the ten-frame.
    Count all the objects in the ten-frames. Write the number.

Chapter 8   two hundred eleven   211

Copyright © Macmillan/McGraw-Hill, a division of The McGraw-Hill Companies, Inc.

Data-Driven Decision Making

Based on the results of the Mid-Chapter Check, use the following resources to review concepts that continue to give students problems.

Exercises	State/Local Standard	What's the Math?	Error Analysis	Resources for Review
1 Lessons 8-2		Count number of objects up to 30.	Does not count the number of objects correctly.	CRM Chapter 8 Resource Masters (Reteach Worksheets)
2–3 Lessons 8-1, 8-2, 8-3		Count, represent, and name a number of objects up to 30.	Does not add any more objects to the total. Does not count correctly. Does not write correct number.	Math Online Concepts in Motion Math Adventures

Peanut Roundup!
Counting

Play with a partner. Take turns.
- Roll the [5].
- Move your cube that number of spaces.
- Take the number of counters shown on the space.
- If you land on a space with a bucket you must put all of your counters back.
- When one player reaches **Finish**, count all of your counters. Who has more?

You Will Need

212   two hundred twelve

Peanut Roundup!

Math Concept:
Counting

Materials: paper, pencils
Manipulatives: number cube, two-colored counters, connecting cubes

Introduce the game on page 212 to your students to play as a class, in small groups, or at a learning workstation to review concepts introduced in this chapter.

Instructions

- Each student uses a connecting cube as a marker. One student uses yellow and the other uses purple.
- Students roll the red number cube and move their marker that number of squares.
- Students take the number of counters indicated on the square they land on.
- If students land on a square with a bucket, they must put all their counters back.
- When one player reaches the finish line, all students count the number of counters they have. The student with the most counters wins the game.

Extend the Game

Have students make their own gameboard using larger numbers on the squares.

Differentiated Practice

Use these leveling suggestions to differentiate the game for all learners.

Level	Assignment
BL Below/Approaching Level	Encourage students to count out their counters one at a time.
OL On Level	Have students play the game with the rules as written.
AL Above/Beyond Level	When students reach the finishline, have them continue to play, moving from the finish back to the starting line before counting their counters.

Lesson Planner _____

Objective

Count to compare groups and numbers to determine which has more, which has less or which is the same or equal.

Review Vocabulary

less (fewer), equals

Resources

Materials: pencils, construction paper, dry cereal, 1–30 number cards, glue, index cards, yarn, markers

Manipulatives: two-colored counters, connecting cubes, color tiles

Literature Connection: *Crayon Counting Book* by Pam Munoz Ryan and Jerry Pallotta

Alternate Lesson: Adapt *Handsful* on p. 125 of *Math Their Way* for practice in one-to-one correspondence, counting and comparing numbers 0 to 30.

Teacher Technology
- TeacherWorks

Focus on Math Background

This lesson focuses on comparing numbers to 30. Numbers 20 to 30 are represented in a ten-frame model. Comparing 26 to 29 is easier when students can visualize the numbers. To understand how to compare numbers, students must have a concrete, visual experience with the concept. To reinforce this concept, display 20 counters lined up vertically and 11 counters lined up vertically, one set next to the other. Have students determine which is longer, which is shorter, and guess which line has more counters than the other.

Daily Routine _____

Use these suggestions before beginning the lesson on p. 213.

5-Minute Check

(Reviews Lesson 8-3)
Have students model numbers 26 and 30 by making a train of 26 connecting cubes, then adding cubes one at a time and counting aloud until the train has 30 cubes.

Problem of the Day

Set out two containers with 18 and 28 counters. Have students count the counters, then write which number is more and which is less.

LINE UP Have five students line up, calling out their numbers one to five. Start a second line with students calling out their numbers from six to 20. Ask students to count the numbers in each line and tell which line has more and which line has less.

Review Math Vocabulary

- Give each pair of students a bag containing 30 connecting cubes. Have students remove a handful of cubes and make a train. Have students count the cubes in their train and write the number.

- **How can you guess what train will be longer?** The train with more cubes will be longer.

- Have pairs compare trains to check their guesses, saying if their number is greater than, **less** than, **equal** to their partner's number.

Visual Vocabulary Cards

Use Visual Vocabulary Card 20 to reinforce the vocabulary reviewed in this lesson. (The Define/Example/Ask routine is printed on the back of each card.)

less

Differentiated Instruction

Small Group Options

Option 1
Below/Approaching Level (BL)
LOGICAL

Materials: two-colored counters, ten-frames

Give 30 two-colored counters and three ten-frames to each student. Have students work in small groups. Have one student in each group use red counters to show 10, and another student use yellow counters to show 21.

What is greater, 10 or 21? How do you know? Sample answer: 21 is greater. There are more yellow counters than red counters.

Option 2
English Language Learners (ELL)
SPATIAL

Materials: cubes, 2-colored counters in sets of 30

Core Vocabulary: chair, each, animal

Common Use Verb: pretend

Do Math This strategy helps students compare numbers.

- Give students 30 cubes and a large handful of counters. Say: "Each counter is an animal."

- Demonstrate putting one counter on a cube. Say "Pretend each cube is a chair. Each animal needs a chair." Have students put "animals" on "chairs." Ask: "How many animals have a chair?" Assist individually or chorally count empty, full, or total animals/chairs.

Independent Work Options

Option 1
Early Finishers (OL) (AL)
VISUAL

Materials: dominoes

- Provide pairs of students with dominoes, each student choosing two dominoes. Have one student show a domino.

- Have the partner respond with a domino that has a different number of dots, and saying more, less, or equal depending on the number of dots on the domino.

- Ask the pairs to take turns showing and responding.

Option 2
Student Technology

Math Online ▷ macmillanmh.com

Math Adventures

Option 3
Learning Station: Social Studies (p. 201H)

Direct students to the Social Studies Learning Station for opportunities to explore and extend the lesson concept.

Leveled Lesson Resources

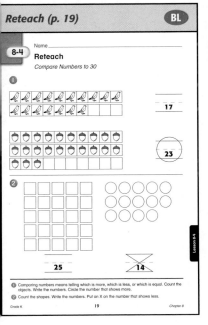

Reteach (p. 19) (BL)

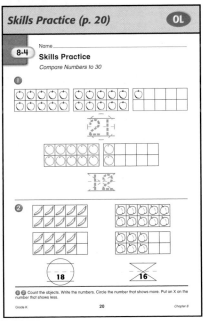

Skills Practice (p. 20) (OL)

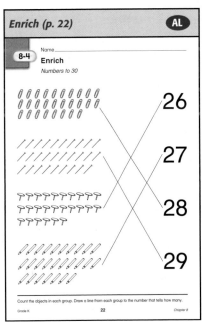

Enrich (p. 22) (AL)

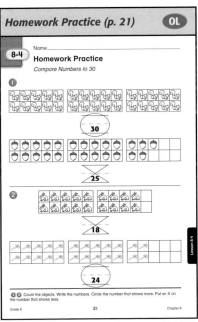

Homework Practice (p. 21) (OL)

1 Introduce

Circle Time

Activity Choice 1 • Literature

Crayon Counting Book
by Pam Munoz Ryan and Jerry Palotta

Materials: pencil, construction paper, colorful dry cereal, number cards from 1 to 30, glue

- Write numbers one to 30 on sheets of construction paper.
- Read the book aloud, have students use counters to model numbers. Emphasize groups of 10, and focus on numbers less than 30.
- Give each student a number card 1 to 30.
- Have students model their number with dry cereal, gluing the cereal to paper.
- In groups of 3, have students compare their numbers by answering what number is more and what number is **less**. Ask students to explain how they know.

Activity Choice 2 • Hands-On

Materials: color tiles, pencil, index cards, yarn, markers

- Show students a mix of 18 green and 25 yellow color tiles. Ask students which color has more tiles.
- Invite volunteers to sort the tiles by color. Ask other volunteers to display each group in rows of five.
- Count each group with students, then write the numbers on separate index cards. Ask a volunteer to place the correct card with its group of color tiles.
- Have a volunteer use yarn to ring the number that shows more.
- Repeat activity with 23 green and 15 yellow color tiles, having students identify the number that is less.

2 Teach

- Direct students to the top of p. 213.
- **How many fire engines are there?** 16 Have students trace the number 16 next to the fire engines.
- **How many police cars are there?** 20 Have students trace the number 20 next to the police cars.
- Guide students to observe that the numbers of fire engines and police cars match what they modeled with their counters and ten-frames.
- **Are there are more fire engines or police cars? How do you know?** Police cars; 16 does not have enough to make 20, and 20 fills two ten-frames; 16 has three rows and one more and 20 has four rows.
- Have students circle the number that shows more objects.

BL Alternate Teaching Strategy

If ➤ students have difficulty using counters to model . . .

Then ➤ use one of these reteach options.

1 CRM **Daily Reteach Worksheet** (p. 19)

2 **Compare Numbers**
- Give each student 30 counters and 3 ten-frames.
- Have students fill the ten-frames with as many counters as they choose.
- Have students write the number of counters they used.
- Have students find a partner.
- Then compare the amount of counters in their ten-frames with the counters in their partners' ten-frame.
- Have each student tell which partner has more, less, or the same/equal amount of counters.
- Have students compare numbers and tell which number represents more, less, or the same as/equal to.

! COMMON ERROR!

Students may have difficulty comparing numbers to 30. Have them use different colored counters to represent each object in Exercises 1 to 6. Have them first count the counters, then count the objects.

Name _____

Compare Numbers to 30

Directions:
1–2. Count the objects in each group. Write the number. Circle the number of the group that shows more objects.

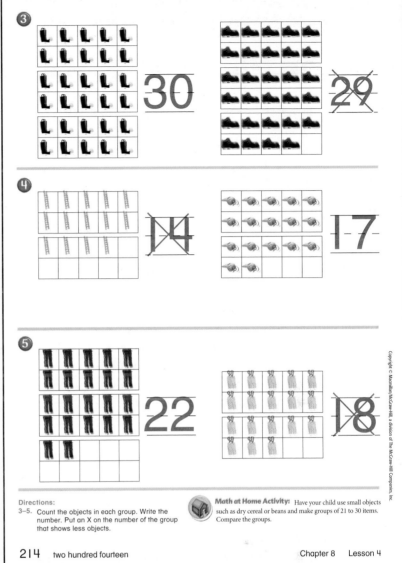

Directions:
3–5. Count the objects in each group. Write the number. Put an X on the number of the group that shows less objects.

Math at Home Activity: Have your child use small objects such as dry cereal or beans and make groups of 21 to 30 items. Compare the groups.

---

3 Practice

Guided Practice

- Direct students to Exercise 1 on p. 213.
- **How many objects are there in each group?** 27, 19
- Have students write the number in the box next to the objects.
- **Which is more, 27 or 19? How do you know?** 27 fills five rows of a ten-frame and part of a sixth row. 19 fills only three rows and part of a fourth row. Circle the number that shows more.
- Repeat for Exercise 2.

Independent Practice

Have students turn to p. 214. Explain the directions. Have students work independently on the exercises.

4 Assess

Formative Assessment

Make a train of 28 connecting cubes.

- **How many cubes are in the train?** 28 **How can you show 29?** Add one more cube.
- Add a cube, and show a train with 29 cubes.
- Which is more, 28 or 29? How do you know?
- Repeat with less and equal using other numbers.

Quick Check | **Are students still struggling with comparing numbers to 30?**

If Yes → Small Group Options (p. 213B)

If No → Independent Work Options (p. 213B)

CRM Skills Practice Worksheet (p. 20)

CRM Enrich Worksheet (p. 22)

Lesson 8-4 Compare Numbers to 30   **214**

Order Numbers to 30

Lesson Planner

Objective
Order numbers from 0 to 30 in sequence.

Review Vocabulary
before, after

Resources
Materials: number lines, masking tape, number cards, paper, pencils
Literature Connection: *Anno's Counting Book* by Mitsumasa Anno
Alternate Lesson: Adapt *Cover Up* on p. 104 of *Math Their Way* for practice in ordering numbers 0 to 30.
Teacher Technology
   💿 TeacherWorks • Concepts in Motion

Focus on Math Background

In this lesson, students will use number lines to order numbers to 30. Number lines help students learn the patterns of the 0 to 9-digit sequence that repeat within decades. For example, students should recognize that any number within a decade ending with the digit 3, such as 23, always comes before a number within the same decade ending with the digit 4.

Daily Routine

Use these suggestions before beginning the lesson on p. 215.

5-Minute Check
(Reviews Lesson 8-4)
Hold up one number card 0 to 30 in each hand. Have students name the numbers and tell which number is more and less. Repeat the activity.

Problem of the Day
Write a number line from zero to 30 on the chalkboard. Omit 2, 12, 22, and 29. Have students copy the number line and add the missing numbers.

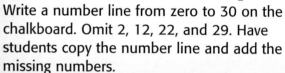 Give number cards to students, from 1 to 30 (or less if there are fewer students). Call students up in groups of 10: 1–10, 11–20, 21–30. Have students identify their number and then line up in order.

Review Math Vocabulary

• Write the numbers one to 20 on index cards. Put them in a bag. Have pairs of students take one card out of the bag without looking. Place the remaining cards on the chalkboard ledge in order, leaving blank spaces where numbers will be inserted.

• Tell students to say a number riddle describing the number they took, such as: "This number is just **after** 13 and just **before** 15. What is the number? How do you know?"

• Have pairs place their number card in the appropriate place on the chalkboard ledge.

Visual Vocabulary Cards

Use Visual Vocabulary Card 2 to reinforce the vocabulary reviewed in this lesson. (The Define/Example/Ask routine is printed on the back of each card.)

Differentiated Instruction

Small Group Options

Option 1

Gifted and Talented (AL)

LOGICAL

Materials: paper, pencil, dark marker

- Have students make a pencil drawing of an object in the classroom. Have them use a dark-colored marker to put 30 numbered dots around the outside of their drawn object.

- Tell students to erase their pencil marks. Have students trade pictures with a partner, then connect the dots in numerical order.

Option 2

English Language Learners (ELL)

LINGUISTIC

Materials: floor, number line, number cards
Core Vocabulary: find your place, count off
Common Use Verb: stand on

Hear Math This strategy helps students order numbers.

- Make a number line on the floor with tape. Label the numbers.

- Give three students a number from one to three. Say: **"Find your place."** Help them stand on the number line. Say: **"Count off"** encouraging all to join in.

- Pass out more numbers (in sequence) and repeat. End strategy in unison by counting.

Independent Work Options

Option 1

Early Finishers (OL) (AL)

LOGICAL

Materials: number cards 0 to 30

- Place number cards, out of order, facedown on a desk.

- Provide a number line for students to use to order the numbers.

- Have students turn the cards over, one at a time, and put them in numerical order.

Option 2

Student Technology

Math Online macmillanmh.com

Math Adventures

Option 3

Learning Station: Social Studies (p. 201H)

Direct students to the Social Studies Learning Station for opportunities to explore and extend the lesson concept.

Leveled Lesson Resources

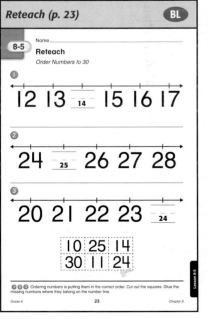

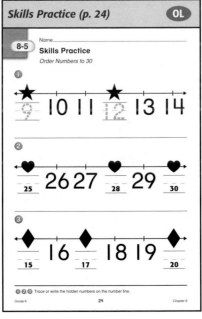

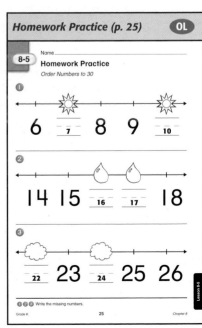

1 Introduce

Circle Time

Activity Choice 1 • Literature

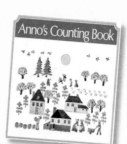

Anno's Counting Book
by Mitsumasa Anno
Materials: masking tape, 1–30
number cards

- Read the book aloud. Put a long piece of masking tape on the floor. Put a 0 card at the left end. Give each student a number card.

- Ask students with cards 1, 2, and 3 to put their numbers in order on the number line.

- Have the student with card 10 put the card on the number line. Discuss how the student decided where to put the card.

- Have remaining students put their number cards on the line. Discuss how they knew where to put their numbers.

Activity Choice 2 • Hands-On

Materials: number lines, paper, pencil

- Write a zero to 30 number line on the chalkboard. Have students read the numbers aloud from zero to 30, and from 30 to zero.

- Show a number line on the chalkboard. Have students write all the numbers from zero to 30 in order on the number line. Have them read the numbers zero-30 and 30-zero.

- **What is different about the number line?** Numbers are missing. **How we can find the missing numbers?** Sample answer: Count and when you reach a number not on the number line, it is missing.

- Ask students to write and say the first number they think is missing. **What number do you think is missing? How do you know?** 7; you say 7 **after** you say 6, but 7 is not on the number line; it is right after 6; it is right **before** 8. Ask a volunteer to write 7 where it belongs.

- Continue counting and repeat the questions for 12 and 26.

- Repeat the activity with different numbers.

2 Teach

- Direct students to the top of p. 215.

- **What do you notice about the number line?** Numbers are in order from 10 to 30.

- Have students point to each number as they count aloud.

- Ask questions using "before" and "after" to name numbers on the number line. For example: "what number comes before 18?" 17

BL Alternate Teaching Strategy

If students are having difficulty understanding numerical order . . .

Then use one of these reteach options.

1 CRM **Daily Reteach Worksheet** (p. 23)

2 **Count a Calendar Month** Display a 30-day month calendar such as April, June, September, or November.

- Have students count aloud the number of days in the month, from one to 30.

- Practice numerical order by having students identify the day that comes before or after a particular day. Identify days only by their number, such as saying day 12 of this month comes before day 13 of this month.

- Repeat the activity, using at least 10 examples from the calendar.

 COMMON ERROR!

Some students may not understand that "just before" and "just after" indicate one place away. Point to and name a number on a number line and have students identify numbers that come just before and just after that number.

Name _____

Order Numbers to 30

10 11 12 13 14 15 16 17 18 19 20 21 22 23 24 25 26 27 28 29 30

①
19   20   ___   22   ___   24

21   23

②
25   ___   ___   28   29   ___

26   27   30

Directions:
1–2. Write the missing numbers.

③
12   13   ___   15   16
11   14

④
___   21   ___   23   24   ___
20   22   25

⑤
17   ___   19   ___   21   22
18   20

⑥
24   ___   ___   ___   28   29
25   26   27

Directions:
3–6. Write the missing numbers. Then look back over the page and circle all the numbers you wrote that are before 20. Put an X on the number you wrote that is between 21 and 23.

Math at Home Activity: Make a number line. Ask your child to write five numbers in order on the number line.

③ Practice

Guided Practice

- Have students compare this number line at the top of the page to the number line in Exercise 1.
- **How can you find the missing number in the number line?** Sample answers: Use the first number line as a guide; count to find the missing numbers.
- Count "19, 20, frog, 22, frog, 24" with the students.
- Tell students that the frogs are sitting on top of a number so that number cannot be seen. Direct students to the top of p. 215 to discover which numbers each frog is covering. Have students write the missing number in the box below the frogs.
- Repeat the same for Exercise 2 as students write the missing numbers.

Independent Practice

Have students turn to p. 216. Explain the directions. Have students work independently on the exercises.

④ Assess

✓ Formative Assessment

Provide each student with a number line from zero to 30 in which three different, nonconsecutive numbers are missing. Have students write in the missing numbers.

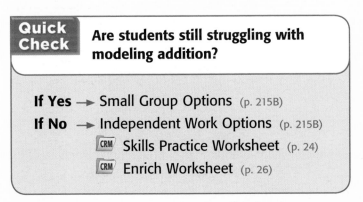

Quick Check — **Are students still struggling with modeling addition?**

If Yes → Small Group Options (p. 215B)
If No → Independent Work Options (p. 215B)
    CRM Skills Practice Worksheet (p. 24)
    CRM Enrich Worksheet (p. 26)

Lesson Planner _____

Objective
Estimate a group of objects and then count them.

Vocabulary
about, **estimate**

Resources
Materials: paper plates, pencils, white board
Manipulatives: two-colored counters, color tiles
Literature Connection: *How Many Snails? A Counting Book* by Paul Giganti, Jr.
Alternate Lesson: Use *Estimate and Checking* on pp. 308 and 309 of *Math Their Way* to provide practice in estimation.
Teacher Technology
  🔘 TeacherWorks

🔍 Focus on Math Background

This lesson emphasizes developing the number sense of students by teaching them strategies to estimate quantities up to 30. This lesson introduces five, 10, and 20, as landmark numbers to compare and anchor other quantities. For example, students will determine how close a quantity is to five, 10, or 20 to arrive at a reasonable estimate.

Daily Routine _____

Use these suggestions before beginning the lesson on p. 217.

5-Minute Check
(Reviews Lesson 8-5)
Give each student a number card. Have them place their cards in order on the chalkboard ledge.

Problem of the Day
1 Hold up a glass jar containing 25 to 30 counters. Tell students to guess, or estimate, how many counters are in the jar.

2 Empty the jar. Count with students. Have them say the estimate closest to the actual number.

 Have students estimate, then count, the number of giant steps needed from their seat to their place in line. Have them say how close their estimate was.

Building Math Vocabulary
Explain that an estimate tells **about** how many, rather than exactly how many. Tell students that when people say, "That costs about a dollar," they are estimating.

• Invite volunteers to close their eyes and **estimate** how many windows are in the room. Say that these numbers are guesses, or estimates, based on what they remembered. Tell students to count to find the exact number of windows.

• Repeat the activity with other objects.

Visual Vocabulary Cards
Use Visual Vocabulary Card 14 to reinforce the vocabulary introduced in this lesson. (The Define/Example/Ask routine is printed on the back of each card.)

Differentiated Instruction

Small Group Options

Option 1 Below/Approaching Level BL

- Draw three rows of stars on the chalkboard. From top to bottom, draw 10 stars, 20 stars, and 30 stars.
- Point to each star one at a time as students count aloud.
- Tell students that each row can help them estimate numbers close to 10, 20, and 30.
- Beneath the stars, draw a row of 12 hearts. Have students estimate how many hearts there are by comparing the row of hearts to the rows of stars.

AUDITORY

Option 2 English Language Learners ELL

Materials: classroom items
Core Vocabulary: closest, team, point
Common Use Verb: guess

Write Math This strategy helps students estimate numbers.

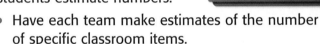

- Have each team make estimates of the number of specific classroom items.
- Count the exact number of each item and record information on the chalkboard.
- Give a point to the team closest to the estimate.

Independent Work Options

VISUAL

Option 1 Early Finishers OL AL

Materials: paper, crayon

- Tell students to look around and guess, or estimate, how many chairs are in the room. Tell them not to count chairs.
- Have students draw a chair, then write their number estimate.
- Have students count the number of chairs and see how close their estimate was to the actual number.

Option 2 Student Technology

Math Online > macmillanmh.com

Option 3 Learning Station: Science (p. 201G)

Direct students to the Science Learning Station for opportunities to explore and extend the lesson concept.

Leveled Lesson Resources

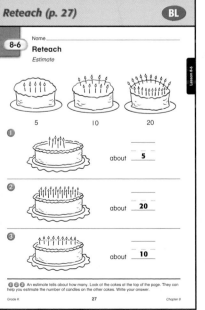

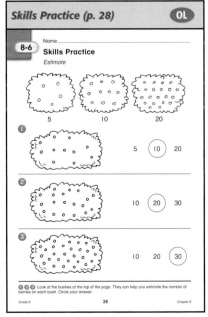

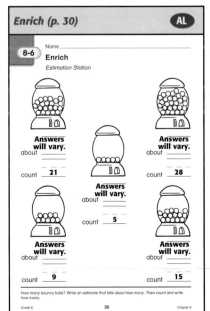

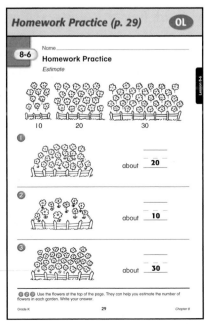

① Introduce

○ircle Time

Activity Choice 1 • Literature

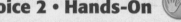

How Many Snails? A Counting Book by Paul Giganti, Jr.

- Before reading each page aloud, ask students to tell **about** how many big gray clouds there are, how many fish there are, and so on.

- As you read, have students **estimate** the answer to each question, and then count to find the answer.

- **What estimating strategies did you use?** counting one page and doubling it, using information from previous pages, counting by fives

- To extend, read aloud *Each Orange Had 8 Slices: A Counting Book* by Paul Giganti, Jr., which is similar, but more challenging.

Activity Choice 2 • Hands-On

Materials: paper plates, counters, whiteboard

- Place five counters on one plate, 10 on another, and 20 on another. Say and write the number of counters on each plate.

- Point to the five counters. **How many counters are on this plate?** five Tell students that knowing the amount is five can help them estimate the number of counters on the other plates.

- Point to the other two plates. **What plate do you think has 10 counters? Why?** Sample answer: The plate of 10 counters has a little more than five counters. Have the class count counters from the plate of 10 counters.

- **How many counters are on the last plate? How do you know?** 20; 20 was the greatest number and this plate has the most counters.

② Teach

- Direct students to the top of p. 217.
- Tell students that the mats at the top of the page match the mats and color tiles discussed while they were in the circle.
- **How many color tiles are on the yellow mat?** five Have students trace the dashed number.
- Repeat for the orange and green mats.

BL Alternate Teaching Strategy

If → students give estimates that are far greater or less than reasonable . . .

Then → use one of these reteach options.

1. CRM **Daily Reteach Worksheet** (p. 27)

2. **Play a Guessing Game** Tell students they will play a guessing, or estimating, game.

- Begin with objects few in number, such as windows or doors, asking students to estimate how many are in the classroom.

- Have students say their estimate aloud. Then have them check their work by making an actual count.

- Work up to larger numbers, such as the number of boys, girls, desks, coat hooks, and so on. After each estimate and counting, help students with using mental counting skills to improve their estimating skills.

COMMON ERROR!

Some students may be anxious about estimating, feeling that their estimate must be accurate. Calling estimation a guessing game should make students more comfortable. Explain that estimating is just looking, thinking, and guessing.

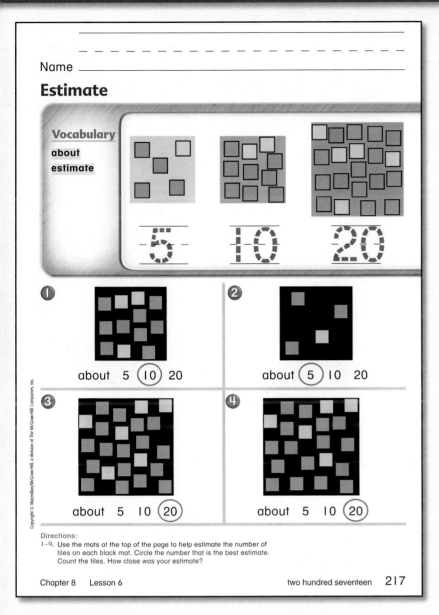

Name

Estimate

Vocabulary
about
estimate

about 5 (10) 20

about (5) 10 20

about 5 10 (20)

about 5 10 (20)

Directions:
1–4. Use the mats at the top of the page to help estimate the number of tiles on each black mat. Circle the number that is the best estimate. Count the tiles. How close was your estimate?

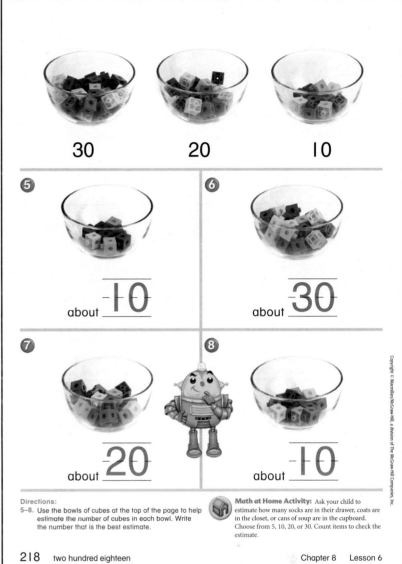

30   20   10

about ___10___

about ___30___

about ___20___

about ___10___

Directions:
5–8. Use the bowls of cubes at the top of the page to help estimate the number of cubes in each bowl. Write the number that is the best estimate.

Math at Home Activity: Ask your child to estimate how many socks are in their drawer, coats are in the closet, or cans of soup are in the cupboard. Choose from 5, 10, 20, or 30. Count items to check the estimate.

③ Practice

Guided Practice

- Direct students to the bottom of student page 217.
- In Exercise 1, have them estimate if the number of tiles on the black mat is about five, 10, or 20. **How many tiles do you think there are? Why do you think so?** About 10; The number of tiles looks more than five, but less than 20. Have students circle their answer. Then have students count the tiles. Ask if their estimate was reasonable.
- Repeat the activity for Exercises 2–4.

Independent Practice

Have students turn to p. 218. Explain the directions and have students work independently on the exercises.

④ Assess

✓ Formative Assessment

- Fill six ten-frames with counters. Separate the ten-frames so students can see three groups of counters: 10, 20, and 30.
- Display 15 red counters and 26 yellow counters.
- Have students write their estimates of red and yellow counters, then count to check their estimates. Ask if their estimate was close to the actual amount.

Quick Check | **Are students still struggling with estimating?**

If Yes → Small Group Options (p. 217B)
If No → Independent Work Options (p. 217B)
   CRM Skills Practice Worksheet (p. 28)
   CRM Enrich Worksheet (p. 30)

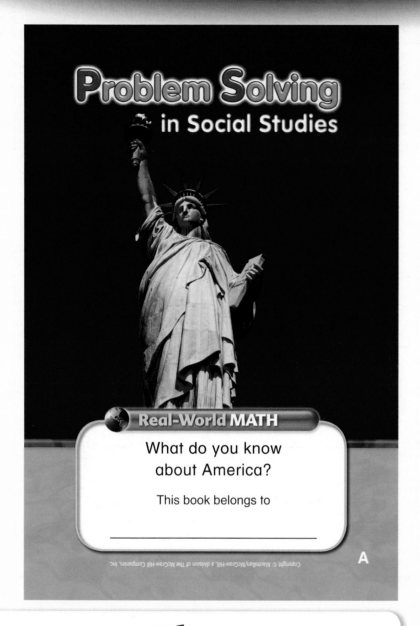

Problem Solving
in Social Studies

Real-World MATH

What do you know about America?

This book belongs to

_____

A

The bald eagle is a symbol of America.

How many eggs do you see?

___3___ eggs

B

Lesson Planner

Objective
Use illustrations to count objects.

National Standard
Students learn about cultural contributions from various regions of the United States and how they helped to form a national heritage.

Activate Prior Knowledge
Before you turn students' attention to the pages, discuss with them things they know about America.

- **What is our country called?** United States of America
- **What does an American flag have on it?** stars and stripes
- **Where have you seen a flag?** school, library, classroom

The bald eagle symbol is on money.

Can you find it?
Circle your answer.

C

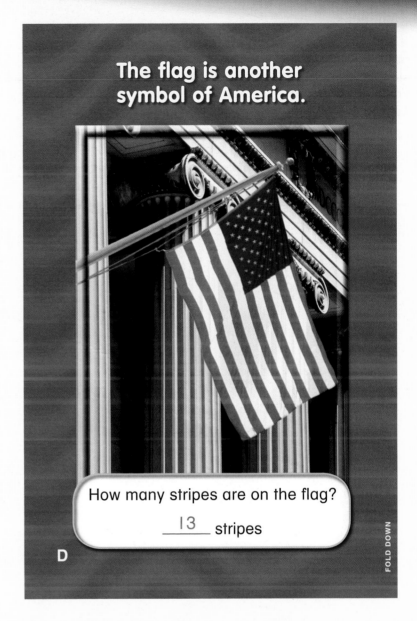

The flag is another symbol of America.

How many stripes are on the flag?

___13___ stripes

D

FOLD DOWN

Create the Book

Guide students to create their book.

- Have them fold the page in half.

- Ask them to write their name on page A.

- Explain that page A is the front cover and page D is the back cover. If necessary, have them practice flipping through the book in order.

- Guide them in reading the information and word problems on each of the pages.

Use the Student Pages

Have students work individually or in pairs to solve the word problems on pages B–D.

Page B Have students point to and touch each egg they see in the nest.

Page C Have students point to each bald eagle they see on the dollar bill and quarters, then count the total number.

Page D Have students mark each stripe, number each stripe, or move a counter when counting.

If necessary, review the problem-solving strategies suggested in Lesson 8-3, p. 209.

WRITING IN ►MATH Have students draw an eagle's nest with more than three eggs in it. Then have them write the number of eggs they drew by the nest.

FOLDABLES Dinah Zike's Foldables

Use these lesson suggestions for incorporating the Foldables during the chapter.

Lesson 8-5 Use the display cases made in Chapter 1 to help students recognize, count, and compare numbers to 30. Determine which groups have *more*, *less*, or the same (*equal*) number of objects. Place a group of objects in one of the display cases. Ask students to estimate the number of objects. Have students count the objects to check the reasonableness of the estimates.

Chapter 8 Project

Number Posters

Lead a discussion on the results of the completed chapter project with the class.

Vocabulary Review

Review chapter vocabulary using one of the following options.

- **Visual Vocabulary Cards** (2, 4, 13, 14, 20, and 25)
- **eGlossary** at macmillanmh.com

Data-Driven Decision Making

Based on the results of the Chapter Review/Test, use the following to review concepts that continue to present students with problems.

Exercises	State/Local Standard	What's the Math?	Error Analysis	Resources for Review
1 Lesson 8-2		Count and write numbers up to 30.	Does not count objects correctly. Writes wrong number.	**CRM** Chapter 8 Resource Masters (Reteach Worksheets)
2 Lesson 8-4		Compare numbers up to 30.	Does not compare numbers correctly. Writes wrong number. Does not circle number showing "less."	**Math Online** Concepts in Motion Math Adventures
3 Lesson 8-5		Orders numbers up to 30 in a sequence.	Does not know how to order numbers. Reverses order when writing in missing numbers.	

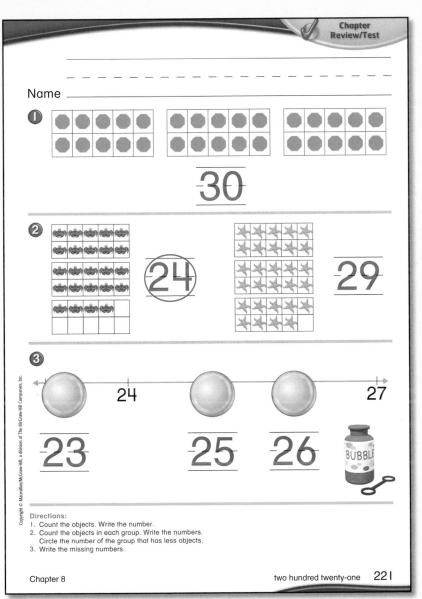

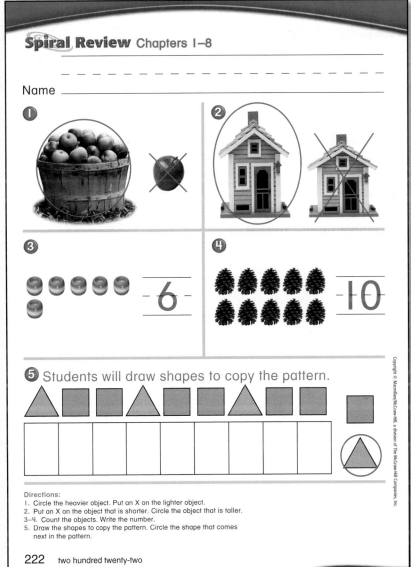

Summative Assessment

Use these alternate leveled chapter tests to differentiate assessment for the specific needs of your students.

Leveled Chapter 8 Tests			
Form	Type	Level	CRM Pages
1	Multiple Choice	BL	38–39
2A	Multiple Choice	OL	40–41
2C	Multiple Choice	OL	42–43
2D	Free Response	AL	44–45

BL = below/approaching grade level
OL = on grade level
AL = above/beyond grade level

Spiral Review

Reviews Chapters 1 to 8

Objective: Review and assess mastery of skills and concepts from previous chapters.

Resources for Review

Based on student results, refer to these lessons for remediation.

- **Exercise 1: Lesson 7-5** (p. 189)
- **Exercise 2: Lesson 7-3** (p. 183)
- **Exercise 3: Lesson 4-3** (p. 105)
- **Exercise 4: Lesson 4-5** (p. 111)
- **Exercise 5: Lesson 3-3** (p. 75)

Test Practice

Chapters 1–8

 Formative Assessment

- You can use Student Edition pp. 223–224 to benchmark student progress.

- Additional practice pages can be found in Chapter 8 Resource Masters.

CRM **Chapter 8 Resource Masters**
   Cumulative Test Practice (p. 96)
- Multiple Choice format (pp. 38-43)
- Free Response format (pp. 44-45)

ExamView®
Assessment Suite Create additional practice worksheets or tests.

Test-Taking Tips

For the Teacher

- It may be helpful to remind students to double check that they put their name on their test.

- It may be beneficial to the students if you review some of the chapter vocabulary prior to taking the test.

For the Student

- Tell students to be neat.

- Encourage students to answer all the questions on the test.

- Encourage students tp fill in the entire oval while answering questions on the test.

- Inform students that if they finish the test early, it can be helpful if they check over their answers.

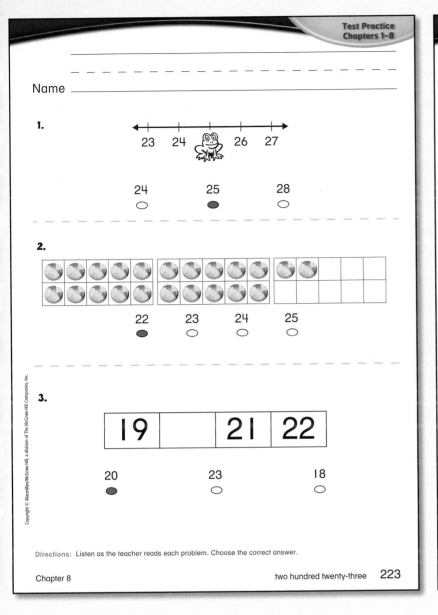

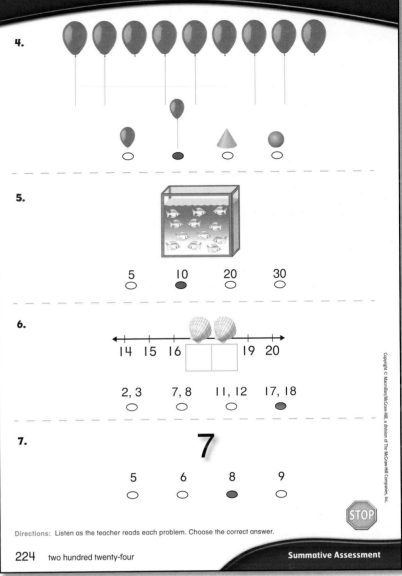

Name _____

1.

2.

3.

4.

5.

6.

7.

Directions: Listen as the teacher reads each problem. Choose the correct answer.

Chapter 8

two hundred twenty-three 223

224 two hundred twenty-four

Directions: Listen as the teacher reads each problem. Choose the correct answer.

Summative Assessment

Test Directions for Teachers

Read the following directions to students before they begin. Then read each question followed by a pause to allow students time to work and choose an answer. The first test item can be worked as a class example.

- **Write your name at the top of the page.**
- **I am going to read each question to you. Listen carefully to the entire question before you choose an answer.**

1. Look at the frog on the number line. Count on to find the missing number. Mark the number that is missing.

2. Look at the beach balls. Count the beach balls. Find the number that shows how many beach balls. Mark the number that shows how many beach balls.

3. Look at the counting pattern. Now look at the numbers below the pattern. Mark the number that is missing from the pattern.

- **Turn the page over.**

4. Look at the ballon pattern. Which object comes next in the pattern? Mark the object.

5. Look at the fish in the tank. Estimate the number of fish in the tank. Mark the number that tells about how many fish are in the tank.

6. Look at the shells on the number line. Count on to find the missing numbers. Mark the numbers that are missing.

7. Look at the number seven. Now look at the numbers under seven. Mark the number that is one more than seven.

Chapter 8 Test Practice **224**

Chapter Overview

Chapter-at-a-Glance

In Chapter 9, students work with concepts of time, sequencing events, using a calendar to keep track of events, and telling time to the hour.

Lesson	Math Objective	State/Local Standards
9-1 **Morning, Afternoon, and Evening** (pp. 229–230)	Identify and discriminate between morning, afternoon, and evening.	
9-2 **Days of the Week** (pp. 231–232)	Name and sequence the days of the week.	
9-3 **Calendar** (pp. 233–234)	Read and use a calendar.	
9-4 **Today, Yesterday, and Tomorrow** (pp. 235–236)	Sequence days of the week to explain today, tomorrow, and yesterday.	
9-5 **Using an Analog Clock** (pp. 239–240)	Tell time to the hour using an analog clock.	
9-6 **Using a Digital Clock** (pp. 241–242)	Read the time on a digital clock.	
9-7 **Problem-Solving Strategy: Make a Table** (pp. 243–244)	Make a table to answer questions.	

Use Time

BIG Idea Words and phrases regarding time are a common part of our everyday language. Greetings such as good morning or good night actually indicate that it is a certain time of day. The use of clocks and calendars are also essential to life in our society. In this chapter, students are introduced to many of the commonly used aspects of time, such as days of the week, months in a year, and hours in a day.

Algebra Students learn to sequence events and days of the week in preparation for Algebra. Lessons 9-1 and 9-2

GK-FP3 *Measurement:* **Ordering objects by measurable attributes**

Children use measurable attributes, such as length or weight, to solve problems by comparing and ordering objects. They compare the lengths of two objects both directly (by comparing them with each other) and indirectly (by comparing both with a third object), and they order several objects according to length.

Skills Trace
Vertical Alignment

PreKindergarten

In PreK, students learned to:

- Understand ordinal concepts: *before, after, what comes next, third, fourth, fifth,* and *last.*

Kindergarten

During this chapter, students learn to:

- Understand the concept of time and units to measure it.
- Demonstrate an understanding of concepts of time and the tools that measure time.
- Name the days of the week.
- Identify the time to the nearest hour.

After this chapter, students will learn to:

- Identify common objects in their environment and describe geometric features.
- Identify and describe common geometric objects (e.g., circle, triangle, square, rectangle, cube, sphere, cone).

First Grade

In first grade, students will learn to:

- Use direct comparison and nonstandard units to describe the measurements of objects.
- Tell time to the nearest half hour and relate time to events (e.g., before/after, shorter/longer).

BackMapping and Vertical Alignment McGraw-Hill's *Math Connects* program was conceived and developed with the final results in mind: student success in Algebra 1 and beyond. The authors, using the **NCTM Focal Points and Focal Connections** as their guide, developed this brand new series by backmapping from Algebra 1 concepts, and vertically aligning the topics so that they build upon prior skills and concepts and serve as a foundation for future topics.

Math Vocabulary

The following math vocabulary words for Chapter 9 are listed in the glossary of the **Student Edition**. You can find interactive definitions in 13 languages in the **eGlossary** at macmillanmh.com.

hour, o'clock (p. 239)

morning, afternoon, evening (p. 229)

today, yesterday, tomorrow (p. 235)

week, month (pp. 231, 233)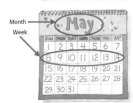

year (p. 233)

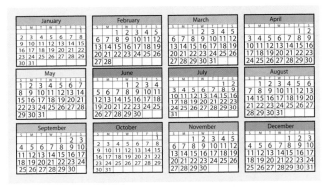

Visual Vocabulary Card Use Visual Vocabulary Cards 3, 15, 24, 26, 28, 46, 47, 49, and 50 to introduce the vocabulary in this chapter. (The Define/Example/Ask routine is printed on the back of each card.)

today

Chapter Planner

Suggested Pacing		
Instruction	Review and Assessment	TOTAL
7 days	2 days	**9 days**

Diagnostic Assessment
Are You Ready? (p. 226)

	Lesson 9-1 Pacing: 1 day	**Lesson 9-2** Pacing: 1 day	**Lesson 9-3** Pacing: 1 day
Lesson/ Objective	**Morning, Afternoon, and Evening** (pp. 229–230) **Objective:** Identify and discriminate between morning, afternoon, and evening.	**Days of the Week** (pp. 231–232) **Objective:** Name and sequence the days of the week.	**Calendar** (pp. 233–234) **Objective:** Read and use a calendar.
State/Local Standards			
Math Vocabulary	**morning afternoon evening**	**week**	**month year**
Lesson Resources	**Materials** chart paper with morning, afternoon, and evening icons, scissors, magazines **Other Resources** CRM Leveled Worksheets (pp. 6–9) Daily Reteach Problem of the Day	**Materials** 7 days-of-the-week cards, calendar **Other Resources** CRM Leveled Worksheets (pp. 10–13) Daily Reteach Problem of the Day	**Materials** months of the year name cards, classroom calendar, blank stickers, markers, masking tape, two-colored dice **Other Resources** CRM Leveled Worksheets (pp. 14–17) Daily Reteach Problem of the Day
Technology Math Online			Concepts in Motion
Reaching All Learners	English Learners, p. 229B ELL Below Level, p. 229B BL Early Finishers, p. 229B OL AL	English Learners, p. 231B ELL Below Level, p. 231B BL Early Finishers, p. 231B OL AL	English Learners, p. 233B ELL Gifted and Talented, p. 233B AL Early Finishers, p. 233B OL AL
Alternate Lesson			*Math Their Way*, p. 156

KEY

BL Below/Approaching Level OL On Level AL Above/Beyond Level ELL English Learners

SE Student Edition TE Teacher Edition CRM Chapter 9 Resource Masters CD-Rom

Transparency Flip Chart Real-World Problem Solving Library

Lesson 9-4 Pacing: 1 day	**Lesson 9-5** Pacing: 1 day	**Lesson 9-6** Pacing: 1 day	

Lesson 9-4   Pacing: 1 day

Today, Yesterday, and Tomorrow
(pp. 235–236)

Objective: Sequence days of the week to explain today, tomorrow, and yesterday.

Lesson 9-5   Pacing: 1 day

Using an Analog Clock
(pp. 239–240)

Objective: Tell time to the hour using an analog clock.

Lesson 9-6   Pacing: 1 day

Using a Digital Clock
(pp. 241–242)

Objective: Read the time on a digital clock.

Lesson/ Objective

State/Local Standards

today
yesterday
tomorrow

hour
o'clock

Math Vocabulary

Materials
days of the week necklace cards, calendar, sticky notes, pencil, chart paper

Materials
chart paper

Manipulatives
demonstration analog clock, student clocks

Materials
digital clock, chart paper, markers, time cards

Manipulatives
demonstration analog clock, counters

Lesson Resources

Other Resources
CRM Leveled Worksheets (pp. 18–21)
Daily Reteach
Problem of the Day

Other Resources
CRM Leveled Worksheets (pp. 22–25)
Daily Reteach
Problem of the Day

Other Resources
CRM Leveled Worksheets (pp. 26–29)
Daily Reteach
Problem of the Day

♪ Math Song Track 5
Math Adventures
Concepts in Motion

♪ Math Song Track 5
Math Adventures

Technology

◁ **Math Online**

English Learners, p. 235B **ELL**
Below Level, p. 235B **BL**
Early Finishers, p. 235B **OL** **AL**

English Learners, p. 239B **ELL**
Below Level, p. 239B **BL**
Early Finishers, p. 239B **OL** **AL**

English Learners, p. 241B **ELL**
Gifted and Talented, p. 241B **AL**
Early Finishers, p. 241B **OL** **AL**

Reaching All Learners

Math Their Way, p. 155

Alternate Lesson

Formative Assessment
Mid-Chapter Check (p. 237)

Game Time: Time for Vacation! (p. 238)

Chapter Planner

	Lesson 9-7 **Pacing:** 1 day
Lesson/ Objective	**Problem-Solving Strategy** **Make a Table** (pp. 243–244) **Objective:** Make a table to answer questions.
State/Local Standards	
Math Vocabulary	
Lesson Resources	**Materials** pictures, pencils, blank calendar sheet **Manipulatives** analog demonstration clock **Other Resources** [CRM] Leveled Worksheets (pp. 30–34) Daily Reteach Problem of the Day *Then and Now*
Technology [Math Online]	
Reaching All Learners	English Learners, p. 243B **ELL** Below Level, p. 243B **BL** Early Finishers, p. 243B **OL** **AL**
Alternate Lesson	**Problem Solving in Music** (p. 245)
✓	**Summative Assessment** • Chapter Review/Test (p. 247) • Test Practice (p. 249)

Assessment Options

✓ Diagnostic Assessment

- **SE** *Option 1:* Are You Ready? (p. 226)
- *Option 2:* Online Quiz (macmillanmh.com)
- *Option 3:* Diagnostic Test (p. 36)

✓ Formative Assessment

- **TE** Alternate Teaching Strategies (every lesson)
- **TE** Writing in Math (every lesson)
- **TE** Line Up (every lesson)
- **SE** Mid-Chapter Check (p. 237)
- **CRM** Mid-Chapter Test (p. 37)

✓ Summative Assessment

- **SE** Chapter Review/Test (p. 247)
- **SE** Test Practice (p. 249)
- **CRM** Leveled Chapter Tests (pp. 42–49)
- **CRM** Cumulative Test Practice (pp. 50–51)
- **CRM** Listening Assessment (pp. 40–41)
- **CRM** Oral Assessment (pp. 38–39)
- ExamView® Assessment Suite
- Advance Tracker

Professional Development

McGraw-Hill

Targeted professional development has been articulated throughout **McGraw-Hill's** *Math Connects* program. The **McGraw-Hill Professional Development Video Library** provides short videos that support the **NCTM Focal Points and Focal Connections**. For more information, visit macmillanmh.com.

Model Lessons	Instructional Strategies

What the Research Says . . .

In this passage, Sydney Schwartz (1984) outlines a developmental sequence for introducing formal time keeping tools, such as calendars, to young children:

"Initially, young children in school want to know what to expect in the sequence of a daily program. They want to know about the sequence of different activities across the period of a week. Slowly, as children develop the ability to anticipate the pattern of their school lives by using a recorded experience, teachers can offer a variety of developmentally appropriate calendars and create a "calendar rich" environment." (p. 109)

Schwartz, Sydney L. 1984. Calendar Reading: a Tradition that Begs Remodeling. *Teaching Children Mathematics*. 1 (2): 104–109.

Teacher Notes

Learning Stations
Cross-Curricular Links

Reading

pairs | **LINGUISTIC**

Candy Colors

- Listen to the story.
- Make a chart.
- Look in the book.
- Draw the color candy.

Teacher Note: Read the book aloud, discussing what Little Pea eats each day. Help students make a chart with the days of the week on the left, and space for students to draw on the right. Have students draw the color candy Little Pea has each day of the week for dinner. Have the book available for students to complete this activity.

Materials:
- *Little Pea* by Amy Krouse Rosenthal
- paper
- crayons

Art

small group | **KINESTHETIC**

Clock Collage

- Cut out five clocks.
- Make a collage.
- Trade with a partner.
- Share your collage.

Teacher Note: Have a collection of magazines available for students to cut up. Students can cut out pictures of watches if they cannot find enough clocks. Tell students to glue their pictures on construction paper. Have students compare collages with a partner by trading.

Materials:
- old magazines
- construction paper
- scissors
- glue

Language Arts

individual | **LINGUISTIC**

Morning Events

- Fold your paper in three columns.
- Draw three things you do in the morning in order.
- Number the boxes.
- Share your pictures.

Teacher Note: Help students fold paper in three columns. After students draw their pictures, have them number the pictures in the order in which they do the activities shown. Have students share their pictures with the rest of the class and discuss similarities and differences.

Materials:
- construction paper
- crayons

Science

individual | SPATIAL

Time Capsule

- Fold the paper to make four boxes.
- Draw four activities that you do from day to day.
- Roll up your paper.

Teacher Note: Help students fold adding machine tape in half two times. Have students count the four boxes made by folding. Magazines could be available for students to use for their pictures if they would rather cut out and glue pictures than draw. Tell students to draw or glue their pictures in the order in which they do the activities. Tell them to draw the weather that might occur on the day of their activity. After students roll up their paper, have them put the paper in a film canister, put the lid on the canister, then label the canister with a sticker on which they have written their name.

Materials:
- blank adding machine tape strips
- pencils
- crayons
- film canisters
- circle stickers
- magazines

Health

small group | SOCIAL

Go for a Minute!

- Try doing something for one minute.
- Time yourself.
- Draw what you did.
- Try something else.

Teacher Note: Model the kinds of activities students can do. Suggest the following activities to students: jumping up and down, clapping hands, running in place, and bouncing a ball. Model how to use a sand timer, and tell students that when all of the sand reaches the bottom, a minute has passed. Encourage students to share their drawings with the rest of the class.

Materials:
- minute sand timer
- paper
- crayons

Calendar Time

Numbering Days of the Month

- Have students make a calendar for the current month.
- Write in the numbers on the calendar.
- Ask students to name the day of the week on which the 10th falls. Repeat with several dates.
- Ask how many days the month has and how many days a week has. Have students tell what day of the week it will be tomorrow.
- Write in any special days on the calendar.

Teacher Note: Help students begin their calendar on the correct day. Do this by looking at the last day of the previous month.

Sunday	Monday	Tuesday	Wednesday	Thursday	Friday	Saturday
	1	2	3	4	5	6
7	8	9	10	11	12	13
14	15	16	17	18	19	20
21	22	23	24	25	26	27
28	29	30	31	January		

Introduce the Chapter

🌐 Real World: Find Clocks

- Line students up for a tour around the school.

- Challenge students to find clocks as they travel.

- Along the way ask students questions about how time relates to the school: Why does the principal need to know the time? How do teachers use time? Why don't we come to school at night? What would happen if there were no clocks or watches to tell time?

Use the Student Page

Have students turn to p. 225. Guide students to discuss the images on the page and answer the Explore questions.

Key Vocabulary

Introduce the key vocabulary in the chapter using the routine below.

<u>Define:</u> **Morning** is the period of time from sunrise to noon.
<u>Example:</u> Morning is usually when you wake up to start the day.
<u>Ask:</u> What is one thing you do in the morning?

Diagnostic Assessment

Check for students' prerequisite skills before beginning the chapter.

- **Option 1:** *Are You Ready for Chapter 9?*
  SE Student Edition, p. 226

- **Option 2:** *Online Assessment Quiz*
  Math Online ⟩ macmillanmh.com

- **Option 3:** *Diagnostic Test*
  CRM Chapter 9 Resource Masters, p. 36

RTI (Response to Intervention)

Apply the Results Based on the results of the diagnostic assessment on student p. 226, use the chart on the next page to address individual needs before and during the chapter.

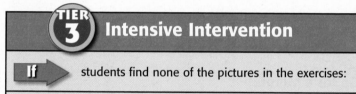

TIER 3	Intensive Intervention
If	students find none of the pictures in the exercises:
Then	use Chapters 2 and 10 of *Math Triumphs*, an intensive math intervention program from McGraw-Hill

 **Dinah Zike's Foldables**

Guide students to create a Three-Tab Book Foldable graphic organizer to understand time.

① Fold a sheet of paper like a hot dog.

② With the paper horizontal, and the fold of the hot dog up, fold the right side toward the center, trying to cover one half of the paper.

③ Fold the left side over the right side to make a book with three folds.

④ Open the folded book. Place your hands between the two thicknesses of paper and cut up the two valleys on one side only. This will form three tabs.

⑤ Label the tabs from left to right: *Today, Tomorrow,* and *Yesterday.*

 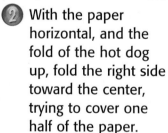 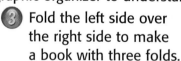   

When to Use It Lessons 9-1, 9-3, and 9-4 (*Additional instructions for using the Foldable with these lessons are found on pp. 237 and 247.*)

Key Vocabulary
morning
afternoon
evening
today
o'clock

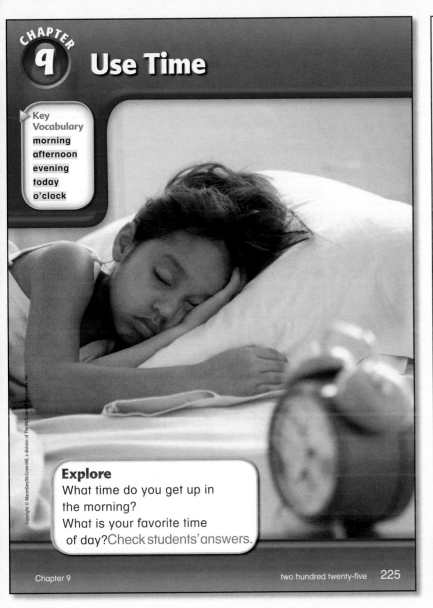

Explore
What time do you get up in the morning?
What is your favorite time of day? Check students' answers.

Name _____

Math Online
Take the Chapter Readiness
Quiz at macmillanmh.com .

Are You Ready for Chapter 9?

Sample answers:

Directions: Circle three things in this picture that tell what day or time it is.

RTI (Response to Intervention)

TIER 2 **Strategic Intervention** below/approaching grade level	TIER 1 **On-Level**	**Above/Beyond Level**
If students find one of the pictures: **Exercises 1–4**	**If** students find two of the pictures: **Exercises 1–4**	**If** students find all of the pictures: **Exercises 1–4**
Then choose a resource:	**Then** choose a resource:	**Then** choose a resource:
CRM Chapter 2 Resource Masters (Reteach Worksheets) Math Online Concepts in Motion	TE Learning Stations (pp. 225G–225H) TE Chapter Project (p. 227) CRM Game: Time and Time Again Math Adventures My Math Zone Chapter 8	TE Learning Stations (pp. 225G–225H) TE Chapter Project (p. 227) Real-World Problem Solving: *Then and Now* My Math Zone Chapters 8 and 9 Math Online Game

WRITING IN ▶ MATH

Starting the Chapter
Have students draw a picture of two things they do in the morning before school. Help students write a caption for their picture or have them dictate a sentence for you to write.

Chapter 9 Project

Student Journals

- Set up a math center with blank calendar grids, analog clock rubber stamps, date stamp, a list of the vocabulary words in the chapter, construction paper, writing paper and art supplies.

- Ask students to visit the center each day or a few times each week to create a journal or calendar page to illustrate the things they are doing that day or special events coming up during the month.

- Help students to write the date on each journal page or have students stamp the date with a date stamp.

- Encourage students to use vocabulary words in their writing and to use drawings and the clock stamp to represent the time of the day they are writing about.

- Help students to organize all journal pages in order, bind them together in a book, and have students share their journals with the class and their families.

Chapter 9 Literature List

Lesson	Book Title	Author
9-1	Isn't It Time?	Judy Hindley
9-2	The Very Hungry Caterpillar	Eric Carle
9-3	How Do You Say It Today, Jesse Bear?	Nancy White Calstrom
9-4	Wednesday Is Spaghetti Day	Maryann Cocca-Leffler
9-5	I Can Tell the Time	Gail Davies
9-6	Time to…	Bruce McMillan
9-7	Brown Rabbit's Day	Alan Baker
Any	Seven Blind Mice	Ed Young
Any	Rabbit's Pajama Party	Stuart J. Murphy
Any	Mañana Iguana	Ann Whitford Paul

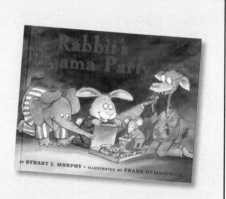

ELL National ESL Standards Alignment for Chapter 9			
Lesson, Page	ESL Standard	Modality	Level
9-1, p. 229B	Goal 1, Standard 2, c	Visual, Intrapersonal	Intermediate
9-2, p. 231B	Goal 1, Standard 3, d	Auditory, Linguistic	Intermediate
9-3, p. 233B	Goal 1, Standard 1, a	Logical	Intermediate
9-4, p. 235B	Goal 1, Standard 3, b	Auditory, Spatial	Intermediate
9-5, p. 239B	Goal 1, Standard 3, k	Auditory	Beginning
9-6, p. 241B	Goal 2, Standard 1, a	Kinesthetic, Visual	Intermediate
9-7, p. 243B	Goal 2, Standard 2, e	Spatial	Advanced

The National ESL Standards can be found in the Teacher Reference Handbook.

English

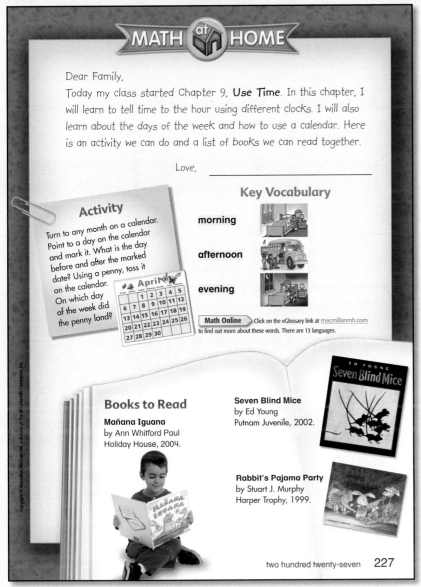

MATH at HOME

Dear Family,
Today my class started Chapter 9, **Use Time**. In this chapter, I will learn to tell time to the hour using different clocks. I will also learn about the days of the week and how to use a calendar. Here is an activity we can do and a list of books we can read together.

Love, _____

Activity
Turn to any month on a calendar. Point to a day on the calendar and mark it. What is the day before and after the marked date? Using a penny, toss it on the calendar. On which day of the week did the penny land?

April

			1	2	3	4	5
6	7	8	9	10	11	12
13	14	15	16	17	18	19
20	21	22	23	24	25	26
27	28	29	30			

Key Vocabulary
morning

afternoon

evening

Math Online Click on the eGlossary link at macmillanmh.com to find out more about these words. There are 13 languages.

Books to Read
Mañana Iguana
by Ann Whitford Paul
Holiday House, 2004.

Seven Blind Mice
by Ed Young
Putnam Juvenile, 2002.

Rabbit's Pajama Party
by Stuart J. Murphy
Harper Trophy, 1999.

two hundred twenty-seven 227

Español

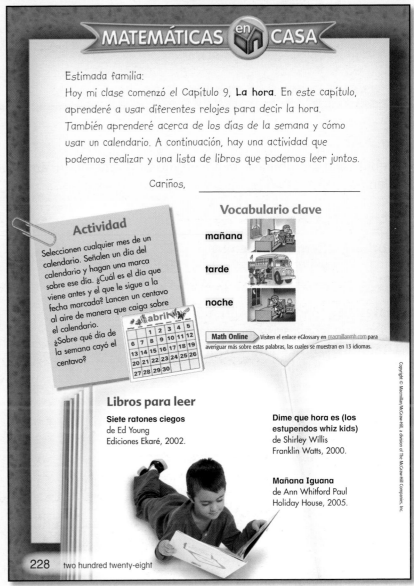

MATEMÁTICAS en CASA

Estimada familia:
Hoy mi clase comenzó el Capítulo 9, **La hora**. En este capítulo, aprenderé a usar diferentes relojes para decir la hora. También aprenderé acerca de los días de la semana y cómo usar un calendario. A continuación, hay una actividad que podemos realizar y una lista de libros que podemos leer juntos.

Cariños, _____

Actividad
Seleccionen cualquier mes de un calendario. Señalen un día del calendario y hagan una marca sobre ese día. ¿Cuál es el día que viene antes y el que le sigue a la fecha marcada? Lancen un centavo al aire de manera que caiga sobre el calendario. ¿Sobre qué día de la semana cayó el centavo?

abril

			1	2	3	4	5
6	7	8	9	10	11	12
13	14	15	16	17	18	19
20	21	22	23	24	25	26
27	28	29	30			

Vocabulario clave
mañana

tarde

noche

Math Online Visiten el enlace eGlossary en macmillanmh.com para averiguar más sobre estas palabras, las cuales se muestran en 13 idiomas.

Libros para leer
Siete ratones ciegos
de Ed Young
Ediciones Ekaré, 2002.

Dime que hora es (los estupendos whiz kids)
de Shirley Willis
Franklin Watts, 2000.

Mañana Iguana
de Ann Whitford Paul
Holiday House, 2005.

228 two hundred twenty-eight

MATH at HOME

- Read the Math at Home letter on p. 227 with the class and have each student sign it.

- Send home copies of the Math at Home letter with each student.

- Use the Spanish letter on p. 228 for students with Spanish-speaking parents or guardians.

Read-Aloud Anthology

For an optional reading activity to introduce this chapter's math concepts, see the Read-Aloud Anthology on p. TR31.

Morning, Afternoon, and Evening

Lesson Planner

Objective
Identify and discriminate between morning, afternoon, and evening.

Vocabulary
morning, afternoon, evening

Resources
Materials: chart paper with morning, afternoon, and evening icons, scissors, magazines
Literature Connection: *Isn't It Time?* by Judy Hindley
Teacher Technology
⊙ TeacherWorks

Focus on Math Background

Students begin to orient themselves in time by sequencing familiar routines within a predictable schedule (e.g., I wake up; then I eat breakfast; then I go to school). As students recognize these daily cycles, they organize their daily events into categories such as morning, afternoon, and evening.

In this lesson, students discuss and order the routines of their daily schedule at school. Then they sort and classify these events into morning, afternoon, and evening. Such understanding lays the foundation for future mathematical vocabulary, such as A.M. and P.M., and how to determine A.M. and P.M. on analog and digital clocks.

Daily Routine

Use these suggestions before beginning the lesson on p. 229.

5-Minute Check
(Reviews Lesson 8-6)
Have students look at a small jar or container filled with attribute buttons. About how many buttons are in the jar? Sample answer: 20 buttons

Problem of the Day
Have students draw a picture of an activity they do in the morning, and another picture of an activity they do in the evening.

LINE UP Have students line up by how they get to school in the morning: by bus, car, van, walking, and so on.

Building Math Vocabulary

- Write **morning**, **afternoon**, and **evening** on the chalkboard. Draw a picture of each time of day next to each word, such as a sunrise, a sun high in the sky, and a moon. Point to the words and discuss them.

- Put students into three groups: morning, afternoon, and evening. Tell each group to jump up and down if the activity you state is done at their group's time of day.

- Call out activities such as eat breakfast, get dressed, brush your teeth, and read a story. Some activities, such as brush your teeth, may cause more than one group to jump.

Visual Vocabulary Cards
Use Visual Vocabulary Card 26 to reinforce the vocabulary introduced in this lesson. (The Define/Example/Ask routine is printed on the back of each card.)

morning

Differentiated Instruction

Small Group Options

Option 1 — Below/Approaching Level BL
VISUAL

Materials: paper, crayons, pencils

- Have students draw pictures of their activities for one day and record what time they did each activity (morning, afternoon, evening).
- Have students form small groups to share memories about their events.

Option 2 — English Language Learners ELL
VISUAL, INTRAPERSONAL

Materials: large paper sun
Core Vocabulary: when, what do you do?, sun
Common Use Verb: show

See Math This strategy helps students determine the differences between morning, afternoon, and evening.

- Show the position of the sun in the morning, at noon, and in the evening by moving it from right to left when facing students.
- Have students draw one activity they do at each time of the day. Ask, "What do you do?" at each time.

Independent Work Options

Option 1 — Early Finishers OL AL
LINGUISTIC

Materials: construction paper, crayons, markers, stickers

- Have students fold a sheet of construction paper in half.
- Have students create scenes using stickers for morning, afternoon, and evening in the middle and the back.
- Have students label each page either *morning, afternoon,* or *evening*.
- Have students write *Morning, Afternoon, and Evening* as a title on the front.

Option 2 — Student Technology

Math Online > macmillanmh.com

Option 3 — Learning Station: Language Arts (p. 225G)

Direct students to the Language Arts Learning Station for opportunities to explore and extend the lesson concept.

Leveled Lesson Resources
Additional support for English Language Learners can be found in the ELL Guide (p. 59). ELL

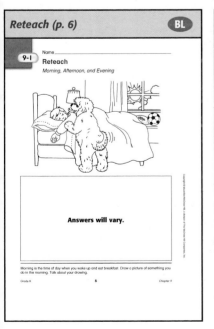

Reteach (p. 6) BL

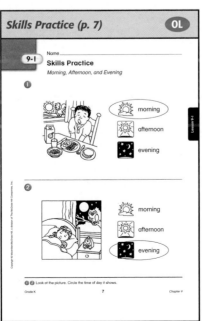

Skills Practice (p. 7) OL

Enrich (p. 9) AL

Homework Practice (p. 8) OL

① Introduce

Circle Time
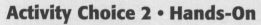
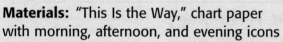

Activity Choice 1 • Literature

Isn't It Time? by Judy Hindley

- Read the book aloud. Discuss the activities specific to morning, afternoon, evening, and night.

- Have a volunteer act out an activity. Ask students to guess the activity and identify whether it occurs during the **morning**, **afternoon**, **evening**, or night.

- Repeat with other volunteers. Display on a chart which activities occur during morning, afternoon, evening, or night.

Activity Choice 2 • Hands-On

Materials: "This Is the Way," chart paper with morning, afternoon, and evening icons

This is the way we brush our teeth, brush our teeth, brush our teeth. This is the way we brush our teeth, early in the morning.

- Gather students together.
- Lead the class in singing the song "This Is the Way."
- Display pictures illustrating routines from the song. Encourage students to act out the verses.
- Repeat song using different activities for the afternoon and evening.

② Teach

- Direct students to the top of p. 229.
- Discuss the activity in the first picture.
- Have students tell about activities in their morning routines.
- Explain the icon for morning.
- Tell students that in the morning the sun comes up, just like the sun is coming up in the picture, and this is called sunrise.
- Repeat the steps above with afternoon and evening.

BL Alternate Teaching Strategy

If students have trouble understanding the difference between morning, afternoon, and evening . . .

Then use one of these reteach options.

1. CRM **Daily Reteach Worksheet** (p. 6)

2. **Make Collages** Read aloud *The Snowy Day* by Ezra Jack Keats.

   - Discuss the activities Peter did in the morning, during the afternoon, or what he may have done in the evening.

   - Have students cut out daytime and nighttime pictures from old magazines or books.

   - Have students make a daytime collage and a nighttime collage by sorting and then gluing their pictures into two categories, day and night, on a sheet of construction paper.

⚠ COMMON ERROR!

Students may have difficulty differentiating between morning and afternoon because the sun can be seen in the morning and in the afternoon. Explain the different positions of the sun during each of these times to help students visualize differences.

Morning, Afternoon, and Evening

Vocabulary
morning
afternoon
evening

morning   afternoon   evening

①

②

Directions:
1–2. Look at the picture. Circle the time of day it shows.

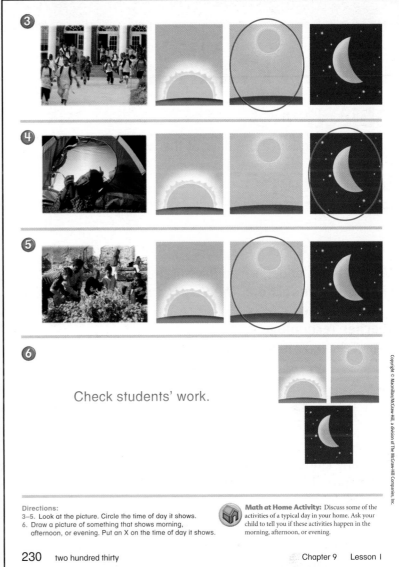

③

④

⑤

⑥ Check students' work.

Directions:
3–5. Look at the picture. Circle the time of day it shows.
6. Draw a picture of something that shows morning, afternoon, or evening. Put an X on the time of day it shows.

Math at Home Activity: Discuss some of the activities of a typical day in your home. Ask your child to tell you if these activities happen in the morning, afternoon, or evening.

③ Practice

Guided Practice

- Direct students to the bottom of p. 229.
- Have them circle the time of day each picture shows.

Independent Practice

Have students turn to p. 230. Explain the directions. Have students work independently on the exercises.

④ Assess

✓ Formative Assessment

Have students tell about an activity that they do in the morning, afternoon, or evening. **What is something you do in the afternoon?** Sample answers: play with friends; eat a meal; ride my bike; read a book

Quick Check   **Are students still struggling to differentiate between morning, afternoon, and evening?**

If Yes → Small Group Options (p. 229B)

If No → Independent Work Options (p. 229B)

    [CRM] Skills Practice Worksheet (p. 7)

    [CRM] Enrich Worksheet (p. 9)

Lesson Planner

Objective
Name and sequence the days of the week.

Vocabulary
week

Resources
Materials: calendar, seven days-of-the-week cards
Literature Connection: *The Very Hungry Caterpillar*
by Eric Carle
Teacher Technology
TeacherWorks

Focus on Math Background

Reciting the days of the week is a common routine in many kindergarten classrooms. This helps students become familiar with the cyclical pattern of a day-to-day schedule.

Categorizing events within intervals, such as morning, afternoon, and evening, helps students develop an understanding of the duration of one entire day.

In this lesson, students will process and sequence the fragmented parts of their day—for example, breakfast, going to school, soccer practice, dinner—into a larger whole quantified by a single unit of time, such as Monday. Students will also identify the order of the days of the week.

Daily Routine

Use these suggestions before beginning the lesson on p. 231.

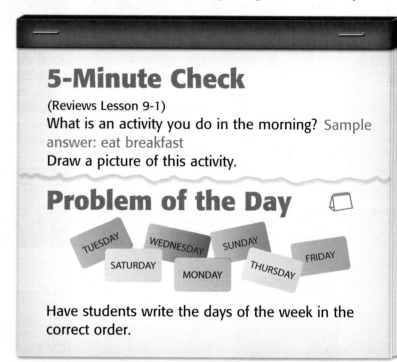

5-Minute Check
(Reviews Lesson 9-1)
What is an activity you do in the morning? Sample answer: eat breakfast
Draw a picture of this activity.

Problem of the Day

Have students write the days of the week in the correct order.

LINE UP As you prepare for recess, lunch, or dismissal, help students recall the order of the days of the week by chanting the sequence.

Building Math Vocabulary

- Write the days of the week on the chalkboard. Point to the days as you discuss them.
- Say that Sunday is the first day of the week.
- **What day comes after Sunday?** Monday
- Have students say the days of the week from Sunday through Saturday.
- **What day comes after Tuesday?** Wednesday
- **What day comes before Saturday?** Friday
- Show students on a calendar that a **week** is seven days in a row, Sunday through Saturday.

Visual Vocabulary Cards
Use Visual Vocabulary Card 49 to reinforce the vocabulary introduced in this lesson. (The Define/Example/Ask routine is printed on the back of each card.)

Differentiated Instruction

Small Group Options

Option 1 — Below/Approaching Level (BL)
VISUAL

Materials: calendar, paper, pencil

- Show students the classroom calendar.
- **How many days are in a week?** seven
- Ask how many Mondays, Tuesdays, Wednesdays, and so on there are in each week.
- **What day does the month begin?** Sample answer: Friday
- Ask if there are any holidays this month, and on what day they fall.

Option 2 — English Language Learners (ELL)
AUDITORY, LINGUISTIC

Materials: calendar
Core Vocabulary: day, week, when you hear
Common Use Verb: clap

Hear Math This strategy helps students hear the ending sounds.

- Tell students they will learn to chant the **days** of the **week.**
- Say: "Clap **when you hear** the word "**day.**" Demonstrate clapping on day as you chant the **days** of the **week.** Have students join in as you chant twice more.
- Show students the classroom calendar.

Independent Work Options

Option 1 — Early Finishers (OL) (AL)
LINGUISTIC

Materials: construction paper, crayons, markers

- Give a seven-page booklet to each student. Tell students they will make a weekly diary.
- Have students copy the days of the week on the pages and then draw a picture of an event that took place on the days that have already passed.
- Students will need reminders for the previous school days about events that may have already taken place.
- Have students take their diaries home and complete the remaining weekend pages.

Option 2 — Student Technology

Math Online macmillanmh.com

Option 3 — Learning Station: Reading (p. 225G)

Direct students to the Reading Learning Station for opportunities to explore and extend the lesson concept.

Leveled Lesson Resources

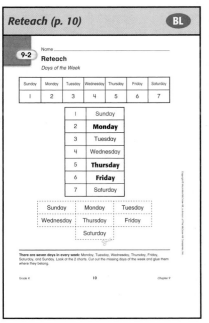

Reteach (p. 10) (BL)

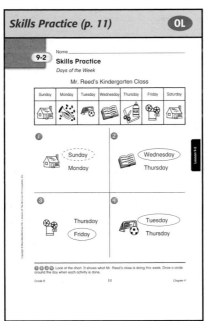

Skills Practice (p. 11) (OL)

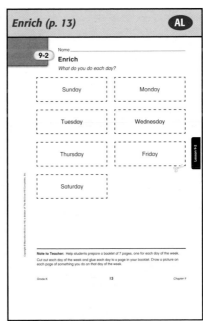

Enrich (p. 13) (AL)

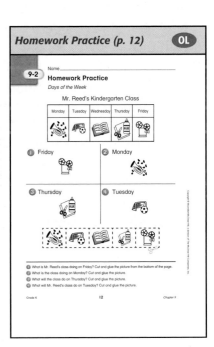

Homework Practice (p. 12) (OL)

① Introduce

Circle Time

Activity Choice 1 • Literature

The Very Hungry Caterpillar
by Eric Carle

Materials: calendar with the names
of the days on it

- Read the book aloud. Discuss days of
the **week**. If possible, demonstrate using
a calendar.
- Have students recite in unison the days of
the week.
- Provide seven days-of-the-week cards to seven
students and have them line up in the correct
order.
- Using the same cards, have seven different
students act out the caterpillar's daily activity.

Activity Choice 2 • Hands-On

Materials: seven days of the week cards

- Call seven students up to the front of the room, and
give each one a card with a different day of the week
on it.
- Say the days of the week in order, and have students
line up accordingly.
- Repeat until all students have had a chance to
participate.
- After students demonstrate an understanding of
how the days are ordered, play a guessing game
with them.
- Tell students to guess the day of the week that
comes after Sunday. If students do not
answer correctly, give them more
clues describing the order. Tell
them that the day comes
before Tuesday, or that it
comes between Sunday
and Tuesday.
- Give clues for different
days until students have
guessed all seven
days of the week.

② Teach

- Direct students to the top of p. 231.
- Name the days of the week with students.
- Guide students to understand the different activities that
occur on each weekday of Mrs. Han's kindergarten class.
- **What activities does the chart show?** art, PE, music,
library, computers
- Discuss the days that your class has special activities.

⒝ Alternate Teaching Strategy

If students have trouble naming the days of the
week . . .

Then use one of these reteach options.

1 ▭ **Daily Reteach Worksheet** (p. 10)

2 **Order Days of the Week** Give students seven objects
and seven cards, each with a day of the week.

- Have students put the days of the week in order.
(You may need to read them out loud.)
- Have students pair an object with each day.
- Have students tell a days-of-the-week story about
those objects. For example:
*On Sunday, I walked on the beach and found a
shell.*

⚠ **COMMON ERROR!**

Students may have difficulty comprehending
the day-to-day passage of time represented
on a calendar. Keep colored labels on the
classroom calendar to help students
differentiate each day of the week.

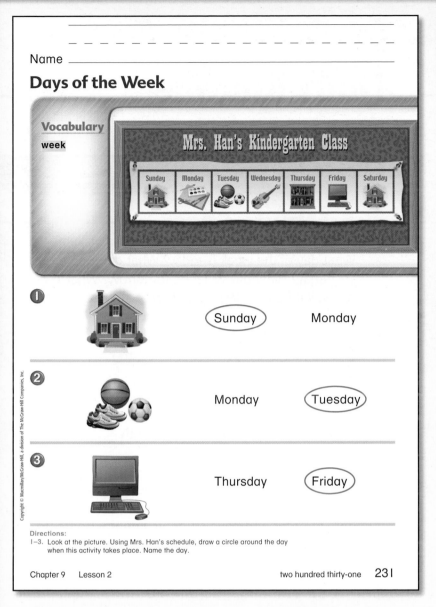

Name _____

Days of the Week

Vocabulary
week

Mrs. Han's Kindergarten Class

Sunday | Monday | Tuesday | Wednesday | Thursday | Friday | Saturday

① (Sunday)   Monday

② Monday   (Tuesday)

③ Thursday   (Friday)

Directions:
1–3. Look at the picture. Using Mrs. Han's schedule, draw a circle around the day when this activity takes place. Name the day.

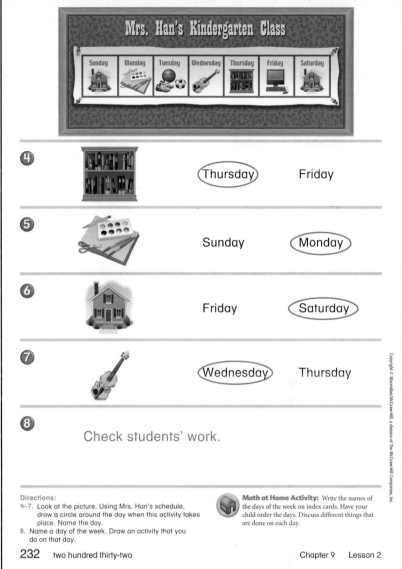

Mrs. Han's Kindergarten Class

Sunday | Monday | Tuesday | Wednesday | Thursday | Friday | Saturday

④ (Thursday)   Friday

⑤ Sunday   (Monday)

⑥ Friday   (Saturday)

⑦ (Wednesday)   Thursday

⑧ Check students' work.

Directions:
4–7. Look at the picture. Using Mrs. Han's schedule, draw a circle around the day when this activity takes place. Name the day.
8. Name a day of the week. Draw an activity that you do on that day.

Math at Home Activity: Write the names of the days of the week on index cards. Have your child order the days. Discuss different things that are done on each day.

---

③ Practice

Guided Practice

- Direct students to p. 231.
- Ask them to look at the picture of the activity.
- Have students draw a circle around the day when that activity takes place.
- Ask them to name the day.

Independent Practice

Have students turn to p. 232. Explain the directions. Have students work independently on exercises.

④ Assess

✓ Formative Assessment

- Ask students how many days there are in a week. Have them name the days.
- Say a day of the week. **What day comes next?** Sample answer: Monday comes after Sunday.

Quick Check   Are students still struggling to name the days of the week?

If Yes → Small Group Options (p. 231B)

If No → Independent Work Options (p. 231B)

    CRM Skills Practice Worksheet (p. 11)

    CRM Enrich Worksheet (p. 13)

Lesson Planner

Objective
Read and use a calendar.

Vocabulary
month, **year**

Resources

Materials: months of the year name cards, classroom calendar, stickers, markers, masking tape, two-colored dice

Literature Connection: *How Do You Say It Today, Jesse Bear?* by Nancy White Calstrom

Alternate Lesson: Adapt *Other Graphs* on page 156 of *Math Their Way* for practice in counting the number of days in school.

Teacher Technology
TeacherWorks • Concepts in Motion

Focus on Math Background

In this lesson, students expand their understanding of units of time to include how weeks build into a month and months build into a year. After learning to sequence activities within a seven-day time span, students will learn to appreciate the calendar as a tool to track events that go beyond one week. Becoming oriented to the layout of a calendar requires students to:

- Look left to right, down, and sweep back to the left.
- Visualize how rows represent weeks and how each of the seven columns designates one day of the week.
- Plot where the first day of the month begins.

Daily Routine

Use these suggestions before beginning the lesson on p. 233.

5-Minute Check
(Reviews Lesson 9-2)
What day of the week is today? What day was yesterday? What day will it be tomorrow? What day will it be two days from now? Sample answers: Tuesday; Monday; Wednesday; Thursday

Problem of the Day
Pass out number cards to each student for each day on this month's calendar. Have students look at a calendar and identify the ordinal numbers from first until the end of the month.

LINE UP Give each student a number card from one to the total number of students in class. Call numbers in order and have students line up. Compare these numbers to the numbers on the calendar.

Building Math Vocabulary

- Write the words **year** and **month** on the chalkboard. Point to the words as you discuss them. Call on students to list the 12 months. Write the name of each month in order on the chalkboard.

- Have students look at the classroom calendar.

- **What month of the year is this?** Sample answer: March

- **What do we use a calendar for?** Sample answers: to tell the day of the week; to remember special days; to count days; to see all months in the year

- Have each student tell what month they were born.

Visual Vocabulary Cards

Use Visual Vocabulary Card 24 to reinforce the vocabulary introduced in this lesson. (The Define/Example/Ask routine is printed on the back of each card.)

month

Differentiated Instruction

Small Group Options

Option 1
Gifted and Talented AL

Materials: blank calendar grids, pencils, one-year calendar

- Have students make a calendar for their birth month.
- Tell students the day their month starts and then have them write in the numbers for each day of their month.
- Have students circle their birthday.
- Count and record how many calendar months were made.
- Use the one-year calendar to name any missing months.

Option 2
English Language Learners ELL

LOGICAL

Materials: poster-size year-long calendar
Core Vocabulary: when is, "X" years old, my birthday is
Common Use Verb: will be

Talk Math This strategy helps students use a calendar.

- Write each students' birthday on a 12-month calendar.
- Have students go to the calendar and find their birthday, then say: "My birthday is in ___. I will be __ years old."
- Scaffold, assist, and restate students' efforts.

Independent Work Options

LOGICAL

Option 1
Early Finishers OL AL

Materials: calendars, crayons

- Have students color every Sunday a color.
- Then, have them color every Monday a different color.
- Repeat using different colors for each day of the week.
- **What pattern do you see?** Sample answer: Each column of color is a different day of the week.

Option 2
Student Technology

Math Online macmillanmh.com

Option 3
Learning Station: Reading (p. 225G)

Direct students to the Reading Learning Station for opportunities to explore and extend the lesson concept.

Leveled Lesson Resources

Reteach (p. 14) BL	Skills Practice (p. 15) OL	Enrich (p. 17) AL	Homework Practice (p. 16) OL

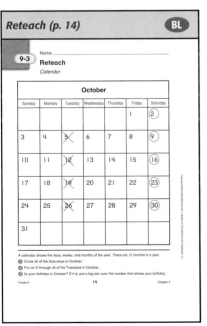

1 Introduce

Circle Time

Activity Choice 1 • Literature

How Do You Say It Today, Jesse Bear? by Nancy White Calstrom

- Read and discuss the book, paying close attention to the activities that occur each **month**.
- Use a calendar to illustrate the order of months in a **year**.
- Prepare twelve cards, each with the name of a month. Reread from the story the three lines that describe each month and allow the student with that card to stand in front of the class. Continue until all months are in order.

Activity Choice 2 • Hands-On

Materials: blank stickers, markers, calendar

- Give each student a blank sticker, and have them write their initials on it.
- Hold a calendar up at the front of the room. Begin by showing the month of January.
- Ask each student a different question that refers to a part of the calendar. Have them come to the front of the room and answer the question by putting their sticker on the calendar. For example, ask what the first Wednesday of January is, or ask where January 17 is.
- Flip the calendar to a new month for each student, flipping back to January after December.

2 Teach

Materials: classroom calendar

- Direct students to the top of p. 233.
- Tell students that a calendar shows the months of the year and the days of the week.
- Model and explain reading a calendar.
- Tell students that the name of the month is located at the top of the calendar. Point to and say the name of that month.
- Explain that every box on a calendar represents a day, has a number, and all seven days in a week are in order.
- Explain that each row stands for one week.

BL Alternate Teaching Strategy

If students have trouble understanding how to read a calendar . . .

Then use one of these reteach options.

1. CRM **Daily Reteach Worksheet** (p. 14)

2. **Play a Calendar Game** Tell students they will play a game called Race to the End of the Month.
   - Create a large 6-by-7-column calendar with masking tape on the floor. Label each column in each row with a colored mouse cutout corresponding to the book *Seven Blind Mice*.
   - Have players take turns rolling two-colored dice, choosing the color closest to the end of the week, then going to the day with that color. Students should move from left to right through the week.
   - If dice are the same color, players go to the white Sunday square and roll again.
   - The first player to get to the end of the month is the winner.

> ⚠ **COMMON ERROR!**
> Students may have difficulty distinguishing weeks. Allow students to color each row/week a different color. They should then be able to identify that there are four weeks in a month because they would have used four colors.

Name _____

Calendar

Vocabulary
month
year

① February

Sunday	Monday	Tuesday	Wednesday	Thursday	Friday	Saturday
					①	2
3	4	5	6	7	8	9
10	11	12	13	14	15	16
17	18	19	20	21	22	23
24	25	26	27	28		

Directions:
1. Draw an X by the name of the month, a circle on the first day of the month, a triangle on the last day of the month, a box around the word *Saturday*, and color the box that shows February 14th.

Chapter 9   Lesson 3   two hundred thirty-three   233

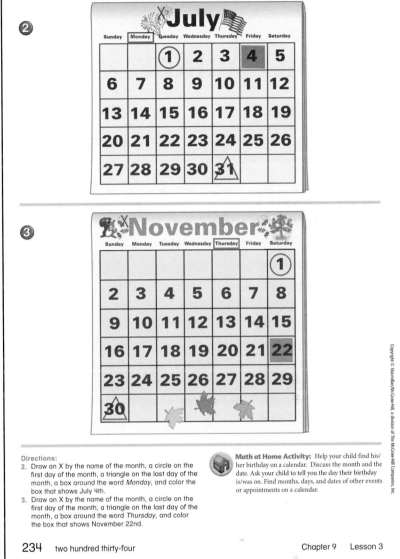

② July

Sunday	Monday	Tuesday	Wednesday	Thursday	Friday	Saturday
	①	2	3	4	5	
6	7	8	9	10	11	12
13	14	15	16	17	18	19
20	21	22	23	24	25	26
27	28	29	30	31		

③ November

Sunday	Monday	Tuesday	Wednesday	Thursday	Friday	Saturday
						①
2	3	4	5	6	7	8
9	10	11	12	13	14	15
16	17	18	19	20	21	22
23	24	25	26	27	28	29
30						

Directions:
2. Draw an X by the name of the month, a circle on the first day of the month, a triangle on the last day of the month, a box around the word *Monday*, and color the box that shows July 4th.
3. Draw an X by the name of the month, a circle on the first day of the month, a triangle on the last day of the month, a box around the word *Thursday*, and color the box that shows November 22nd.

Math at Home Activity: Help your child find his/ her birthday on a calendar. Discuss the month and the date. Ask your child to tell you the day their birthday is/was on. Find months, days, and dates of other events or appointments on a calendar.

234   two hundred thirty-four   Chapter 9   Lesson 3

---

③ Practice

Guided Practice

- Direct students to Exercise 1 on p. 233.
- Ask students to do the following:
  - Draw an "X" on the name of the month.
  - Draw a circle on the first day of the month.
  - Draw a triangle on the last day of the month.
  - Draw a box around the word *Saturday*.
  - Color the box that shows February 14.

Independent Practice

Have students turn to p. 234. Read the directions and have students answer independently.

④ Assess

Formative Assessment

Use the current month's calendar.

- **Are there any holidays this month? What day of the week has a holiday?** Sample answer: yes; Sunday
- **What day of the week is the first day of the month? the last day?** Sample answer: Thursday; Saturday

Quick Check   Are students still struggling to read a calendar?

If Yes → Small Group Options (p. 233B)
If No → Independent Work Options (p. 233B)
CRM Skills Practice Worksheet (p. 15)
CRM Enrich Worksheet (p. 17)

Today, Yesterday, and Tomorrow

Lesson Planner

Objective

Sequence days of the week to explain today, tomorrow, and yesterday.

Vocabulary

today, **yesterday**, **tomorrow**

Resources

Materials: days of the week necklace cards, calendar, sticky notes, pencil, chart paper

Literature Connection: *Wednesday Is Spaghetti Day* by Maryann Cocca-Leffler

Alternate Lesson: Use *Other Graphs* on page 155 of *Math Their Way* to provide practice in understanding the concepts of today, tomorrow, and yesterday.

Teacher Technology
- 💿 TeacherWorks

Focus on Math Background

In this lesson, students use math vocabulary—*yesterday, today,* and *tomorrow*—to describe the passage of time. To make sense of temporal concepts such as yesterday, today, and tomorrow, students must:

- Sequence activities as coming before, during, and after an event.
- Visualize how days have beginning and ending points (morning and night), which measure a time span and repeat within a week in a larger, predictable cycle.
- Navigate days on a calendar from left to right and describe and locate each day in relation to other days of the week.
- Categorize the passage of time as past, present, and future events.

Daily Routine

Use these suggestions before beginning the lesson on p. 235.

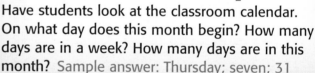

5-Minute Check

(Reviews Lesson 9-3)

1. What month does the calendar show? May
2. Which day of the month is Mother's Day? Sunday, May 13
3. Which day of the month is Memorial Day? Monday, May 28

May						
SUN	MON	TUES	WED	THUR	FRI	SAT
		1	2	3	4	5
6	7	8	9	10	11	12
13	14	15	16	17	18	19
20	21	22	23	24	25	26
27	28	29	30	31		

Problem of the Day

Have students look at the classroom calendar. On what day does this month begin? How many days are in a week? How many days are in this month? Sample answer: Thursday; seven; 31

LINE UP Have a volunteer place a sticker on a day of the week on the classroom calendar. That individual then chooses another student to answer either what day it was yesterday or what it will be tomorrow. If that student answers correctly they both can line up. Repeat until all students are in line.

Building Math Vocabulary

- Write **yesterday**, **today**, and **tomorrow** on the chalkboard.
- Have students discuss yesterday, today, and tomorrow by recalling special activities.
- **What special activity did we do yesterday? What will we do today? What is planned for tomorrow?** Sample answers: painted; read a book; perform a play

Visual Vocabulary Cards

Use Visual Vocabulary Card 47 to reinforce the vocabulary introduced in this lesson. (The Define/Example/Ask routine is printed on the back of each card.)

tomorrow

Differentiated Instruction

Small Group Options

Option 1 Below/Approaching Level BL

Materials: seven cards, each with a day of the week, three cards saying "yesterday," "today," and "tomorrow"

- Have students work in pairs. Have a student put "today" next to a day of the week. The partner should then put "tomorrow" or "yesterday" next to the correct day.

Option 2 English Language Learners ELL

Materials: index cards, classroom calendar, tape
Core Vocabulary: how old, candles, cake
Common Use Verb: was/were

Hear Math This strategy reinforces past and future verb tenses.

- Give each student an index card with their birthday on the bottom. Have students write their name and draw a cake. Help students figure out how many candles to draw. Model "you will be five/were four."
- Tape their cakes under their month on the calendar and say, for example, "I was four" or "I will be five."
- Prompt students by restating and scaffolding language.

Independent Work Options

Option 1 Early Finishers OL AL

Materials: construction paper, crayons

- Have students make a weekly planner.
- Distribute sheets of paper divided into three columns and labeled: *Yesterday, Today, Tomorrow.*
- Ask students to draw pictures of what they did yesterday, what they will do today, and what they will do tomorrow.
- Ask volunteers to talk about their pictures.

Option 2 Student Technology

Math Online > macmillanmh.com

Option 3 Learning Station: Science (p. 225H)

Direct students to the Science Learning Station for opportunities to explore and extend the lesson concept.

Leveled Lesson Resources

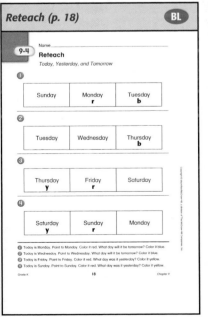

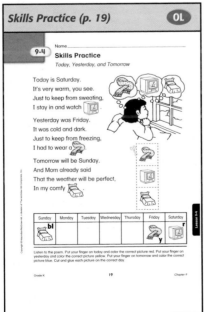

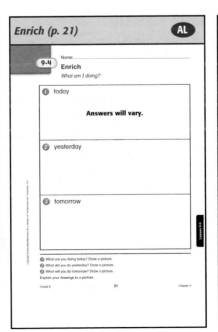

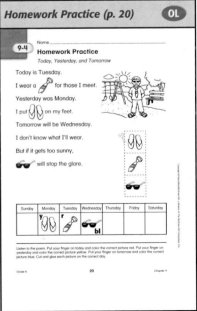

1 Introduce

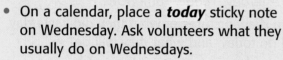ircle Time

Activity Choice 1 • Literature

Wednesday Is Spaghetti Day
by Maryann Cocca-Leffler

Materials: calendar; three sticky notes labeled *today, yesterday, tomorrow*; pencil

- On a calendar, place a **today** sticky note on Wednesday. Ask volunteers what they usually do on Wednesdays.

- Read the book aloud, discussing what Catrina does on Wednesday (today). Ask them when certain activities occur. For example, Scruffy makes the salad today. Continue to emphasize the concept of today by asking this type of question.

- **Which day will tomorrow be?** Thursday

- Put a *tomorrow* sticky note on Thursday.

- **What day was yesterday?** Tuesday Put a *yesterday* sticky note on Tuesday.

Activity Choice 2 • Hands-On

Materials: days of the week necklace cards

- Invite seven volunteers to wear a day of the week necklace card.

- Ask students to line up three volunteers by yesterday, today, and tomorrow. Repeat this activity with other days.

- Have students form groups of three, with one student representing today. Have the other two students arrange themselves by yesterday and tomorrow.

- Have students take turns.

2 Teach

- Direct students to the top of p. 235.

- Explain that *yesterday*, *today*, and *tomorrow* are words that describe what day of the week it is.

- Point to Today in the poem. Read the first line. Point to the hat. Read aloud the line from the poem about the hat. Have students repeat after you.

- Say that *today* refers to the day that is happening right now.

- Point to Yesterday in the poem. Read that line aloud. Point to the balloon. Read that line. Have students repeat.

- Say that *yesterday* refers to the day before today.

- Point to Tomorrow in the poem. Read that line and the next line aloud. Point to the rain. Read the rest of the poem. Have students repeat.

- Say that *tomorrow* refers to the day that will come after today.

Alternate Teaching Strategy

 students have trouble understanding yesterday, today, and tomorrow . . .

Then use one of these reteach options.

1 **CRM** **Daily Reteach Worksheet** (p. 18)

2 **Match Pictures** Make a one-row, seven-column table on chart paper to display the lunch menu selections for students for each day of the week.

- Have students match or draw a picture of each lunch item within the corresponding box on the menu table.

- **What did we eat for lunch yesterday?** Sample answer: spaghetti

- **What was for lunch today?** Sample answer: sandwich

- **What will we eat tomorrow?** Sample answer: pizza

! COMMON ERROR!

Students may have trouble identifying and locating *yesterday*, *today*, and *tomorrow* on a single-row, seven-column chart. Continue using the icons in the poem to help students find these words on the weekly schedule.

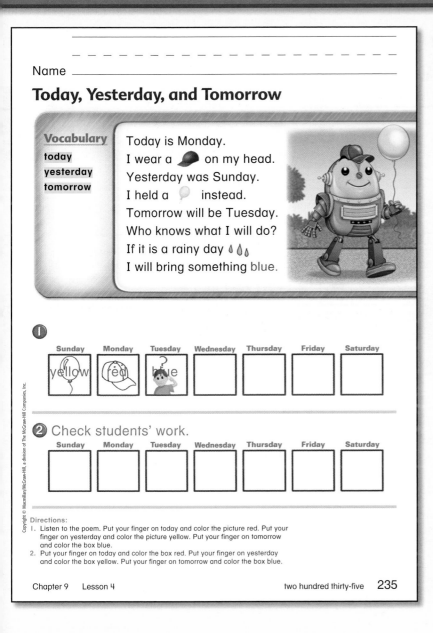

Name _____

Today, Yesterday, and Tomorrow

Vocabulary
today
yesterday
tomorrow

Today is Monday.
I wear a 🧢 on my head.
Yesterday was Sunday.
I held a 🎈 instead.
Tomorrow will be Tuesday.
Who knows what I will do?
If it is a rainy day 💧💧💧
I will bring something blue.

①

Sunday	Monday	Tuesday	Wednesday	Thursday	Friday	Saturday
yellow	red	blue				

② Check students' work.

Sunday	Monday	Tuesday	Wednesday	Thursday	Friday	Saturday

Directions:
1. Listen to the poem. Put your finger on today and color the picture red. Put your finger on yesterday and color the picture yellow. Put your finger on tomorrow and color the box blue.
2. Put your finger on today and color the box red. Put your finger on yesterday and color the box yellow. Put your finger on tomorrow and color the box blue.

---

③

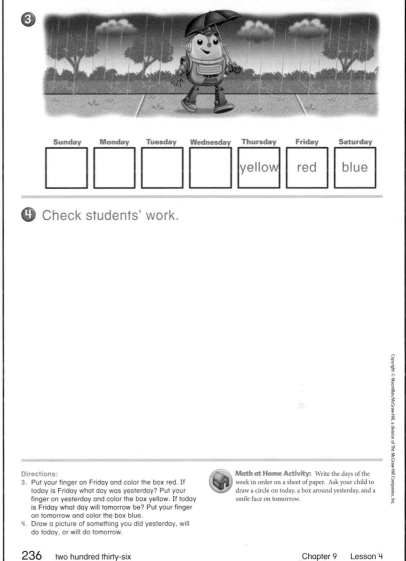

Sunday	Monday	Tuesday	Wednesday	Thursday	Friday	Saturday
				yellow	red	blue

④ Check students' work.

Directions:
3. Put your finger on Friday and color the box red. If today is Friday what day was yesterday? Put your finger on yesterday and color the box yellow. If today is Friday what day will tomorrow be? Put your finger on tomorrow and color the box blue.
4. Draw a picture of something you did yesterday, will do today, or will do tomorrow.

Math at Home Activity: Write the days of the week in order on a sheet of paper. Ask your child to draw a circle on today, a box around yesterday, and a smile face on tomorrow.

---

❸ Practice

Guided Practice

- Direct students to the bottom of p. 235.
- Read the poem aloud.
- **In the poem, what day is today?** Monday
- Help students identify Monday in Exercise 1 by locating the picture of the cap that matches the cap shown in the poem.
- For Exercises 1 and 2, have students color the boxes to identify today, yesterday, and tomorrow.

Independent Practice

Have students turn to p. 236. Explain the directions.
Have students work independently on the exercises.

❹ Assess

Formative Assessment

- Use the calendar to discuss today, tomorrow, and yesterday.
- Have a volunteer identify today by pointing to it on the calendar. Have other students say the name of the day aloud.
- Repeat for yesterday and tomorrow.

> **Quick Check** Are students still struggling to use today, yesterday, and tomorrow?

If Yes → Small Group Options (p. 235B)
If No → Independent Work Options (p. 235B)
  [CRM] Skills Practice Worksheet (p. 19)
  [CRM] Enrich Worksheet (p. 21)

Mid-Chapter Check

Lessons 9-1 to 9-4

 Formative Assessment

Use the Mid-Chapter Check to assess students' progress in the first half of the chapter.

ExamView®
Assessment Suite Customize and create multiple versions of your Mid-Chapter Check and the test answer keys.

FOLDABLES® Dinah Zike's Foldables

Use these lesson suggestions for incorporating the Foldables during the chapter.

Lesson 9-4 Make a Three-Tab Book Foldable, and label the tabs as illustrated. Under the *Today* tab, record things that occur on the current day. Discuss things that occurred the day before, and record them under the *Yesterday* tab. Discuss things that might happen tomorrow, and record them under the *Tomorrow* tab.

Lesson 9-2 Use poster board to make a Four-Tab Book Foldable, and cut each of the four tabs in half. Label the first tab *Days of the Week,* and label the remaining tabs with the seven days of the week. Practice naming the days of the week. Under the tabs, record things that happen to the class on each day of the week. When possible, use pictures.

Lesson 9-1 Make and use a Three-Tab Book Foldable, and label the tabs *Morning, Afternoon,* and *Evening.* Divide the class into three groups. Have each group draw things that happen in the morning, afternoon, and evening. Select and glue example pictures under the appropriate tabs.

Name _____

1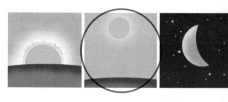

2

Wednesday Thursday

3

Copyright © Macmillan/McGraw-Hill, a division of The McGraw-Hill Companies, Inc.

Directions:
1. Look at the picture. Circle the time of day it shows.
2. Look at the picture. Using Mrs. Han's schedule, draw a circle around the day when the activity takes place.
3. Draw an X by the name of the month, a circle on the first day of the month, a triangle on the last day of the month, a box around the word *Wednesday,* and color the box that shows April 5th.

Chapter 9   two hundred thirty-seven 23

Data-Driven Decision Making

Based on the results of the Mid-Chapter Check, use the following resources to review concepts that continue to give students problems.

Exercises	State/Local Standard	What's the Math?	Error Analysis	Resources for Review
1 Lesson 9-1		Understand concepts of time of morning, afternoon, evening.	Cannot distinguish between morning, afternoon, and evening.	**CRM** Chapter 9 Resource Masters (Reteach Worksheets)
2 Lesson 9-2		Name the days of the week.	Does not know days of week. Cannot read "Wednesday" or "Thursday."	**Math Online**
3 Lesson 9-3		Demonstrate an understanding of how to read and use a calendar.	Does not follow directions. Draws an "X," a circle, a triangle, or a box around the wrong item, or colors the wrong box.	Concepts in Motion Math Adventures

Time for Vacation!

Using A Calendar

Play with a partner. Take turns.
- Roll the **5**.
- Move your.
- Follow the numbers in order. If you land on a day that has an arrow, move one space in the direction the arrow points.
- The first person to get to **Finish** wins!

You Will Need

March

Sunday	Monday	Tuesday	Wednesday	Thursday	Friday	Saturday
			Start	1	2	3
4	5	6	7	8	9	10
11➡	12	13	14	15	⬅16	17
18	19	20➡	21	22	23	⬅24
25	26	27	⬅28	29	30	**Vacation 31 Finish**

Time for Vacation!

Math Concept: Using a Calendar

Manipulatives: number cube, connecting cubes

Introduce the game on page 238 to your students to play as a class, in small groups, or at a learning workstation to review concepts introduced in this chapter.

Instructions

- Assign each student a connecting cube as a game piece.
- Have players take turns rolling a number cube.
- Players move their game piece the number of spaces they roll, following the numbers on the calendar in order.
- If players land on a day with an arrow, they move 1 space in the direction the arrow points.
- The first player to reach the finish wins.

Extend the Game

Have students make their own gameboard for a different month, using a blank calendar.

Differentiated Practice

Use these leveling suggestions to differentiate the game for all learners.

Level	Assignment
BL Below/Approaching Level	Have students put a sticker at the beginning and end of rows to remind them of how to move on the calendar.
OL On Level	Have students play the game with the rules as written.
AL Above/Beyond Level	Have students say the day and date of the calendar square they land on, such as: Friday, March 2.

Lesson Planner

Objective

Tell time to the hour using an analog clock.

Vocabulary

hour, o'clock

Resources

Materials: chart paper
Manipulatives: demonstration analog clock, student clocks
Literature Connection: *I Can Tell the Time* by Gail Davies
Teacher Technology
  TeacherWorks • Concepts in Motion

Focus on Math Background

Clocks are present everywhere in the environment and attract the interest of young children. However, using clocks to measure time is challenging for most kindergarteners.

Most kindergarteners struggle to comprehend the proportional relationship of 60 minutes to one hour. They do not understand that when the minute hand makes a complete cycle around the clock, the hour hand moves only one twelfth of this distance.

This lesson focuses on telling time only to the hour and comparing events that last the same as, less than, or about one minute. Students also develop a sense of the duration of one hour.

Daily Routine

Use these suggestions before beginning the lesson on p. 239.

5-Minute Check

(Reviews Lesson 9-4)
Have students look at the classroom calendar and tell what day of the week was yesterday, what day is today, and what day will be tomorrow.

Problem of the Day

Draw an analog clock set to 6:00, another set to 9:00, and another set to 2:00. What times are shown on the clocks? 6:00, 9:00, 2:00

LINE UP As you prepare for recess, lunch, or dismissal, show a time on the demonstration analog clock. Have students say the time and line up.

Building Math Vocabulary

- Show students the demonstration analog clock set to 5 **o'clock**. Move the minute hand around the clock to show 6 o'clock.
- Tell students that each number represents a different **hour** of the day.
- Ask a volunteer to move the clock hand to show 7 o'clock. Lead a discussion about activities that students do at 7 o'clock.
- If students give answers that suggest two different hours—such as eating breakfast and eating dinner—remind them that 7 o'clock can be a morning hour or an evening hour.

Visual Vocabulary Cards

Use Visual Vocabulary Card 28 to reinforce the vocabulary introduced in this lesson. (The Define/Example/Ask routine is printed on the back of each card.)

o'clock

Differentiated Instruction

Small Group Options

Option 1
LOGICAL

Below/Approaching Level (BL)

Materials: demonstration analog clock, index cards with numbers 1–12 written on them

- Show a time on the demonstration clock and say the time. Have students repeat the time.
- Give students a number card. Ask a volunteer to say the number and then show it as a time on the demonstration analog clock.
- Repeat with other students.

Option 2
AUDITORY

English Language Learners (ELL)

Materials: transparency of a face in a circle that fits within a transparency of a clock face

Core Vocabulary: face, clock, round
Common Use Verb: go around

Hear Math This strategy introduces new vocabulary.

- Run your finger around the perimeter of your **face,** saying: "This is a **face.** It is **round**."
- Have students repeat. Say: "Go around your **face**." Repeat on the transparencies. Say: "This is also a **face,** a **clock face**."
- Repeat "going around" the **clock face,** noting numbers, as time permits.

Independent Work Options

Option 1
LINGUISTIC

Early Finishers (OL) (AL)

Materials: two number cubes, clocks with numbers but no hands

- Roll both cubes. Count the number of dots.
- Draw the hands on a clock to show that number as if it were time on the clock.

Option 2
Student Technology

Math Online macmillanmh.com

Math Adventures

Option 3
Learning Station: Art (p. 225G)

Direct students to the Art Learning Station for opportunities to explore and extend the lesson concept.

Leveled Lesson Resources
Additional support for English Language Learners can be found in the ELL Guide (p. 109). (ELL)

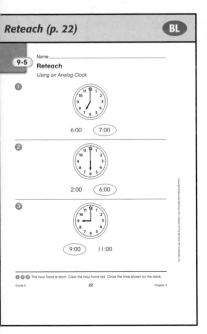

Reteach (p. 22) (BL)

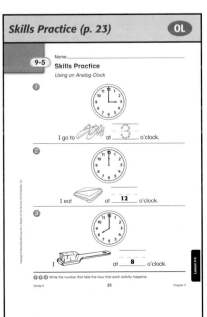

Skills Practice (p. 23) (OL)

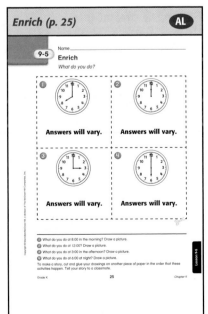

Enrich (p. 25) (AL)

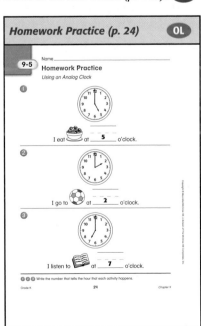

Homework Practice (p. 24) (OL)

1 Introduce

Circle Time

Activity Choice 1 • Literature

I Can Tell the Time
by Gail Davies

- Read aloud and discuss the book, having students take turns setting the clock on the book to the correct time.
- Then ask students questions to identify the times of daily activities. Have students set the clock to match the times.
- Discuss with students the times they get up, eat dinner, and so on. Encourage students to use the word **o'clock** in their answers.
- Create a chart showing the students' daily schedule in hourly increments.

Activity Choice 2 • Hands-On

Materials: demonstration analog clock, student clocks

- Have students count off to work in groups of three.
- Tell student 1 to choose a time of day and set the clock to that **hour**.
- Have the other two students in the group say the time aloud.
- Student 2 should draw a picture of an activity or event that might take place at that hour.
- Student 3 then acts out the activity or event shown in the drawing, while the rest of the class guesses.
- Have each group complete the exercise one at a time, and encourage each group to set the clock to a different hour than the previous groups used.

2 Teach

- Distribute demonstration clocks to each student or to student pairs.
- Identify the parts of the clock by referring to the example shown at the top of p. 239.
- Have students point to and identify the matching part on their clocks as you introduce each feature on your clock.
- Guide students on how to arrange each hand on their demonstration clocks to show 9 o'clock.
- Ask students to show 10 o'clock. Say that from 9:00 to 10:00 is one hour.

BL Alternate Teaching Strategy

If students have trouble reading an analog clock . . .

Then use one of these reteach options.

1 CRM **Daily Reteach Worksheet** (p. 22)

2 **Clock Practice** Have students work in pairs. Give each pair a clock with numbers and moveable hands.
- Have students set the clock to 12 o'clock to begin.
- Have one student roll a number cube, and the partner move the clock hand clockwise to show that hour on the clock.
- Have partners switch roles.

! COMMON ERROR!

Students may confuse the clock hands, especially when referred to as the "big" hand and the "little" hand. "Big" could refer to thickness, and the hour (little) hand is thicker. Use the words "long" and "short" to describe the hands to clarify which is the minute and which is the hour hand.

Name _____

Using an Analog Clock

Vocabulary
hour
o'clock

School starts at _9_ o'clock.

①

I eat 🍳 at
_7_ o'clock.

②

I go 🏠 at
_3_ o'clock.

Directions:
1–2. Write the number that tells the hour that each activity happens.

③

I go to ⚽ at
_4_ o'clock.

④

I eat 🥞 at
_6_ o'clock.

⑤

I take a  at
_8_ o'clock.

⑥

I eat 🍱 at
_12_ o'clock.

Directions:
3–6. Write the number that tells the hour that each activity happens.

Math at Home Activity: Draw different clocks or cut clocks from magazines that show time to the nearest hour. Ask your child to tell the time.

③ Practice

Guided Practice

- Direct students to Exercise 1 on p. 239.
- Have students look at the analog clock and tell the time.
- Talk about what activity occurs at that time.
- Demonstrate how to write the number in the designated space.
- Follow the same procedure with Exercise 2.

Independent Practice

- Have students turn to p. 240. Explain the directions.
- Have students work independently on the exercises.

④ Assess

Formative Assessment

- **What is the time on each clock?** 7:00, 3:00, 4:00, 6:00, 8:00, 12:00
- **What is the same about the long hands on each clock?** The long hand is on the 12.

Quick Check	Are students still struggling to use analog clocks?

If Yes → Small Group Options (p. 239B)

If No → Independent Work Options (p. 239B)

CRM Skills Practice Worksheet (p. 23)

CRM Enrich Worksheet (p. 25)

Lesson 9-5 Using an Analog Clock   **240**

Using a Digital Clock

Lesson Planner _____

Objective

Read the time on a digital clock.

Review Vocabulary

twelve, zero

Resources

Materials: digital clock, chart paper, markers, time cards
Manipulatives: demonstration analog clock, counters
Literature Connection: *Time to…* by Bruce McMillan
Teacher Technology
  TeacherWorks • Math Song Track 5

Focus on Math Background

Prior to this lesson, students learn to read time in analog form. Then they compare and transfer this information to a digital clock. When seeing 3:00 on a digital clock, students learn that the digits before the colon tell the hour, and the digits after the colon tell the minutes. As with analog clocks, kindergarteners only tell time to the hour on digital clocks.

Daily Routine _____

Use these suggestions before beginning the lesson on p. 241.

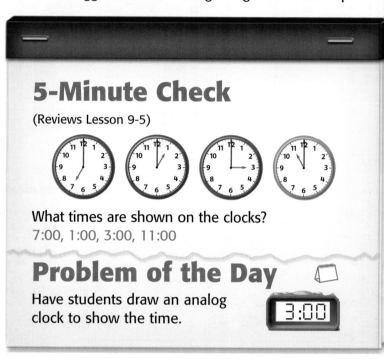

5-Minute Check

(Reviews Lesson 9-5)

What times are shown on the clocks?
7:00, 1:00, 3:00, 11:00

Problem of the Day

Have students draw an analog clock to show the time.

LINE UP Give students index cards with various times, some on a digital clock and some on an analog clock. Have students find the person whose time matches theirs, then line up in order with their partner.

▶ Review Math Vocabulary

• Show 6:00 on the demonstration analog clock. Ask students what time it is. Explain that when the hand is on the **twelve**, it means that a new hour is starting.

• Show 6:00 on the digital clock. Explain that two **zeroes** after the colon mean the same as the long hand being on the 12 on an analog clock: the beginning of a new hour.

• Show 2 o'clock on the analog clock.

• Ask students to write in the air what time the other clock would say. Show the correct answer on the board *2:00*. Repeat with other times.

Differentiated Instruction

Small Group Options

Option 1
SPATIAL

Gifted and Talented **AL**

Materials: paper, pencil

- Write times on the chalkboard: 8:00, 4:00, 5:00, 9:00.
- Have small groups draw analog and digital clocks for these times. Have groups compare clocks to check answers.

Option 2
KINESTHETIC, VISUAL

English Language Learners **ELL**

Materials: floor number line
Core Vocabulary: slow, stand on
Common Use Verb: jump

Jumping is slow   Hopping is quick

Hours are quick
Days are slow

Do Math This strategy kinesthetically demonstrates digital clocks.

- Say: "The left side of the digital clock is hours. Hours go by fast. Let's show hours by hopping on one foot."
- Show a digital clock and explain that there are 24 hours in one day. Days go by slowly. Let's show days by hopping slowly on both feet.
- Repeat as time permits.

Independent Work Options

Option 1
LINGUISTIC

Early Finishers **OL** **AL**

Materials: index cards, pencil

- Make sets of 12 index cards, showing the 12 hours on a digital clock.
- Give a set of cards to each student.
- Have students form pairs to play a game.
- Both players draw a card from their set and show the times.
- Explain that the player whose card has the greater number keeps the pair of cards in their discard pile.
- Explain that the player with more cards in the discard pile is the winner.

Option 2
Student Technology

Math Online macmillanmh.com

♪ Math Song "Tick Tock" Track 5

Math Adventures

Option 3
Learning Station: Art (p. 225G)

Direct students to the Art Learning Station for opportunities to explore and extend the lesson concept.

Leveled Lesson Resources
Additional support for English Language Learners can be found in the ELL Guide (p. 111). **ELL**

Reteach (p. 26) **BL**	*Skills Practice (p. 27)* **OL**	*Enrich (p. 29)* **AL**	*Homework Practice (p. 28)* **OL**
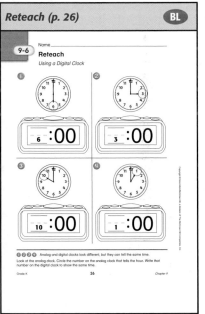	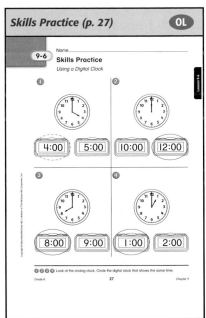	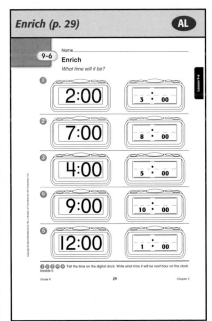	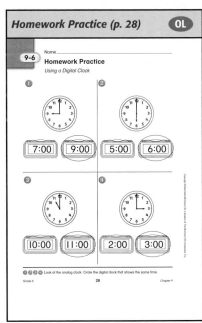

① Introduce

 ircle Time

Activity Choice 1 • Literature

Time to… by Bruce McMillan

- Read the book aloud, discussing the digital clocks at the bottom of each page.

- Then ask students to identify the time of daily activities. Record responses in digital time.

- Have students take turns recording digital time from the time shown on an analog clock, and vice versa. Remind students that when an analog clock shows the longer hand on **twelve**, the digital clock should show two **zeroes** following the colon.

Activity Choice 2 • Hands-On

Materials: digital clock, chart paper, marker

- Discuss with students their observations of the digital clock they analyzed in the discovery center.

- **What do you notice about the digital clock?** Sample answer: There are two dots between the numbers.

- Write responses on chart paper. Have students say and write key attributes about digital clocks. **How is a digital clock different from an analog clock?** Sample answers: It has numbers before and after the colon; there are no hands; it is not round.

- Have students identify various times on the digital clock.

② Teach

- Have students look at the analog and digital clocks at the top of p. 241. Point to similarities as you discuss.

- Explain to students that they can use a digital clock and an analog clock to show and tell the same time.

- Review the vocabulary word *hour.*

- Say that the number on the left of the digital clock matches the number shown by the hour hand on the analog clock because these numbers tell the hour.

- Explain that just like the minute hand on the analog clock, the numbers on the right of the digital clock count the number of minutes that have passed in the hour.

BL **Alternate Teaching Strategy**

If students have trouble reading a digital clock . . .

Then use one of these reteach options.

1 **CRM** **Daily Reteach Worksheet** (p. 26)

2 **Match the Hours** Give each student 12 counters and a list of digital clock times, beginning with 12:00 and ending with 11:00.

- Use a demonstration analog clock set to 9 o'clock and show it to all students.

- Have students say the time aloud.

- Have students look at the number on the analog clock to which the short hand is pointing. Have them find the matching number on their list of digital clock times.

- When students find the match, have them put the number of counters next to the digital time that matches the number of the hour. For 9 o'clock, students should put nine counters next to the 9:00 on their list.

- Repeat with other times until students have reviewed all 12 hours.

> **! COMMON ERROR!**
>
> Students might not read the numbers on digital clocks from left to right. Put a dot or sticker to the left of the clock display to remind students where to start.

Name _____

Using a Digital Clock

8 o'clock   8 o'clock

①   **②**

12:00   (2:00)   (5:00)   3:00

Copyright © Macmillan/McGraw-Hill, a division of The McGraw-Hill Companies, Inc.

Directions:
1–2. Look at the analog clock. Circle the digital clock that shows the same time.

Chapter 9   Lesson 6   two hundred forty-one   241

③   **④**

(7:00)   2:00   9:00   (4:00)

⑤   **⑥**

(6:00)   3:00   (10:00)   1:00

Directions:
3–6. Look at the analog clock. Circle the digital clock that shows the same time.

Math at Home Activity: Compare telling time on the hour using digital and analog clocks in your home. Tell your child to write the time as it appears on the digital clock. Look for digital clocks and analog clocks in other surroundings.

Copyright © Macmillan/McGraw-Hill, a division of The McGraw-Hill Companies, Inc.

242   two hundred forty-two   Chapter 9   Lesson 6

❸ Practice

Guided Practice

- Direct students to the bottom of p. 241.
- Tell students to look at the analog clock and then circle the digital clock that shows the same time.

Independent Practice

Have students turn to p. 242. Explain the directions. Have students work independently on the exercises.

❹ Assess

✓ Formative Assessment

- Put two groups of cards on a table—each showing the same times. One group should show digital clocks; the other group should show analog clocks.
- Have students go to the table one at a time and pair up one card from each group.

Quick Check   **Are students still struggling to tell time on a digital clock?**

If Yes → Small Group Options (p. 241B)

If No → Independent Work Options (p. 241B)
    CRM Skills Practice Worksheet (p. 27)
    CRM Enrich Worksheet (p. 29)

Lesson Planner _____

Objective

Make a table to answer questions.

Resources

Materials: pictures, pencils, blank calendar sheet
Manipulatives: analog demonstration clock
Literature Connection: *Brown Rabbit's Day*
by Alan Baker
Teacher Technology
● TeacherWorks
📖 **Real-World Problem Solving Library**
Math and Social Studies: *Then and Now*
Use these leveled readers to reinforce and extend
problem-solving skills and strategies.

Leveled for:
OL On Level
ELL Sheltered English
ELL Spanish

For additional support, see the Real-World Problem
Solving Teacher Guide.

*On-level title is available in
classroom Big Book.*

Daily Routine _____

Use these suggestions before beginning the lesson on p. 243.

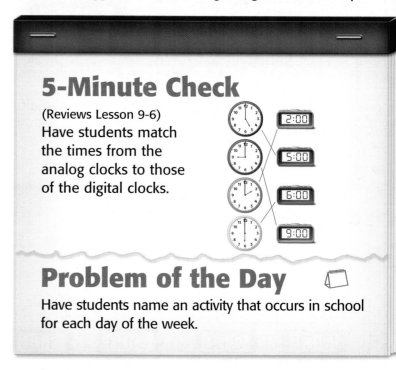

5-Minute Check

(Reviews Lesson 9-6)
Have students match
the times from the
analog clocks to those
of the digital clocks.

Problem of the Day 📆

Have students name an activity that occurs in school
for each day of the week.

LINE UP As you prepare for recess, lunch, or dismissal,
ask students to share something they do in the
evening, then line up.

Differentiated Instruction

Small Group Options

Option 1 — Below/Approaching Level (BL)
LOGICAL

Materials: paper, pencil, crayons

- Help students make a three-column table on paper.
- Have them label the columns in order: *Morning*, *Afternoon*, and *Evening*. Have students write or draw an activity they do during each time of the day.
- Have students form small groups and compare tables.

Option 2 — English Language Learners (ELL)
SPATIAL

Core Vocabulary: arms, hours
Common Use Verb: show

Do Math This strategy shows how digital and analog clocks are used to tell time.

- Show a class schedule. Replace activities time with a picture of an analog or digital clock to the hour.
- Assign students to demonstrate "analog" times with their arms and "digital" times by jumping forward while the class counts orally.
- Have students act out the class schedule by rotating each activity shown using analog or digital clocks to the hour.

Independent Work Options

Option 1 — Early Finishers (OL) (AL)
LINGUISTIC

Materials: class schedule, index cards with each time, and index cards with each activity either spelled or drawn.

- Students will look at the class schedule and use index cards to build a different table with the same information.
- Across the top will be the times.
- Across the bottom will be the corresponding activities.

Option 2 — Student Technology

Math Online ▷ macmillanmh.com

Option 3 — Learning Station: Health (p. 225H)

Direct students to the Health Learning Station for opportunities to explore and extend the lesson concept.

Leveled Lesson Resources

Reteach (pp. 30-31) **BL**	Skills Practice (p. 32) **OL**	Enrich (p. 34) **AL**	Homework Practice (p. 33) **OL**
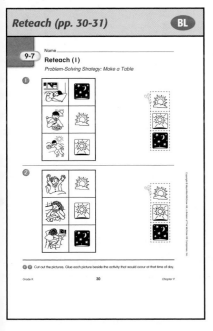	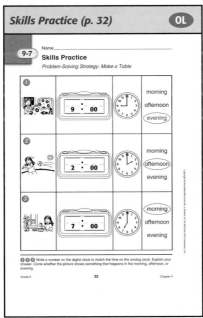	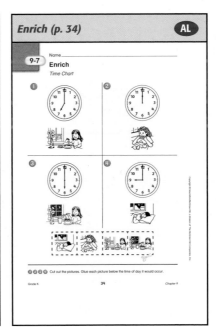	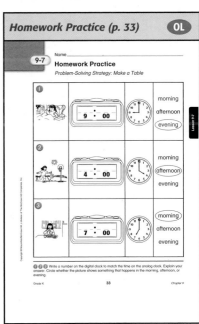

1 Introduce

Circle Time
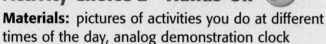

Activity Choice 1 • Literature

Brown Rabbit's Day
by Alan Baker
Materials: pencils, blank calendar sheet

* Read *Brown Rabbit's Day* aloud, emphasizing time words.

* Write on the chalkboard and discuss: *morning, breakfast, lunch,* and *afternoon.*

* Remind students that one week is seven of Brown Rabbit's days.

* Have students fill in the days of the week on a blank calendar sheet. Reinforce how a calendar is like a table.

Activity Choice 2 • Hands-On

Materials: pictures of activities you do at different times of the day, analog demonstration clock

* Show a picture of an activity you do in the morning.

* Ask students whether the picture shows an activity you do in the morning, afternoon, evening, or night.

* Ask a volunteer to show a time on the instructional clock that could match the picture.

* Repeat with different pictures.

* Ask volunteers to share activities they do in the morning, afternoon, evening, or night.

2 Teach

The *make a table* strategy helps students to see data in an organized way and to use all information at hand in order to solve a problem.

* Direct students to p. 243.

* Have students look at the table. Tell them that a table is a way to show information. **What information does this table show?** activities girls and boys do, clocks, words to tell about different times during the day

* **How do the pictures help you understand what time of day it is?** Sample answer: The pictures show the sun or moon and that tells us the time of day.

* Tell students they will use the pictures and clocks in the table to decide what time of day the child does each activity.

BL Alternate Teaching Strategy

If students have trouble understanding how to use the a table to understand concepts about time . . .

Then use one of these reteach options.

1 CRM **Daily Reteach Worksheet** (pp. 30-31)

2 **Sequence Picture Cards** Have students work in pairs. Each pair sequences picture cards that show morning, afternoon, and evening.

* Ask students how they know the cards are in order.

* Have students draw pictures in order to show an activity they do in the morning, afternoon, and evening.

! COMMON ERROR!

Students may have difficulty using a table to understand information. Discuss the information in a table and how to use this information to answer questions.

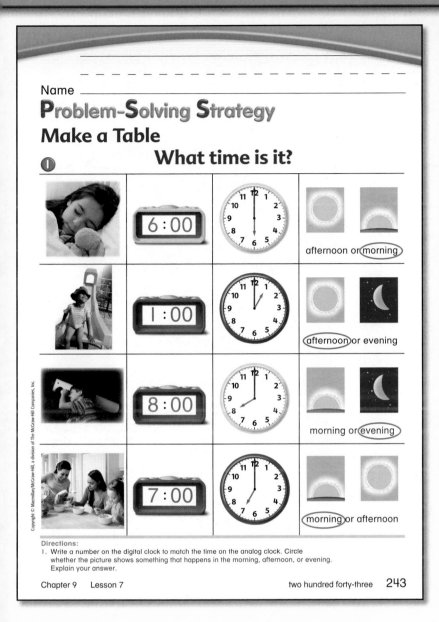

Name _____

Problem-Solving Strategy
Make a Table
① What time is it?

Directions:
1. Write a number on the digital clock to match the time on the analog clock. Circle whether the picture shows something that happens in the morning, afternoon, or evening. Explain your answer.

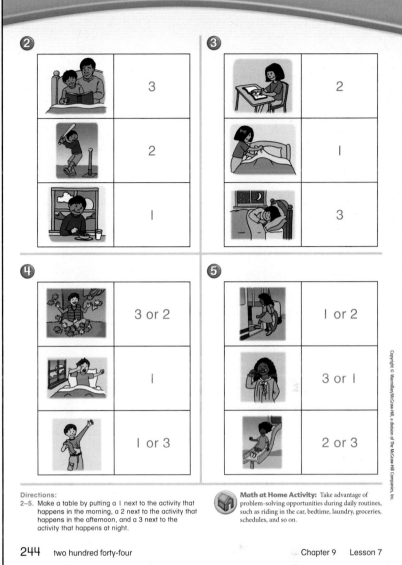

② | | 3 |
③ | | 2 |

④ | | 3 or 2 |
⑤ | | 1 or 2 |

Directions:
2–5. Make a table by putting a 1 next to the activity that happens in the morning, a 2 next to the activity that happens in the afternoon, and a 3 next to the activity that happens at night.

Math at Home Activity: Take advantage of problem-solving opportunities during daily routines, such as riding in the car, bedtime, laundry, groceries, schedules, and so on.

③ Practice

Guided Practice

- Direct students to p. 243.
- Tell students to look at the first picture in the row.
- Have students write numbers on the digital clock to match the time on the analog clock.
- Ask students to circle whether the picture shows something that happens in the morning, afternoon, or evening depending on the picture in the first box and the time in the next box.

Independent Practice

Have students turn to p. 244. Explain the directions. Have students work independently on the exercises.

- Ask students to share another strategy that could be used and how it might be used.
- Ask students what other information would be helpful to show in a table.

④ Assess

Formative Assessment

- Show students pictures of activities or events that take place in the morning, afternoon, and evening.
- Have students put the pictures in the order in which the events take place.

Quick Check	Are students still struggling to solve problems using a table of information?

If Yes → Small Group Options (p. 243B)

If No → Independent Work Options (p. 243B)

    CRM Skills Practice Worksheet (p. 32)

    CRM Enrich Worksheet (p. 34)

Problem Solving in Music

Real-World MATH

Namida is a Native American dancer. She has to practice the dances.

This book belongs to

_____

A

This dancer hears the beat. He has to count his steps.

B

Lesson Planner

Objective

Use a chart to record information.

National Standard 🎵

Students describe in simple terms how elements of music are used in music examples from various cultures of the world.

Activate Prior Knowledge

Before you turn students' attention to the pages, discuss Native American dancing.

- Share with students that some people dress up for special Native American dances.
- **How is this boy's outfit different than the one you are wearing today?** Sample answers: It is bright and colorful. It has feathers.
- **What type of activities do you practice outside?** Sample answer: I practice playing soccer outside.
- **Have you ever used an instrument to create a beat? What type of instrument was it?** Sample answer: Yes, I have used a drum to create a beat.

Elan practices on Monday, Wednesday, Thursday, and Saturday.
Color to show when he practices.

Sunday	
Monday	▢
Tuesday	
Wednesday	▢
Thursday	▢
Friday	
Saturday	▢

How many days does he practice?

__4__ days

C

What do you practice doing?
Sample answers:
swimming, piano, baseball

D

FOLD DOWN

Create the Book

Guide students to create their book.

- Have them fold the page in half.

- Ask them to write their name on page A.

- Explain that page A is the front cover and page D is the back cover. If necessary, have them practice flipping through the book in order.

- Guide them in reading the information and word questions on each of the pages.

Use the Student Pages

Page B Read the page together. Practice counting possible dance steps.

Page C Help students color the boxes on the chart to show what days Elan practices.

Page D Discuss the activities students practice at school and outside of school.

WRITING IN ▶MATH Have students draw a picture of themselves playing a sport or enjoying a hobby. Help them write a caption to tell about their picture.

FOLDABLES Dinah Zike's Foldables

If students have not completed their Foldables, guide them to create and fill in the appropriate information using the instructions on pp. 225 and 237.

You may choose to use the Foldable to help students review the concepts presented in this chapter and as a tool for studying for the Chapter Test.

Vocabulary Review

Review chapter vocabulary using one of the following options.

- **Visual Vocabulary Cards** (3, 15, 24, 26, 28, 46, 47, 49, 50)
- **eGlossary** at <u>macmillanmh.com</u>

Data-Driven Decision Making

Based on the results of the Chapter Review/Test, use the following to review concepts that continue to present students with problems.

Exercises	State/Local Standards	What's the Math?	Error Analysis	Resources for Review
1 Lesson 9-1		Understand units to measure time such as morning, afternoon, and evening.	Does not understand words "morning," "afternoon," "evening." Draws undistinguishable, confusing picture.	CRM Chapter 9 Resource Masters (Reteach Worksheets) **Math Online** Concepts in Motion Math Adventures
2 Lesson 9-4		Demonstrate an understanding of concepts of time such as yesterday, today, and tomorrow.	Misreads directions. Does not understand words "yesterday," "today," "tomorrow."	
3 Lesson 9-5		To the nearest hour, identify the time of an everyday event using an analog clock.	Does not know how to write time.	
4 Lesson 9-6		Identify the time on an analog clock and circle the corresponding digital clock.	Cannot read digital clock. Cannot read analog clock. Circles both clocks for the answer.	

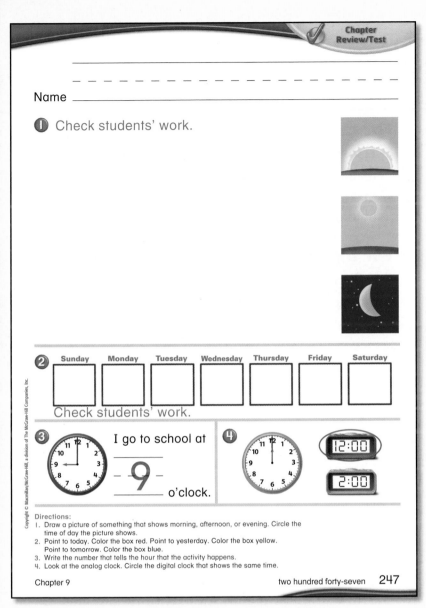

Name

① Check students' work.

② | Sunday | Monday | Tuesday | Wednesday | Thursday | Friday | Saturday |

Check students' work.

③ I go to school at

-9 o'clock.

④

12:00

2:00

Directions:
1. Draw a picture of something that shows morning, afternoon, or evening. Circle the time of day the picture shows.
2. Point to today. Color the box red. Point to yesterday. Color the box yellow. Point to tomorrow. Color the box blue.
3. Write the number that tells the hour that the activity happens.
4. Look at the analog clock. Circle the digital clock that shows the same time.

Chapter 9   two hundred forty-seven 247

Name

① 12   12

② 24   28

③ -2 -4 -1

Directions:
1. Count the objects in each group. Write the numbers. Draw a box around the groups if they are the same.
2. Count the objects in each group. Write the number of objects that each group contains. Put an X on the group that has less objects.
3. Count the boxes to find out how many of each animal there are. Write the number.

248   two hundred forty-eight

Summative Assessment

Use these alternate leveled chapter tests to differentiate assessment for the specific needs of your students.

Leveled Chapter 9 Tests			
Form	Type	Level	CRM Pages
1	Multiple Choice	BL	42–43
2A	Multiple Choice	OL	44–45
2C	Multiple Choice	OL	46–47
2D	Free Response	AL	48–49

BL = below/approaching grade level
OL = on grade level
AL = above/beyond grade level

Spiral Review

Review Chapters 1 to 9

Objective: Review and assess mastery of skills and concepts from previous chapters.

Resources for Review

Based on student results, refer to these lessons for remediation.

- **Exercise 1: Lesson 6-1** (p. 153)
- **Exercise 2: Lesson 8-4** (p. 213)
- **Exercise 3: Lesson 5-1** (p. 131)

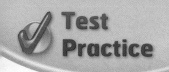

Test Practice

Chapters 1–9

 Formative Assessment

- You can use Student Edition pp.249–250 to benchmark student progress.

- Additional practice pages can be found in Chapter 9 Resource Masters. Create additional practice worksheets or tests.

CRM **Chapter 9 Resource Masters**
Cumulative Test Practice

- Multiple Choice format (pp. 42-47)

- Free Response format (pp. 48-49)

 Create additional practice worksheets or tests.

Test-Taking Tips

For the Teacher

- Make sure you have the students' attention before reading the test questions.

- Make sure each student understands the directions before beginning the test.

For the Student

- Make sure students check that they have filled in an oval for each test question.

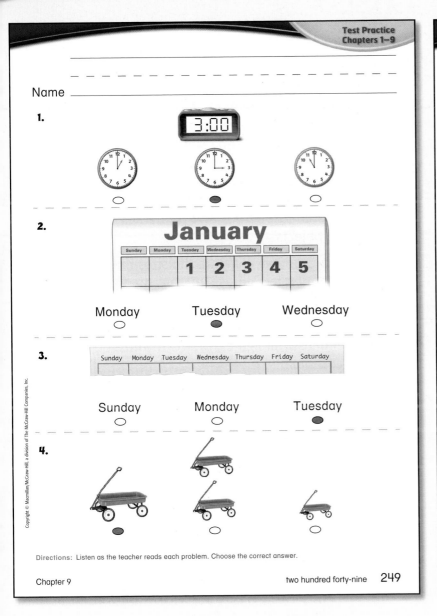

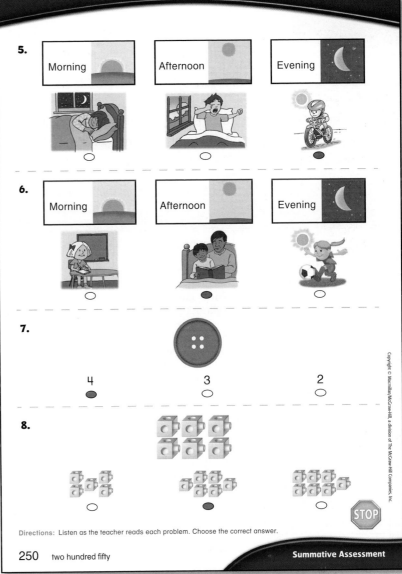

Directions: Listen as the teacher reads each problem. Choose the correct answer.

Chapter 9   two hundred forty-nine   249

250   two hundred fifty

Summative Assessment

Test Directions for Teachers

Read the following directions to students before they begin. Then read each question followed by a pause to allow students time to work and choose an answer. The first test item can be worked as a class example

- **Write your name at the top of the page.**
- **I am going to read each question to you. Listen carefully to the entire question before you choose an answer.**

1. Look at the digital clock. Find and mark the clock that shows the same time.

2. Look at this calendar. Find and mark the day of the week that is the first day of January.

3. Look at this calendar. Find and mark the day of the week that comes before Wednesday.

4. Look at the row of wagons. Find the wagon that holds more than the wagon above. Mark the wagon.

5. Look at the pictures in the row. They show morning, afternoon, and evening. Find and mark the activity you might do in the afternoon.

6. Look at the pictures in a row. They show morning, afternoon, and evening. Find and mark the activity you might do in the evening.

7. Look at the button holes. Find the number that tells how many button holes are in the button. Mark the number.

8. Look at the row of cubes. Find the group that shows the same amount of cubes as the group above. Mark the group.

Chapter Overview

Chapter-at-a-Glance

In Chapter 10, the emphasis is on identifying, classifying, and comparing three-dimensional and two-dimensional figures.

Lesson	Math Objective	State/Local Standards
10-1 Three-Dimensional Figures (pp. 255–256)	Identify and describe three-dimensional figures including sphere, cone, cube, and cylinder.	
10-2 Compare Three-Dimensional Figures (pp. 257–258)	Sort three-dimensional objects by varied attributes: roll, stack, and slide.	
10-3 Two-Dimensional and Three-Dimensional Figures (pp. 259–260)	Match the surface of three-dimensional figures to two-dimensional figures.	
10-4 Squares and Rectangles (pp. 261–262)	Identify and describe squares and rectangles.	
10-5 Circles and Triangles (pp. 263–264)	Identify and describe circles and triangles.	
10-6 Problem-Solving Strategy: Draw a Picture (pp. 267–268)	Determine figures missing in a design, and draw figures to complete the pictures.	
10-7 Equal parts (pp. 269–270)	Identify things divided into equal parts or halves.	
10-8 Two-Dimensional Figures In Position (pp. 271–272)	Explore the attributes of two-dimensional figures in different forms and orientations.	

Describe Geometric Figures

BIG Idea Geometry gives students the opportunity to observe items in their environments and to begin to compare and classify. Geometric figures are everywhere! Studying geometry gives students the opportunity to relate math to the real world. Looking for figures in the environment helps students see that objects have different properties and properties can be used to describe objects.

Algebra Students compare the sizes of figures and objects formed by figures. This lays the foundation for students to understand equalities. Lesson 10-5

Geometry As students observe geometric properties of three-dimensional figures, they categorize objects that roll, stack, and slide.
Lessons 10-2 and 10-6

GK-FP2 *Geometry:* **Describe shapes and space**

Children interpret the physical world with geometric ideas (e.g., shape, orientation, spatial relations) and describe it with corresponding vocabulary. They identify, name, and describe a variety of shapes, such as squares, triangles, circles, rectangles, (regular) hexagons, and (isosceles) trapezoids presented in a variety of ways (e.g., with different sizes or orientations), as well as such three-dimensional shapes as spheres, cubes, and cylinders. They use basic shapes and spatial reasoning to model objects in their environment and to construct more complex shapes.

Skills Trace
Vertical Alignment

PreKindergarten

In PreK, students learned to:

- Recognize, describe, and name figures (e.g., circles, triangles, rectangles—including squares).

Kindergarten

During this chapter, students learn to:

- Identify three-dimensional and two-dimensional figures.
- Compare two-dimensional figures.
- Compare sizes and positions of two-dimensional and three-dimensional figures.

After this chapter, students will learn to:

- Add numbers with each number less than or the same as (equal to) 9.
- Work with simple subtraction problems.

First Grade

In first grade, students will learn to:

- Identify common three-dimensional geometric figures.
- Identify faces and corners.
- Give and follow directions.

Backmapping and Vertical Alignment

McGraw-Hill's *Math Connects* program was conceived and developed with the final results in mind: student success in Algebra 1 and beyond. The authors, using the **NCTM Focal Points and Focal Connections** as their guide, developed this brand new series by backmapping from Algebra 1 concepts, and vertically aligning the topics so that they build upon prior skills and concepts and serve as a foundation for future topics.

Math Vocabulary

The following math vocabulary words for Chapter 10 are listed in the glossary of the *Student Edition*. You can find interactive definitions in 13 languages in the *eGlossary* at macmillanmh.com.

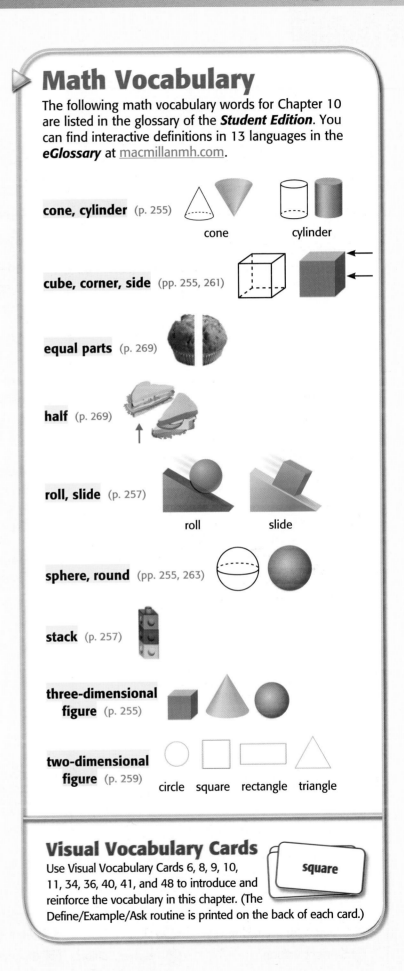

cone, cylinder (p. 255)

cone   cylinder

cube, corner, side (pp. 255, 261)

equal parts (p. 269)

half (p. 269)

roll, slide (p. 257)

roll   slide

sphere, round (pp. 255, 263)

stack (p. 257)

three-dimensional figure (p. 255)

two-dimensional figure (p. 259)

circle   square   rectangle   triangle

Visual Vocabulary Cards

Use Visual Vocabulary Cards 6, 8, 9, 10, 11, 34, 36, 40, 41, and 48 to introduce and reinforce the vocabulary in this chapter. (The Define/Example/Ask routine is printed on the back of each card.)

square

Chapter Planner

	Suggested Pacing	
Instruction	**Review and Assessment**	**TOTAL**
8 days	2 days	**10 days**

✓ **Diagnostic Assessment**
Are You Ready? (p. 252)

	Lesson 10-1 Pacing: 1 day	**Lesson 10-2** Pacing: 1 day	**Lesson 10-3** Pacing: 1 day
Lesson/ Objective	**Three-Dimensional Figures** (pp. 255–256) **Objective:** Identify and describe three-dimensional figures including sphere, cone, cube, and cylinder.	**Compare Three-Dimensional Figures** (pp. 257–258) **Objective:** Sort three-dimensional objects by varied attributes: roll, stack, and slide.	**Two-Dimensional and Three-Dimensional Figures** (pp. 259–260) **Objective:** Match the surface of three-dimensional figures to two-dimensional figures.
State/Local Standards			
Math Vocabulary	**three-dimensional figure, cube, sphere, cone, cylinder**	**roll, stack, slide**	**two-dimensional figure, square, rectangle, circle, triangle**
Lesson Resources	**Materials** pencils, classroom objects, yarn, scissors, glue, real-world objects **Manipulatives** building blocks, geometric solids **Other Resources** [CRM] Leveled Worksheets (pp. 6-9) 🖌 Daily Reteach 📖 Problem of the Day	**Materials** classroom objects, playground ball, pencils, chart paper, markers, real-world objects **Manipulatives** geometric solids **Other Resources** [CRM] Leveled Worksheets (pp. 10-13) 🖌 Daily Reteach	**Materials** pencils, sand, container **Manipulatives** blocks, geometric solids **Other Resources** [CRM] Leveled Worksheets (pp. 14-17) 🖌 Daily Reteach 📖 Problem of the Day
Technology [Math Online]	Concepts in Motion		🌐 Math Adventures Concepts in Motion
Reaching All Learners	English Learners, p. 255B **ELL** Below Level, p. 255B **BL** Early Finishers, p. 255B **OL** **AL**	English Learners, p. 257B **ELL** Gifted and Talented, p. 257B **AL** Early Finishers, p. 257B **OL** **AL**	English Learners, p. 259B **ELL** Below Level, p. 259B **BL** Early Finishers, p. 259B **OL** **AL**
Alternate Lesson	*Math Their Way,* pp. 74–75 *IMPACT Mathematics:* Unit F	*IMPACT Mathematics:* Unit F	*Math Their Way,* pp. 76–77 *IMPACT Mathematics:* Unit F

KEY

BL Below/Approaching Level	**OL** On Level	**AL** Above/Beyond Level	**ELL** English Learners
SE Student Edition	**TE** Teacher Edition	**CRM** Chapter 1 Resource Masters	💿 CD-Rom
🖌 Transparency	📖 Flip Chart	📖 Real-World Problem Solving Library	

	Lesson 10-4 Pacing: 1 day	**Lesson 10-5** Pacing: 1 day	**Lesson 10-6** Pacing: 1 day	

Lesson 10-4   Pacing: 1 day

Squares and Rectangles
(pp. 261–262)

Objective: Identify and describe squares and rectangles.

Lesson 10-5   Pacing: 1 day

Circles and Triangles
(pp. 263–264)

Objective: Identify and describe circles and triangles.

Lesson 10-6   Pacing: 1 day

Problem-Solving Strategy
Draw a Picture
(pp. 267–268)

Objective: Determine figures missing in a design, and draw figures to complete the pictures.

Lesson/Objective

State/Local Standards

corner, side

round

Math Vocabulary

Materials
graph paper, pencils, paper, crayons, paper figures

Manipulatives
attribute buttons

Other Resources
CRM Leveled Worksheets (pp. 18-21)
Daily Reteach
Problem of the Day

Materials
drawing paper, crayons, paper figures, pencils

Manipulatives
attribute buttons

Other Resources
CRM Leveled Worksheets (pp. 22-25)
Daily Reteach
Problem of the Day

Materials
crayons, paper

Manipulatives
pattern blocks

Other Resources
CRM Leveled Worksheets (pp. 26-30)
Daily Reteach
Problem of the Day

Lesson Resources

Math Adventures

Math Adventures

Math Adventures

Technology
Math Online

English Learners, p. 261B **ELL**
Below Level, p. 261B **BL**
Early Finishers, p. 261B **OL** **AL**

English Learners, p. 263B **ELL**
Gifted and Talented, p. 263B **AL**
Early Finishers, p. 263B **OL** **AL**

English Learners, p. 267B **ELL**
Below Level, p. 267B **BL**
Early Finishers, p. 267B **OL** **AL**

Reaching All Learners

IMPACT Mathematics: Unit G

IMPACT Mathematics: Unit G

Alternate Lesson

Formative Assessment
Mid-Chapter Check (p. 265)

Game Time: Finding Figures
(p. 266)

	Lesson 10-7 **Pacing:** 1 day	Lesson 10-8 **Pacing:** 1 day
Lesson/ Objective	**Equal Parts** (pp. 269–270) **Objective:** Identify things divided into equal parts or halves.	**Two-Dimensional Figures In Position** (pp. 271–272) **Objective:** Explore the attributes of two-dimensional figures in different forms and orientations.
State/Local Standards		
Math Vocabulary	equal parts, half	
Lesson Resources	**Materials** construction paper figures, drawing paper, pencils **Manipulatives** geometric solids **Other Resources** CRM Leveled Worksheets (pp.31-34) Daily Reteach Problem of the Day	**Materials** paper figures, drawing paper, pencil **Manipulatives** pattern blocks **Other Resources** CRM Leveled Worksheets (pp. 35-38) Daily Reteach Problem of the Day
Technology [Math Online]	Math Adventures	Math Adventures
Reaching All Learners	English Learners, p. 269B ELL Below Level, p. 269B BL Early Finishers, p. 269B OL AL	English Learners, p. 271B ELL Below Level, p. 271B BL Early Finishers, p. 271B OL AL
Alternate Lesson		*Math Their Way*, pp. 38–39 *IMPACT Mathematics*: Unit G

Problem-Solving in Social Studies (p. 273)

Summative Assessment
- Chapter Review/Test (p. 275)
- Test Practice (p. 278)

Assessment Options

Diagnostic Assessment

SE *Option 1:* Are You Ready? (p. 252)
Option 2: Online Quiz (macmillanmh.com)
CRM *Option 3:* Diagnostic Test (p. 40)

Formative Assessment

TE Alternate Teaching Strategies (every lesson)
TE Writing in Math (every lesson)
TE Line Up (every lesson)
SE Mid-Chapter Check (p. 265)
CRM Mid-Chapter Test (p. 41)

Summative Assessment

SE Chapter Review/Test (p. 275)
SE Test Practice (p. 277)
CRM Leveled Chapter Tests (pp. 46-53)
CRM Cumulative Test Practice (p. 54-55)
CRM Listening Assessment (p. 44-45)
CRM Oral Assessment (p. 42-43)
ExamView® Assessment Suite
Advance Tracker

Assessment Tips

Vocabulary is an essential part of geometry and it requires students to be able to "say it," "read it," "write it," "define it," and "draw it."

- Have students create vocabulary cards for each word in the chapter.
- Conduct a vocabulary interview each day with a couple of different students.
- Ask them to tell you all about one of their vocabulary cards, providing the word, definition, and drawing.
- Probe for their understanding of the vocabulary words and record your observations on index cards that can be put in their file folders.

Teacher Notes

McGraw Hill Professional Development

Targeted professional development has been articulated throughout the **McGraw-Hill's** *Math Connects* program. The **McGraw-Hill Professional Development Video Library** provides short videos that support the **NCTM Focal Points and Focal Connections**. For more information, visit macmillanmh.com.

| Model Lessons | Instructional Strategies |

CHAPTER 10

Learning Stations
Cross-Curricular Links

Reading

Read All About It
- Listen to the story.
- Draw pictures of objects from the story.
- Draw figures from the story.
- Trade drawings with someone. Count and compare how many figures there are.

Teacher Note: Read The Shape of Things *aloud. Do not show the photos or pictures as you read. Have students draw pictures of the objects in the story, and draw some of the same figures as in the story. Have students form small groups and trade papers. Count how many of the same figures the students each drew. Have students describe, identify, and compare each figures drawn.*

Materials:
- *The Shape of Things* by Dayle Ann Dodds
- drawing paper
- crayons

Health

Walk the Shapes
- Walk around the figures.
- How was walking around the figures the same?
- How was it different?

Teacher Note: Help students make these large figures on the floor with masking tape: square, triangle, circle, and rectangle. Have students walk around the figures and identify each figure. Have them describe and compare how walking each figure was the same and different. For example, ask how many turns they made.

Materials:
- masking tape

Technology

Sorting Shapes
- Choose the Attribute Blocks button. Choose the workmat with two circles for sorting.
- Sort the figures.
- Sort the figures into two groups.
- Sort figures another way.

Materials:
- Math Tool Chest: Attribute Blocks tool

Teacher Note: Have students use the two-circle workmat in order to sort figures. You can provide students with ways to sort the figures such as: figures that stack, figures that do not stack, or allow the students to sort figures any way they choose. Have students justify their sort by explaining it to a classmate.

Science

 pair | KINESTHETIC, SOCIAL, LOGICAL

Slide and Roll

- Make a ramp with books.
- Will the block roll or slide?
- Put the block in the correct circle.

Teacher Note: Help students set up a hardcover book as ramp. Use string to make a large circle on the floor or table for objects that roll and to make another string circle for objects that slide. Tell pairs to get a block and decide whether the block will roll or slide down the ramp. Have them test by putting their block at the top of the book and seeing if it rolls or slides. Have pairs put the object in the correct circle. Have them repeat with other objects.

Materials:

- hardcover book
- string
- geometric solids

 ## Social Studies

  small group | KINESTHETIC, VISUAL, LOGICAL

Create a Store

- Play a game called *"Store"*.
- Put your objects on the shelf.
- What figures can be stacked? What figures cannot be stacked?

Teacher Note: Tell the class that they will play a game called "Store". Have students work in small groups. Give each group a set of everyday objects. Tell them to think of how to set up a shelf of groceries with the objects. Have them test their ideas by putting the objects on the shelf, finding out what objects can be stacked or not stacked. Have groups report their findings and tell how the objects are sorted.

Materials:

- everyday objects such as boxes, soup cans, and containers that would be found in a store

Calendar Time

Shape Stickers

- Put a shape sticker on each day of the month. Use circles, squares, rectangles, and triangles.
- Have students tell what the shape is each day. Have them say the number of sides and the number of corners of each shape.

Teacher Note: Make sure the stickers are arranged so that each shape is evenly distributed throughout the month. Use approximately the same number of stickers for each shape.

Introduce the Chapter

Real World: Geometry

Share with students that they are going to learn about geometry, the study of three-dimensional figures. Three-dimensional figures are also referred to as three-dimensional shapes or solid shapes. Two-dimensional figures are also referred to as two-dimensional shapes or plane shapes. Tell them that we can see figures all around us in our environment.

- Show students a square pattern block. Ask students to identify the shape. Invite volunteers to name objects in the room that have the same shape.
- Show other shapes of pattern blocks. Have students identify classroom objects with the same shape.
- Have students name objects outside the room with the same shape as the pattern blocks.

Use the Student Page

Have students turn to p. 251. Guide students to discuss the images on the page and answer the Explore questions.

Key Vocabulary

Introduce the key vocabulary in the chapter using the routine below.

Define: A **two-dimensional figure** (or plane shape) is a shape that lies flat.

Example: A square and a triangle are each two-dimensional figures.

Ask: How many other two-dimensional figures can you name?

Diagnostic Assessment

Check for students' prerequisite skills before beginning the chapter.

- **Option 1:** *Are You Ready for Chapter 10?*
  SE Student Edition, p. 252

- **Option 2:** *Online Assessment Quiz*
  Math Online ⟩ macmillanmh.com

- **Option 3:** *Diagnostic Test*
  CRM Chapter 10 Resource Masters, p. 40

RTI (Response to Intervention)

Apply the Results Based on the results of the diagnostic assessment on p. 252, use the chart on the next page to address individual needs before and during the chapter.

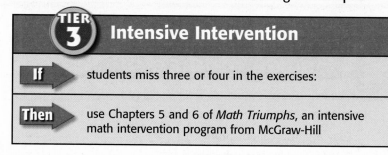

TIER 3	**Intensive Intervention**
If	students miss three or four in the exercises:
Then	use Chapters 5 and 6 of *Math Triumphs*, an intensive math intervention program from McGraw-Hill

---

FOLDABLES Study Organizer **Dinah Zike's Foldables**

Guide students to create a Standing Cube Foldable graphic organizer to collect information about two-dimensional and three-dimensional figures.

① Use two sheets of the same size paper. Fold each like a hamburger with one side of one half inch shorter than the other side.

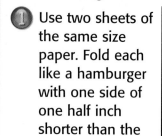

② Fold the long side over the short side of both sheets of paper, making tabs.

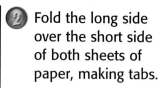

③ On one of the folded papers, place a small amount of glue along the small folded tab, next to the valley, but not in it.

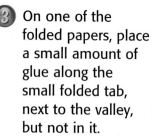

④ Place the non-folded edge of the second sheet square into the valley and fold the glue-covered tab over this sheet. Press flat until the glue holds. Repeat with the other side.

⑤ Allow the glue to dry. Then, the cube can be collapsed flat to allow students to work at their desks. The cube can also be folded into fourths for moving it or storing it.

When to Use It *Lessons 10-1 and 10-3 (Additional instructions for using the Foldable with these lessons are found on pp. 265 and 275.)*

CHAPTER 10

Describe Geometric Figures

Key Vocabulary
equal parts
half

Explore
Look around the classroom.
What figures can you find that
look like the ones in this picture?
Check students' answers.

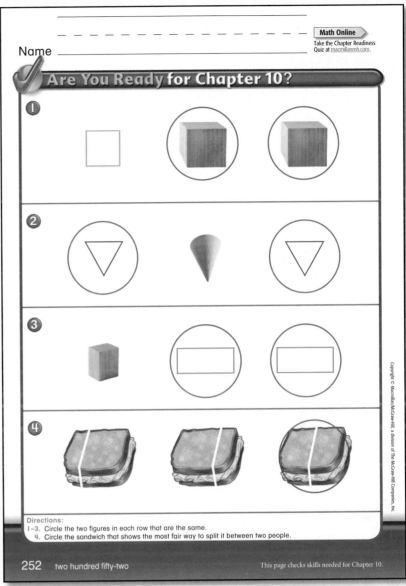

Math Online
Take the Chapter Readiness
Quiz at macmillanmh.com.

Are You Ready for Chapter 10?

①

②

③

④

Directions:
1–3. Circle the two figures in each row that are the same.
  4. Circle the sandwich that shows the most fair way to split it between two people.

RTI (Response to Intervention)

TIER 2 Strategic Intervention below/approaching grade level	TIER 1 On-Level	Above/Beyond Level
If students miss two in: **Exercises 1–4**	**If** students miss one in: **Exercises 1–4**	**If** students miss none in: **Exercises 1–4**
Then choose a resource:	**Then** choose a resource:	**Then** choose a resource:
CRM Chapter 1 Resource Masters (Reteach Worksheets) Math Online Concepts in Motion	TE Learning Stations (pp. 251G–251H) TE Chapter Project (p. 253) CRM Game: What is That Masked Shape? Math Adventures My Math Zone Chapter 9	TE Learning Stations (pp. 251G–251H) TE Chapter Project (p. 253) Real-World Problem Solving: *Playground Shapes* My Math Zone Chapters 9 and 10 Math Online Game

WRITING IN ►MATH

Starting the Chapter

Ask students to write one of the chapter's vocabulary words in their Math Journal. Have them draw a simple illustration to represent that word.

Chapter 10 Project

Shapes Museum Display

- Ask students to bring in empty containers and objects from home that represent various three-dimensional figures they learn about throughout the chapter.

- Provide a table or space in the classroom where these objects can be displayed.

- Give students time to visit the figures museum during each week so students can sort the containers and objects depending on their size, shape, and other attributes.

- Have students draw pictures of items in the figures museum and label each item with a vocabulary word that describes it: *round, cube, sphere, cone, cylinder, circle, triangle, rectangle, roll,* or *stack*. Students may also use letter stamps to stamp a word below each picture.

Chapter 10 Literature List

Lesson	Book Title	Author
10-1	Cubes, Cones, Cylinders, and Spheres	Tana Hoban
10-2	Math Counts Shape	Henry Pluckrose
10-3	Color Zoo	Lois Ehlert
10-4	Shapes, Shapes, Shapes	Tana Hoban
10-5	The Shape of Things	Dayle Ann Dodds
10-6	Shape Space	Cathryn Falwell
10-7	Captain Invincible and the Space Shapes	Stuart J. Murphy
10-8	When a Line Bends . . . A Shape Begins	Rhonda Gowler Greene
Any	Color Farm	Lois Ehlert

COLOR FARM

Lois Ehlert

ELL National ESL Standards Alignment for Chapter 10

Lesson, Page	ESL Standard	Modality	Level
10-1, p. 257B	Goal 2, Standard 1, h	Logical	Intermediate
10-2, p. 259B	Goal 2, Standard 3, a	Kinesthetic/Auditory	Intermediate
10-3, p. 261B	Goal 2, Standard 2, f	Linguistic	Intermediate
10-4, p. 263B	Goal 2, Standard 1, f	Logical	Advanced
10-5, p. 265B	Goal 2, Standard 3, h	Kinesthetic, Visual/Interpersonal	Intermediate
10-6, p. 269B	Goal 2, Standard 3, k	Intrapersonal	Intermediate
10-7, p. 271B	Goal 1, Standard 3, f	Visual/Spatial, Logical	Intermediate
10-8, p. 259B	Goal 1, Standard 3, k	Intrapersonal, Interpersonal	Intermediate

The National ESL Standards can be found in the Teacher Reference Handbook.

MATH at HOME

Dear Family,

Today my class started Chapter 10, **Describe Geometric Figures**. In this chapter, I will learn about two- and three-dimensional figures, equal parts, and halves. Here is an activity we can do and a list of books we can read together.

Love, _____

Activity

Have your child look around the house and find an example of one of each: cube, sphere, cone, triangle, square, rectangle, and circle. Draw the object.

Key Vocabulary

three-dimensional figures

two-dimensional figures

half

Math Online Click on the eGlossary link at macmillanmh.com to find out more about these words. There are 13 languages.

Books to Read

Color Farm
by Lois Ehlert
HarperCollins Publishers, 1997.

The Shape of Things
by Dayle Ann Dodds
Sagebrush, 1999.

Captain Invincible and the Space Shapes
by Stuart J. Murphy
HarperCollins
Publishers, 2001.

two hundred fifty-three 253

MATEMÁTICAS en CASA

Estimada familia,

Hoy mi clase comenzó el Capítulo 10, **Describe figuras geométricas**. En este capítulo, aprenderé sobre las formas 2- y 3-dimensional figuras, partes iguales, y mitades. A continuación, hay una actividad que podemos realizar y una lista de libros que podemos leer juntos.

Cariños, _____

Actividad

Pídanle a su hijo(a) que busque en la casa objetos que tengan forma de cubo, esfera, cono, triángulo, cuadrado, rectángulo y círculo. Dibujen el objeto con su hijo(a).

Vocabulario clave

figura tridimensional

figura bidimensional

mitad

Math Online Visiten el enlace eGlossary en macmillanmh.com para averiguar más sobre estas palabras, las cuales se muestran en 13 idiomas.

Libros para leer

Haciendo formas
de Jenifer Van Voorst
Red Brick, 2006.

La forma de las cosas
de Dayle Ann Dodds
Sagebrush, 1999.

Las figuras
de Weekly Reader
Early Learning Library, 2005.

254 two hundred fifty-four

MATH at HOME

- Read the Math at Home letter on p. 253 with the class and have each student sign it.

- Send home copies of the Math at Home letter with each student.

- Use the Spanish letter on p. 254 for students with Spanish-speaking parents or guardians.

Read-Aloud Anthology

For an optional reading activity to introduce this chapter's math concepts, see the Read-Aloud Anthology on p. TR32.

Lesson Planner

Objective

Identify and describe three-dimensional figures including sphere, cone, cube, and cylinder.

Vocabulary

three-dimensional figure, cube, sphere, cone, cylinder

Resources

Materials: pencils, classroom objects, yarn, scissors, glue, real-world objects

Manipulatives: building blocks, geometric solids

Literature Connection: *Cubes, Cones, Cylinders, and Spheres* by Tana Hoban

Alternate Lesson: Adapt *Descriptions* on pages 74 and 75 of *Math Their Way* for practice in describing three-dimensional figures.

Use *IMPACT* Mathematics: Unit F to provide practice with identifying and describing three-dimensional figures.

Teacher Technology

● TeacherWorks • Concepts in Motion

Focus on Math Background

This lesson links students' knowledge about solid figures to the corresponding three-dimensional representations used in formal geometry. Students will label and classify familiar objects such as balls, boxes, hats, or cans, with matching geometrical vocabulary and terminology including spheres, cubes, cones, and cylinders. Students will also describe the geometric features of these three-dimensional figures.

Daily Routine

Use these suggestions before beginning the lesson on p. 255.

5-Minute Check

(Reviews Lesson 9-8)

Show three pictures: a three-tiered snowman with a hat, coal eyes, a carrot nose, and stick arms; a three-tiered snowman with nothing on it; and two stacked balls of snow. Have students tell the order of events in building the snowman.

Problem of the Day

Show an assortment of cubes and spheres. Have students help you sort the objects by shape. Record answers in a graph.

LINE UP As they line up, have students answer a question by naming a three-dimensional figure.
What three-dimensional figure looks like a basketball? A box? A can? A holder for ice cream? sphere; cube; cylinder; cone

Building Math Vocabulary

Materials: building blocks, geometric solids

● Have students work with these four three-dimensional geometric figures: **cube, sphere, cone, and cylinder**.

● Discuss each **three-dimensional figure** with students. Show each figure one at a time, asking students to identify, name, and describe each one. Invite volunteers to tell what they know about the figures.

Visual Vocabulary Cards

Use Visual Vocabulary Card 10 to reinforce the vocabulary introduced in this lesson. (The Define/Example/Ask routine is printed on the back of each card.)

cube

Differentiated Instruction

Small Group Options

Option 1 — Below/Approaching Level BL
LINGUISTIC

Materials: three-dimensional figures, classroom objects shaped like spheres, cubes, cones, and cylinders

- Show a sphere.
- Have groups hold a sphere, then match the sphere to two classroom objects. Have groups discuss their work.
- Repeat with students identifying cubes, cylinders, and cones in the classroom.

Option 2 — English Language Learners ELL
KINESTHETIC, LOGICAL

Materials: paper clock face
Core Vocabulary: nose, flat, feel
Common Use Verb: sticks out

See Math This strategy introduces vocabulary to describe three-dimensional figures.

- Say: "The clock face is **flat**, but my face isn't flat. My **nose sticks out**."
- Tell students to feel both faces.
- Post a picture of a face and label the parts that stick out.

Independent Work Options

Option 1 — Early Finishers OL AL
KINESTHETIC/LOGICAL

Materials: fabric bags, three-dimensional figures

- Put one of each of the three-dimensional figures in a bag and one of each on a table.
- Have students take turns reaching into the bag and holding a figure.
- Have students choose the same figure on the table. Then have them pull the figure out of the bag and see whether they have guessed correctly.

Option 2 — Student Technology

Math Online macmillanmh.com

Option 3 — Learning Station: Reading (p. 251G)

Direct students to the Reading Learning Station for opportunities to explore and extend the lesson concept.

Leveled Lesson Resources

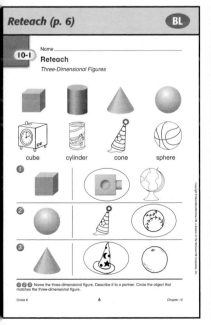
Reteach (p. 6) BL

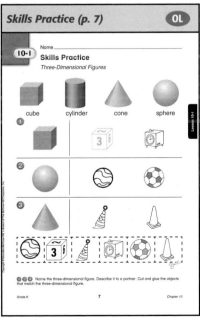
Skills Practice (p. 7) OL

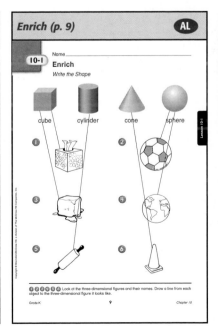
Enrich (p. 9) AL

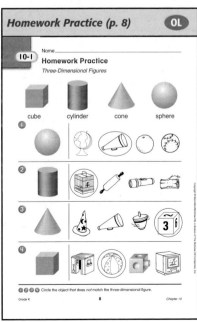
Homework Practice (p. 8) OL

① Introduce

Circle Time

Activity Choice 1 • Literature

Cubes, Cones, Cylinders, and Spheres by Tana Hoban

- Read the book aloud, discussing the pages and identifying **three-dimensional figures** in the room.
- Invite volunteers to identify these three-dimensional figures within the room: **cubes**, **cones**, **cylinders**, and **spheres**.
- Have students work in small groups to identify additional three-dimensional figures in the room.
- Lead the class in a discussion of how the three-dimensional figures are similar and different.

Activity Choice 2 • Hands-On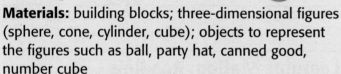

Materials: building blocks; three-dimensional figures (sphere, cone, cylinder, cube); objects to represent the figures such as ball, party hat, canned good, number cube

- Provide time for students to explore the blocks.
- Discuss ways the blocks are alike and different. Have students point out blocks that roll and stack.
- Play a guessing game of "I Spy." Describe a three-dimensional figure and ask the students to find that figure.
- As students discover the figure in their collection ask them to hold it up. Hold up and name a sphere since students might say *ball*.
- Continue the game with each figure.
- When all figures have been discussed, introduce real-world examples. Work with students to match the real-world object with the figure. Point out that three-dimensional figures come in all sizes.
- Give students an opportunity to recognize, describe, and compare each solid figure and match it to a real-world object.

② Teach

Direct students to the top of p. 255.

- Ask volunteers to name and describe each three-dimensional figure.
- Discuss the figures with the class. Compare each figure to the real world example.
- Have students draw a line from the three-dimensional figure to the object that is the same figure.

BL Alternate Teaching Strategy

If students have trouble identifying and describing three-dimensional figures . . .

Then use one of these reteach options.

1 CRM **Daily Reteach Worksheet** (p. 6)

2 **Match Figures** Lay classroom objects and three-dimensional figures on the floor.
- Have students match the classroom objects with the figures and explain why they match.
- Have students connect each classroom object to its matching figure with yarn.

COMMON ERROR!

Students may think an object and a three-dimensional figure must be the same size. Say that figure sizes can be different, and still be the same three-dimensional figure.

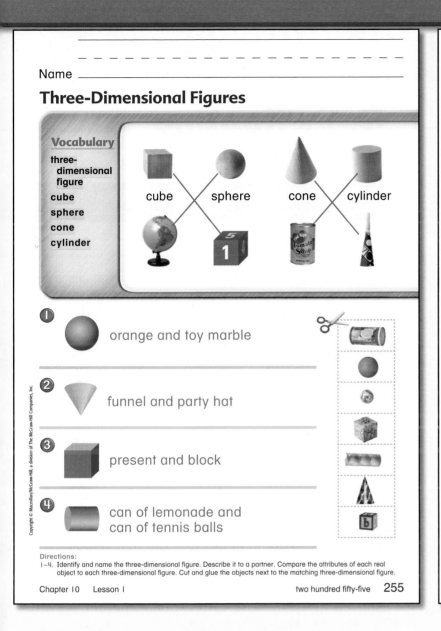

Name _____

Three-Dimensional Figures

Vocabulary
three-dimensional figure
cube
sphere
cone
cylinder

cube   sphere   cone   cylinder

① orange and toy marble

② funnel and party hat

③ present and block

④ can of lemonade and can of tennis balls

Directions:
1–4. Identify and name the three-dimensional figure. Describe it to a partner. Compare the attributes of each real object to each three-dimensional figure. Cut and glue the objects next to the matching three-dimensional figure.

Chapter 10   Lesson 1   two hundred fifty-five   **255**

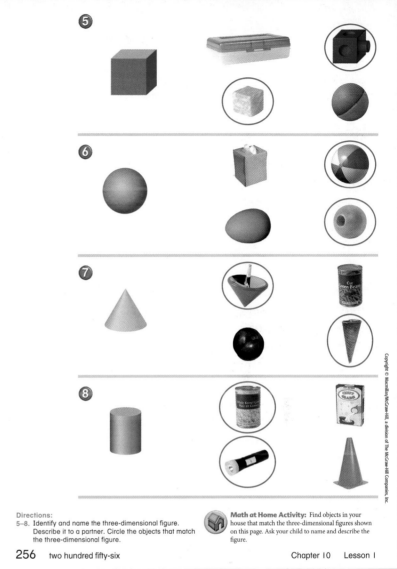

⑤

⑥

⑦

⑧

Directions:
5–8. Identify and name the three-dimensional figure. Describe it to a partner. Circle the objects that match the three-dimensional figure.

 Math at Home Activity: Find objects in your house that match the three-dimensional figures shown on this page. Ask your child to name and describe the figure.

256   two hundred fifty-six   Chapter 10   Lesson 1

---

③ Practice

Guided Practice

- Direct students to p. 255.

- Ask students to name and describe each three-dimensional figure in Exercises 1–4. Have students name and describe each real life object.

- Read the directions aloud. Guide students in cutting out the objects.

- Help students compare each real-life object to the sphere. Have them paste the objects that match the sphere on their paper beside the sphere.

- Repeat the above steps for the cone, then the cube, and then the cylinder.

Independent Practice

Have students turn to p. 256 and work independently on the exercises after the directions have been explained.

④ Assess

Formative Assessment

- Hold up three-dimensional figures one at a time.

- Ask students to recognize, describe, and compare all figures.

Quick Check — **Are students still struggling to name and describe three-dimensional figures?**

If Yes → Small Group Options   (p. 255B)

If No → Independent Work Options   (p. 255B)
   CRM   Skills Practice Worksheet   (p. 7)
   CRM   Enrich Worksheet   (p. 9)

Lesson 10-1 Three-Dimensional Figures   **256**

Lesson Planner

Objective

Sort three-dimensional objects by varied attributes: roll, stack, and slide.

Vocabulary

roll, **stack**, **slide**

Resources

Materials: classroom objects, playground ball, pencils, chart paper, markers, real-world objects as examples of figures

Manipulatives: geometric solids

Literature Connection: *Math Counts Shape* by Henry Pluckrose

Alternate Lesson: Use *IMPACT Mathematics*: Unit F to provide practice with sorting three-dimensional objects by attributes.

Teacher Technology
- TeacherWorks

Focus on Math Background

In this lesson, students will expand their geometric vocabulary for describing three-dimensional objects by comparing the properties of geometric solids. Kindergarteners make sense of geometric properties such as flat, round, and slanted, by manipulating three-dimensional figures (solids). This type of hands-on experience helps students see similarities and differences and then provides the opportunity to classify three-dimensional figures into categories including objects that roll, stack, or slide.

Daily Routine

Use these suggestions before beginning the lesson on p. 257.

5-Minute Check

(Reviews Lesson 10-1)
Show students a sphere, cone, cube, and cylinder. Ask them to name and describe the objects.

Problem of the Day

Find classroom objects shaped like a cube, sphere, or cylinder. Sort the objects into groups by shape.

LINE UP Before they get in line, have students name a classroom object that can roll. Repeat for stack and slide. Give hints to allow all students to line up.

Building Math Vocabulary

Materials: building blocks

- Prompt discussion about things that **roll**. Have students pick a block that could roll.
- Repeat the activity with the words **stack** and **slide**. Have students focus on real-world objects before choosing blocks that display these attributes.

Differentiated Instruction

Small Group Options

Option 1 — Gifted and Talented (AL)

Materials: unit blocks

- Have students form pairs. Give the same four blocks to each student. Have partners sit back to back.
- Have one student build a structure with the blocks and describe it. Have the other student build a duplicate structure based on the description. Have students look at both structures to see whether they look the same.
- Challenge students by using more blocks and/or making a pattern.

Option 2 — English Language Learners (ELL)

KINESTHETIC/AUDITORY

Core Vocabulary: clay, ball, box
Common Use Verb: roll/pinch

Do Math This strategy compares three-dimensional figures. Model and vocalize making a ball with clay.

- Write and say: "Roll a ball." Repeat for "Pinch a box."
- Point to names and have students create figures.

Independent Work Options

KINESTHETIC/AUDITORY

Option 1 — Early Finishers (OL) (AL)

Materials: chart paper, pencils, crayons

- Have students make and label Venn diagrams for *stack* and *slide*.
- Have students draw objects that can stack and slide in the intersection of the Venn Diagram circles.
- Have students draw pictures of objects that either stack or slide in the individual circles.
- Allow students to identify and describe each object on his or her diagram.

Option 2 — Student Technology

Math Online ▸ macmillanmh.com

Option 3 — Learning Station: Science (p. 251H)

Direct students to the Science Learning Station for opportunities to explore and extend the lesson concept.

Leveled Lesson Resources

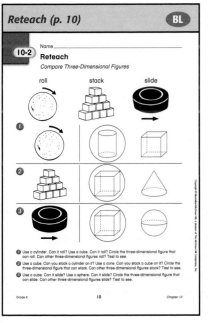

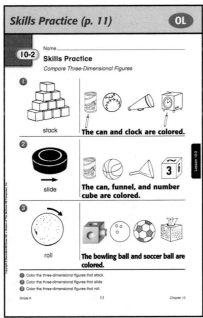

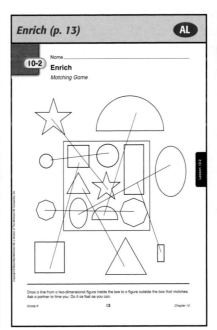

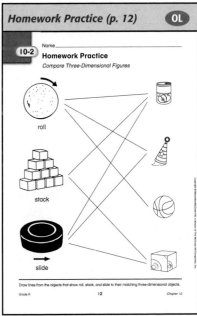

1 Introduce

Circle Time

Activity Choice 1 • Literature

Math Counts Shape
by Henry Pluckrose

- Read the book aloud, discussing the pages. Focus on three-dimensional figures and their attributes: shape, size, roundness, corners.

- Show students the following three-dimensional figures: cubes, spheres, cones, and cylinders. Compare them to the figures in the book.

- Give students sets of these three-dimensional figures. Have them work in pairs to determine what will **roll**, **stack**, or **slide**.

- Record findings in a three-column chart labeled *roll, stack, slide.*

Activity Choice 2 • Hands-On

- Gather students in the circle. Roll a ball to each student. Ask students to identify, describe, and name the three-dimensional shape of the ball.

- Hold up a cube. Use the words *roll* and *slide* to compare the two figures. Demonstrate *roll* once again with the ball.

- Ask students to experiment with objects to discover which ones roll.

- Demonstrate slide with a cube by sliding it across the floor or down a book slide. Ask students to take turns choosing blocks and real-world objects to discover which ones slide.

- Demonstrate stack using a cylinder. Ask students to find other solid figures that will stack.

- Allow students to experiment with three-dimensional figures and real-world objects testing which will stack, roll, and slide. Have students predict to see which figures will roll, slide, or stack.

2 Teach

Direct students to the top of p. 257.

- Ask students what the dog in the picture is doing. Invite volunteers to roll like a dog.

- **What is a three-dimensional figure that rolls?** Sample answer: sphere

- Ask students what the dog is doing in the next picture.

- **What is a three-dimensional figure that slides?** Sample answer: cube

- Repeat the activity with the word *stack*. Choose stuffed animals to stack.

BL Alternate Teaching Strategy

If students have trouble sorting three-dimensional objects by their attributes . . .

Then use one of these reteach options.

1 CRM **Daily Reteach Worksheet** (p. 10)

2 **Sort Figures** Sort objects with help.
- Give each student a three-dimensional figure. Help students name the figure.
- Draw on chart paper an example of each figure.
- Demonstrate rolling. Call it *roll*. Ask students to hold up their object if it rolls. Repeat for *stack* and *slide*.

COMMON ERROR!

Students may forget the difference between rolling and sliding. Tell them to think of rolling a ball or watching wheels that roll. Remind them that only round objects can roll.

Name

Compare Three-Dimensional Figures

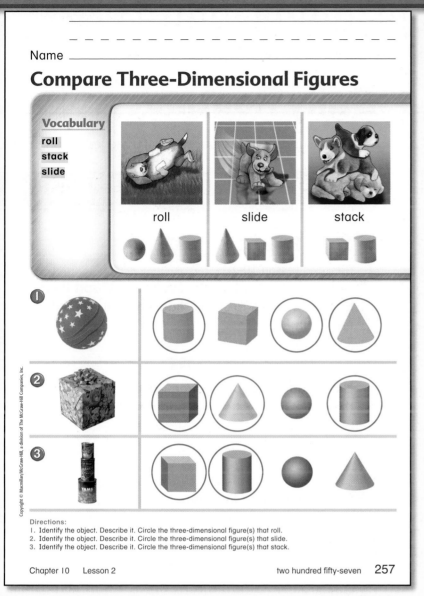

Vocabulary
roll
stack
slide

roll   slide   stack

Directions:
1. Identify the object. Describe it. Circle the three-dimensional figure(s) that roll.
2. Identify the object. Describe it. Circle the three-dimensional figure(s) that slide.
3. Identify the object. Describe it. Circle the three-dimensional figure(s) that stack.

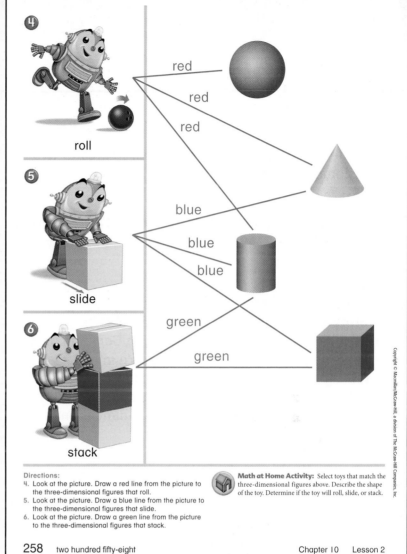

red
red
red

blue

blue

blue

green

green

roll

slide

stack

Directions:
4. Look at the picture. Draw a red line from the picture to the three-dimensional figures that roll.
5. Look at the picture. Draw a blue line from the picture to the three-dimensional figures that slide.
6. Look at the picture. Draw a green line from the picture to the three-dimensional figures that stack.

Math at Home Activity: Select toys that match the three-dimensional figures above. Describe the shape of the toy. Determine if the toy will roll, slide, or stack.

③ Practice

Guided Practice

- Direct students' attention to Exercise 1 on p. 257. Ask them to describe the real world object and to name it as a three-dimensional figure. Circle all of the the figures that roll.

- Repeat for Exercise 2, having students circle figures that slide.

- Repeat for Exercise 3, having students circle figures that stack.

Independent Practice

Have students turn to p. 258 and work independently on the exercises after the directions have been explained.

④ Assess

Formative Assessment

Show three-dimensional figures to students.

- Hold up a sphere. Ask students to name it and tell whether it can roll, stack, or slide.

- Repeat the activity with a cone, cube, and cylinder.

Quick Check — Are students still struggling to describe objects that roll, stack, and slide?

If Yes → Small Group Options (p. 257B)

If No → Independent Work Options (p. 257B)

CRM Skills Practice Worksheet (p. 11)

CRM Enrich Worksheet (p. 13)

Two-Dimensional and Three-Dimensional Figures

Lesson Planner

Objective
Match the surface of three-dimensional figures to two-dimensional figures.

Vocabulary
two-dimensional figure, **square**, **rectangle**, **circle**, **triangle**

Resources
Materials: sand, container, pencils
Manipulatives: blocks, geometric solids
Literature Connection: *Color Zoo* by Lois Ehlert
Alternate Lesson: Adapt *Tiptoe: A Sorting Game* on pages 76 and 77 of *Math Their Way* for practice in matching three-dimensional figures and two-dimensional figures. Use *IMPACT Mathematics*: Unit F to provide practice with matching the surface of two- and three-dimensional figures.
Teacher Technology
TeacherWorks • Concepts in Motion

Focus on Math Background

This lesson helps students connect two-dimensional (plane) figures to the matching faces on three-dimensional (solid) figures. Kindergarteners often inaccurately label three-dimensional figures (solids) with two-dimensional terminology. For example, students may say a ball is shaped like a circle instead of classifying it as a sphere. By learning the two-dimensional figure (shape) made from the side of a three-dimensional figure (solid shape), students will make appropriate connections between two- and three-dimensional geometry.

Daily Routine

Use these suggestions before beginning the lesson on p. 259.

5-Minute Check
(Reviews Lesson 10-2)
Hold up various objects. Have students sort them by their abilities to stack, slide, and roll. Record results in a chart.

Problem of the Day
Have students name a three-dimensional figure that rolls, one that stacks, and one that slides.

LINE UP Ask students if they ate something yesterday that came in a square, rectangle, circle, or triangle shaped container. If not, have them think of a food or food container that is one of these shapes, such as cheese, crackers, cereal, or a sandwich. Have students form different lines based on the shapes of the food or container.

Building Math Vocabulary
Materials: masking tape, geometric solids
- Make shapes on the floor with masking tape: **square**, **rectangle**, **circle**, **triangle**.
- Hold up a geometric solid, such as a cube. Have students identify the three-dimensional figure. Ask them to look at the shapes on the floor and find the **two-dimensional figure** that is made from the three-dimensional figure.
- **What two-dimensional figure is made from a cube?** square Continue with other three-dimensional figures.

Visual Vocabulary Cards
Use Vocabulary Card 6 to reinforce the vocabulary introduced in this lesson. (The Define/Example/Ask routine is printed on the back of each card.)

Differentiated Instruction

Small Group Options

Option 1
Below/Approaching Level BL
SPATIAL

Materials: cardboard, scissors, pencils, paper, crayons

- Cut rectangles, triangles, circles, and squares out of cardboard. Have students form small groups. Help students identify the shapes.
- Have students make their own shapes by tracing each shape on paper. Have groups match shapes on their paper to the cardboard shapes, and name each shape.

Option 2
English Language Learners ELL
LINGUISTIC

Materials: paper figures, glue
Core Vocabulary: flat, looks at, feels like
Common Use Verb: is/isn't

Write Math This strategy compares two- and three-dimensional figures.

- Pair students. Allow them to feel their face as they look at their partner's face. Say: "What figures do you feel?" Accept answers, noting the figures that stick out.
- Use the paper figures to make a face.

Independent Work Options

Option 1
Early Finishers OL AL
LINGUISTIC

Materials: two-dimensional figures

- Have students work in groups to create place settings for a meal in a restaurant.
- Tell them to use circles for plates, squares for napkins, cylinders for cups, rectangles for forks, and triangles for flower vases at each place setting.
- Have groups make a place setting for each student in the group.
- Have groups point to, name, and describe each figure.

Option 2
Student Technology

Math Online ▷ macmillanmh.com
Math Adventures

Option 3
Learning Station: Technology (p. 251G)
Direct students to the Technology Learning Station for opportunities to explore and extend the lesson concept.

Leveled Lesson Resources
Additional support for English Language Learners can be found in the ELL Guide (p. 129).

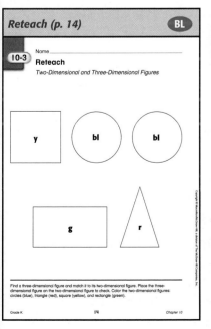

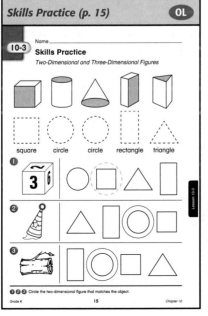

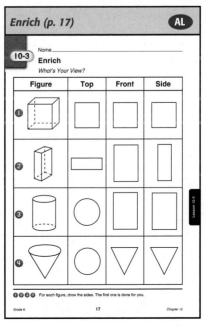

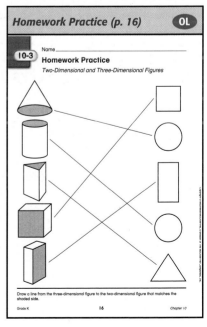

① Introduce

Circle Time

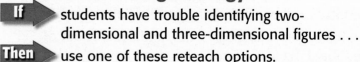

Activity Choice 1 • Literature

Color Zoo by Lois Ehlert

- Read the book aloud, naming the figures and colors.
- Explain that all figures in the book are **two-dimensional figures** because they are flat.
- Display the book's example of a **rectangle**. Ask students to find this figure in the room.
- Repeat with other figures in the book: **square**, **circle**, and **triangle**.

Activity Choice 2 • Hands-On

Materials: blocks, sand, container

- Ask students to find a cube, cone, and a cylinder in the block collection and to name them.
- Show students a triangular prism and a rectangular prism. Name them for students.
- Show students moistened sand in a container. Press a cube into the sand. Show students the figure made in the sand.
- **What is the name of the figure you see in the sand?** square
- Point out that each side of the cube is a square.
- Repeat with other block figures including a cone, cylinder, triangular prism, and rectangular prism to show the two-dimensional figure made from each three-dimensional figure.
- Show students a square, rectangle, and a triangle. Have students identify each figure.
- Combine the two- and three-dimensional figures.
- Have students sort the figures and describe how they are sorted.

② Teach

- Direct students to the top of p. 259.
- Have students identify three-dimensional figures and two-dimensional figures that are made from solids.
- Have them name and trace the dashed two-dimensional figure below each three-dimensional figure.

BL Alternate Teaching Strategy

If students have trouble identifying two-dimensional and three-dimensional figures . . .

Then use one of these reteach options.

1. **CRM Daily Reteach Worksheet** (p. 14)

2. **Compare Figures** Hold up a cube.
   - **Can you trace the face of a cube to make a circle?** no
   - **What figure can you make by tracing the side of a cube?** a square
   - Continue showing other geometric figures and asking other questions to help students match three-dimensional figures to two-dimensional figures.

! COMMON ERROR!

Students may confuse a square with a cube. Explain that a cube has six square sides. Provide examples of objects that are cubes, allowing students to feel the three dimensions.

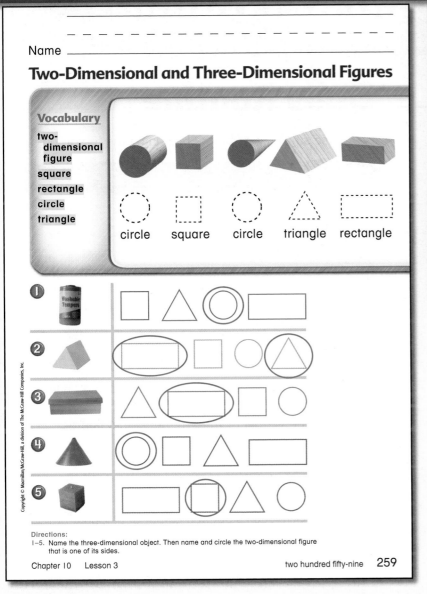

Two-Dimensional and Three-Dimensional Figures

Vocabulary

two-dimensional figure
square
rectangle
circle
triangle

circle   square   circle   triangle   rectangle

Directions:
1–5. Name the three-dimensional object. Then name and circle the two-dimensional figure that is one of its sides.

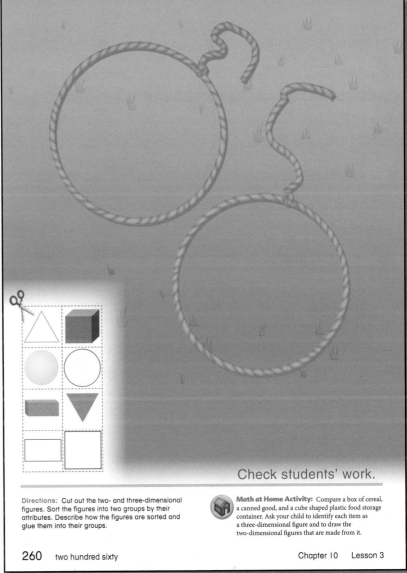

Check students' work.

Directions: Cut out the two- and three-dimensional figures. Sort the figures into two groups by their attributes. Describe how the figures are sorted and glue them into their groups.

Math at Home Activity: Compare a box of cereal, a canned good, and a cube shaped plastic food storage container. Ask your child to identify each item as a three-dimensional figure and to draw the two-dimensional figures that are made from it.

③ Practice

Guided Practice

- Direct students to Exercise 1 on p. 259.
- Have students identify and describe the real-world object and the two-dimensional figure that is made from that object. Instruct students to circle the two-dimensional figure.
- Repeat progess for Exercises 2–5.

Independent Practice

Have students turn to p. 260 and work independently on the exercise after directions are explained.

④ Assess

✓ Formative Assessment

- Give students sets of three-dimensional and two-dimensional figures. Have students compare and match the three-dimensional and two-dimensional figures.
- Ask students to explain why these figures belong together.

Quick Check	Are students still struggling to match three-dimensional and two-dimensional figures?

If Yes → Small Group Options (p. 259B)

If No → Independent Work Options (p. 259B)

     CRM Skills Practice Worksheet (p. 15)

     CRM Enrich Worksheet (p. 17)

Lesson 10-3 Two-Dimensional and Three-Dimensional Figures   **260**

Squares and Rectangles

Lesson Planner

Objective
Identify and describe squares and rectangles.

Vocabulary
corner, side

Resources
Materials: graph paper, pencils, paper, crayons, paper figures
Manipulatives: attribute buttons
Literature Connection: *Shapes, Shapes, Shapes* by Tana Hoban
Alternate Lesson: Use *IMPACT Mathematics*: Unit G to provide practice with identifying and describing squares and rectangles.
Teacher Technology
- TeacherWorks

Focus on Math Background

This lesson focuses on describing geometrical properties of squares and rectangles. By comparing these two quadrilaterals, students will discover similarities and differences. For example, students will understand how a square and rectangle are alike because both figures have four straight sides. Then, by observing the differences of each figure, students will generalize that the square is a special type of rectangle because all of its sides are the same (equal) in size.

Daily Routine

Use these suggestions before beginning the lesson on p. 261.

5-Minute Check
(Reviews Lesson 10-3)
Make a four-column chart. Draw a sphere, cone, cube, and cylinder for the headings. Have students identify attributes of objects and put them in the correct columns.

Problem of the Day
Show students pictures of different objects. Have them compare the objects and identify them as two-dimensional or three-dimensional figures. Record results in a T-chart.

LINE UP Give each student a cutout of a square or rectangle. Have students line up according to whether they have a paper shaped like a square or a rectangle.

Building Math Vocabulary
Materials: cutouts of squares
- Give each student a square. Hold up a square and ask students to hold up their paper shaped like a square.
- Point to a **corner** of your square, saying that this is a corner. Ask students to point to a corner of their square.
- Repeat the activity with the word *side*.
- Ask students to describe the words *corner* and *side* on their own, using their squares.

Visual Vocabulary Cards
Use Visual Vocabulary Card 9 to reinforce the vocabulary introduced in this lesson. (The Define/Example/Ask routine is printed on the back of each card.)

corner

Differentiated Instruction

Small Group Options

Gifted and Talented (AL)

Materials: paper, squares and rectangles, scissors, glue

- Have students form small groups. Give each group paper divided into two columns labeled with the words *rectangle* and *triangle*, pictures of rectangles and triangles in different positions and sizes, six paper squares, five paper rectangles, and scissors.

- Have groups cut squares into rectangles and squares into triangles. Have groups glue their shapes in the proper column, exchange papers, and check each other's work.

Option 2
KINESTHETIC, SOCIAL

English Language Learners (ELL)

Core Vocabulary: hold hands, arms out, corner
Common Use Verb: meet

Do Math This strategy allows students to kinesthetically learn about squares and rectangles.

- Show a square. Say: "Where the sides **meet** is a corner. A square has corners."

- Have four students come up and make a square by holding hands.

- Show a rectangle. Allow students to figure out how to change the "human square" into a rectangle. (Add people to make 2 sides longer.)

Independent Work Options

Option 1
LOGICAL/KINESTHETIC

Early Finishers (OL) (AL)

Materials: paper, crayons

- Have students make shape books.

- Have them make pages for different shapes, focusing on squares and rectangles.

- Have them draw objects that represent the shapes on the pages.

Option 2

Student Technology

Math Online > macmillanmh.com

Math Adventures

Option 3

Learning Station: Art (p. 251G)

Direct students to the Art Learning Station for opportunities to explore and extend the lesson concept.

Leveled Lesson Resources

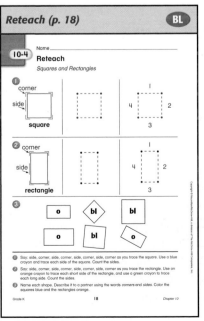

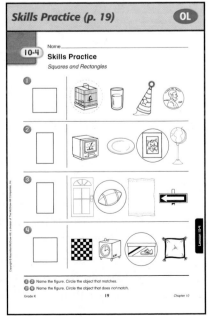

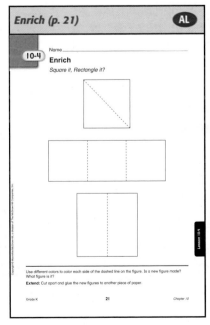

1 Introduce

 ircle Time

Shapes, Shapes, Shapes
by Tana Hoban

Activity Choice 1 • Literature

Shapes, Shapes, Shapes
by Tana Hoban
Materials: graph paper, pencils,
paper, crayons

- Read the book aloud, identifying squares and rectangles appearing in the illustrations. Describe attributes of **sides** and **corners**.

- Ask volunteers to identify and describe squares and rectangles in the room. Record responses on a T-chart.

- Describe squares and rectangles using the words *sides* and *corners*.

- Have students draw a picture using only squares and rectangles. Have them exchange with classmates and explain their pictures.

Activity Choice 2 • Hands-On

Materials: construction paper squares and rectangles

- Ask students to identify the construction paper figures.

- Have students find items in the classroom that are shaped like a square and a rectangle.

- Have them compare their findings to the paper figures by describing each.

- Introduce and define the words *corner* and *sides*.

- Ask students to count the corners and sides of each square and rectangle found in the classroom.

- Show students the construction paper square and rectangle.

- **How are they the same?** four sides and four corners **How are they different?** Sides are different lengths.

- Explain that a square has four sides that are all the same length and that a rectangle has four sides in which two sides are short and two are long.

2 Teach

Materials: pencils, crayons

- Direct students to the top of p. 261.

- Have students identify the figure on the left, trace it, and count the number of sides and corners.

- **What is this figure? How many sides does it have? How many corners?** rectangle; four; four

- Repeat for the square.

- **What is this figure? How many sides does it have? How many corners?** square; four; four

- Have students compare the number of sides and corners on a square and a rectangle.

- **What makes a square and a rectangle different if they have the same number of sides and corners?** Sample answer: A square has four equal sides and a rectangle has four sides with two sides that are longer.

BL Alternate Teaching Strategy

If students have trouble identifying and describing squares and rectangles . . .

Then use one of these reteach options.

1 CRM **Daily Reteach Worksheet** (p. 18)

2 **Find Squares and Rectangles** Show students attribute buttons with different shapes.

- Have students choose an attribute button with four sides.

- Have students choose an attribute button with four corners.

- Draw a rectangle and then trace an attribute square.

- Ask students to explain the difference between the two shapes.

 COMMON ERROR!

Students may not understand that a square is a type of rectangle. Explain that a square and a rectangle have four sides and four corners, but all the sides of a square are all the same length. Explain that a rectangle has two sides that are longer than the other two sides.

Name

Squares and Rectangles

Vocabulary

corner
side

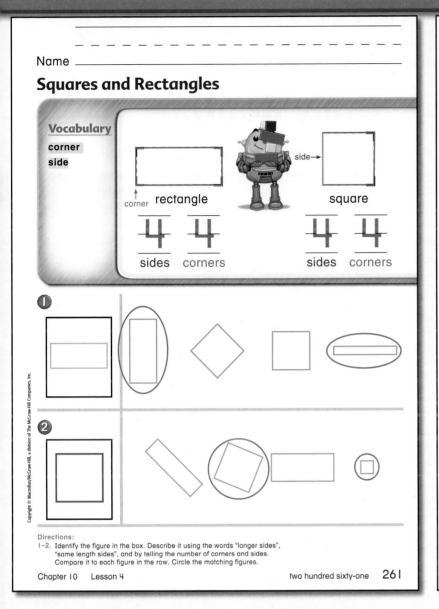

side →

rectangle

square

4 sides   4 corners

4 sides   4 corners

1

2

Directions:
1–2. Identify the figure in the box. Describe it using the words "longer sides", "same length sides", and by telling the number of corners and sides. Compare it to each figure in the row. Circle the matching figures.

Chapter 10   Lesson 4

two hundred sixty-one   261

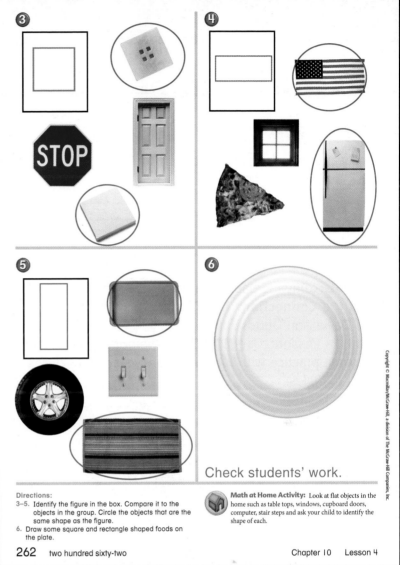

3

4

STOP

5

6

Check students' work.

Directions:
3–5. Identify the figure in the box. Compare it to the objects in the group. Circle the objects that are the same shape as the figure.
6. Draw some square and rectangle shaped foods on the plate.

Math at Home Activity: Look at flat objects in the home such as table tops, windows, cupboard doors, computer, stair steps and ask your child to identify the shape of each.

262   two hundred sixty-two

Chapter 10   Lesson 4

---

3 Practice

Guided Practice

- Direct students to p. 261.
- In Exercise 1, have students identify the figure using the terms *sides* and *corners* and telling the number of corners and sides.
- Guide students to circle the rectangles.
- Repeat with Exercise 2, having students circle the squares.

Independent Practice

Have students turn to p. 262 and work independently on the exercises after directions are explained.

4 Assess

Formative Assessment

Hold up a square and a rectangle.

- **What is a figure that has four sides?** square, rectangle
- **What is a figure that has four corners?** rectangle, square
- **How is a square different from a rectangle?** Sample answer: A square has four equal sides and a rectangle also has four sides, but two sides are longer.

Quick Check | **Are students still struggling to identify and describe squares and rectangles?**

If Yes → Small Group Options (p. 261B)

If No → Independent Work Options (p. 261B)

CRM Skills Practice Worksheet (p. 19)

CRM Enrich Worksheet (p. 21)

Lesson 10-4 Squares and Rectangles   **262**

Lesson Planner

Objective
Identify and describe circles and triangles.

Vocabulary
round

Resources
Materials: drawing paper, crayons, paper shapes, pencils
Literature Connection: *The Shape of Things* by Dayle Ann Dodds
Alternate Lesson: Use *IMPACT Mathematics*: Unit G to provide practice with identifying and describing circles and triangles.
Teacher Technology
- TeacherWorks

Focus on Math Background

In this lesson, students will describe and compare the properties of circles and triangles. By making comparisons between these two different figures, students will develop more sophisticated geometric vocabulary. For example, they will be able to describe how a circle is a round figure created by a curved line and how a triangle is created by three straight lines that connect at endpoints called corners.

Daily Routine

Use these suggestions before beginning the lesson on p. 263.

5-Minute Check
(Reviews Lesson 10-4)
Show a picture of a square object and a picture of a rectangular object. Have students identify what is a square. Repeat with other picture sets of objects.

Problem of the Day
Ask students to identify classroom objects as rectangles or squares. Record results in a T-chart.

LINE UP Have half the students identify a circular classroom object and then line up. Have the other half identify a triangular classroom object and then line up.

Building Math Vocabulary
Materials: construction paper triangles and circles
- Give each student a triangle and a circle. Ask them to find the corners and sides on the triangle.
- Explain that a triangle has three sides and three corners. Point out the sides and corners.
- Name the circle. Ask students to find the sides and corners.
- Explain that a circle has no sides or corners and instead has **round** edges.

Differentiated Instruction

Small Group Options

SPATIAL

Option 1
Gifted and Talented AL

Materials: reference sources about flags, such as encyclopedias or handouts; paper, pencils, crayons

- Give students reference materials about flags.
- Have students choose flags and discuss figures they see in them. Ask them to focus on triangles and circles.
- Have students create their own flags with various figures.

Option 2
English Language Learners ELL

Core Vocabulary: round, bigger, joined hands
Common Use Verb: must curve

Do Math This strategy introduces circles and triangles kinesthetically.

- Show a paper triangle. Allow students to model it. Note that their joined hands are not corners.
- Repeat for a circle. Say: "There are no corners in a circle, so you must curve your arms."
- Allow students to experiment with larger versions and record how many corners are in each figure.

Independent Work Options

LOGICAL

Option 1
Early Finishers OL AL

- Tell students that they will play a game called *I Spy*.
- Model how to play the game. Tell students that you spy a circle in the room. Describe an object, then have them guess the object.
- Repeat the game for spying a triangle in the room.
- Have students take turns spying circles and triangles in the room, and identifying and describing the objects.

Option 2
Student Technology

Math Online macmillanmh.com

Math Adventures

Option 3
Learning Station: Reading (p. 251G)

Direct students to the Reading Learning Station for opportunities to explore and extend the lesson concept.

Leveled Lesson Resources
Additional support for English Language Learners can be found in the ELL Guide (p. 127). ELL

Reteach (p. 22) BL	Skills Practice (p. 23) OL	Enrich (p. 25) AL	Homework Practice (p. 24) OL
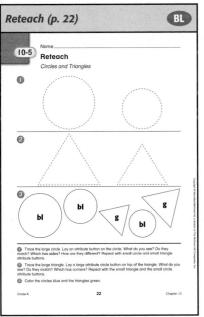	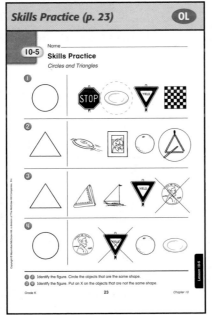	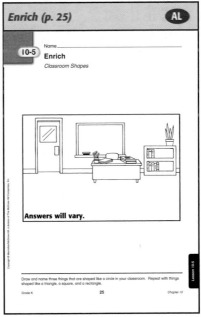	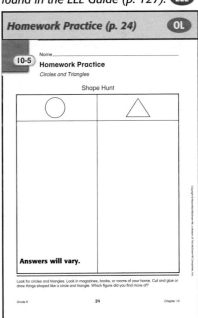

① Introduce

ircle Time

Activity Choice 1 • Literature

The Shape of Things
by Dayle Ann Dodds
Materials: drawing paper, crayons

- Read the book aloud, identifying circles and triangles in the illustrations.
- Have students identify and describe circles and triangles in the room.
- Record responses on a T-chart.
- Have students draw a picture using only circles and triangles. Ask volunteers to share their pictures with the class.

Activity Choice 2 • Hands-On

Materials: construction paper circles, triangles, rectangles, and squares.

- Ask students to identify the construction paper figures.
- Have students find items shaped like a triangle and a circle.
- Have them compare their findings to the paper figures by describing each. Emphasize the word *round* to describe a circle.
- **Are the circles all the same?** no **What does that tell us about circles?** They can be different sizes.
- Remind students of corners and sides and count the corners and sides of each triangle.
- **Are they the same?** yes **What does that tell us about triangles?** All triangles have three corners and three sides.
- Place a pile of construction paper circles, triangles, rectangles, and squares in the middle of circle time. One at a time have students come and take a figure.
- When all students have a figure have them sort themselves by the figure they are holding. Have each group describe their figure and compare it to the other figure.

② Teach

Direct students to the top of p. 263.

- Have students identify the figure on the left (circle) and trace it.
- Repeat for the figure on the right (triangle).
- Have students compare the number of corners on a circle with the corners on a triangle. Have them write the numbers for each in the appropriate spaces. Have students compare the number of sides and write the numbers.
- Identify the figure in the center of the page as a shape person.
- **What is missing from this person?** a head
- Have students draw a circle for the head.
- Have students draw a triangular hat on the circle head.

BL Alternate Teaching Strategy

If students have trouble identifying and describing circles and triangles . . .

Then use one of these reteach options.

1 CRM **Daily Reteach Worksheet** (p. 22)

2 **Compare and Contrast Figures** Show students a circle and a triangle.

- **How are the two figures the same?** Sample answer: They are both two-dimensional figures.
- **How are the figures different?** Sample answers: The triangle has sides, the circle does not. The triangle has corners, the circle does not.
- Have students cut out a circle and emphasize *round* as they cut.
- Have students cut out a triangle emphasizing *corner* and *side* as they cut.
- Have students draw circles on the cutout circle.
- Have students draw triangles on the cutout triangle.

 COMMON ERROR!

Students may not identify a triangle if it looks different from the "typical" triangles they see. Remind students that a figure that has three sides and three corners is always a triangle. Show some examples and count sides and corners with students.

Name _____

Circles and Triangles

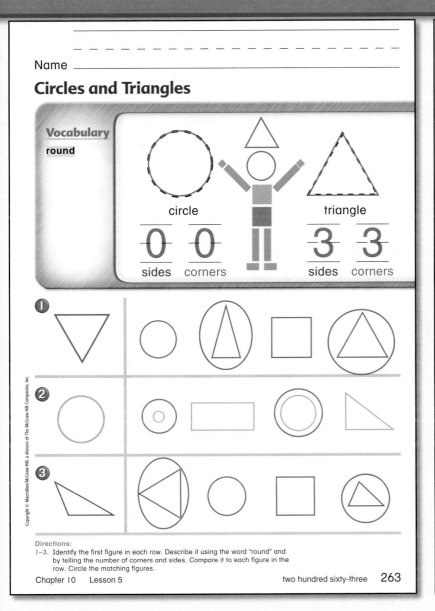

Vocabulary
round

circle
0 sides 0 corners

triangle
3 sides 3 corners

① ② ③

Directions:
1–3. Identify the first figure in each row. Describe it using the word "round" and by telling the number of corners and sides. Compare it to each figure in the row. Circle the matching figures.

Chapter 10   Lesson 5

two hundred sixty-three   263

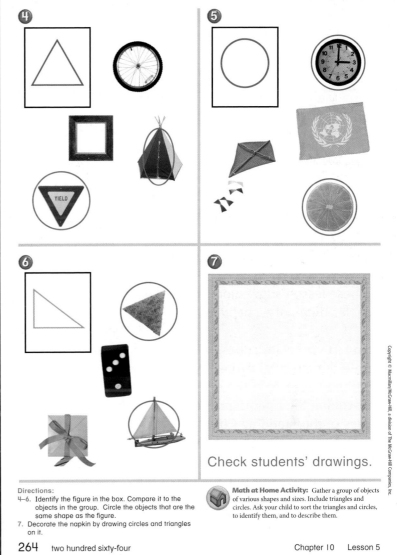

④ ⑤

⑥ ⑦

Check students' drawings.

Directions:
4–6. Identify the figure in the box. Compare it to the objects in the group. Circle the objects that are the same shape as the figure.
7. Decorate the napkin by drawing circles and triangles on it.

Math at Home Activity: Gather a group of objects of various shapes and sizes. Include triangles and circles. Ask your child to sort the triangles and circles, to identify them, and to describe them.

264   two hundred sixty-four

Chapter 10   Lesson 5

---

③ Practice

Guided Practice

- Direct students to p. 263.
- In Exercise 1, have students name, describe, and identify the figures, by telling the number of corners and sides of each.
- Have students circle the other triangles in the row.
- Repeat with Exercise 2, having students circle the circles.
- Repeat with Exercise 3, having students circle triangles.

Independent Practice

Have students turn to p. 264 and work independently on the exercises after directions are given.

④ Assess

Formative Assessment

- **What figure has no sides?** circle
- **What figure has three sides and three corners?** triangle
- Hold up a triangle. Have students name, identify, and describe it.
- Repeat with circle.

Quick Check   Are students still struggling to identify circles and triangles?

If Yes → Small Group Options (p. 263B)
If No → Independent Work Options (p. 263B)
　　　CRM Skills Practice Worksheet (p. 23)
　　　CRM Enrich Worksheet (p. 25)

Mid-Chapter Check

Lessons 10-1 to 10-5

 **Formative Assessment**

Use the Mid-Chapter Check to assess students' progress in the first half of the chapter.

ExamView
Assessment Suite

Customize and create multiple versions of your Mid-Chapter Check and the test answer keys.

FOLDABLES® Dinah Zike's Foldables

Use these lesson suggestions for incorporating the Foldables during the chapter.

Lesson 10-1 Relate cubes, spheres, and cones to three-dimensional figures by finding pictures of common objects in the environment and describing their geometric features on the four sides of the Standing Cube.

Lesson 10-3 Find and/or draw pictures of circles, squares, rectangles, and triangles and glue them to the four sides of the Standing Cube.

Name

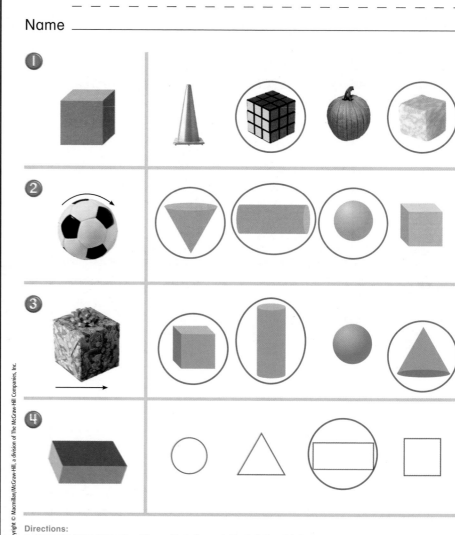

Directions:
1. Name the three-dimensional figure. Circle the real objects that match the three-dimensional figure.
2. Identify the object. Circle the three-dimensional figure(s) that roll.
3. Identify the object. Circle the three-dimensional figure(s) that slide.
4. Name the three-dimensional figure. Circle the two-dimensional figure that is the shape of one of its sides.

Chapter 10   two hundred sixty-five   **265**

Copyright © Macmillan/McGraw-Hill, a division of The McGraw-Hill Companies, Inc.

Data-Driven Decision Making

Based on the results of the Mid-Chapter Check, use the following resources to review concepts that continue to give students problems.

Exercises	State/Local Standards	What's the Math?	Error Analysis	Resources for Review
1 Lesson 10-1		Identify common three-dimensional figures in the environment.	Does not know characteristics of "cube." Confuses cube and square.	**CRM** Chapter 10 Resource Masters (Reteach Worksheets)
2-3 Lesson 10-2		Sort three-dimensional figures or objects by varied attributes.	Does not understand the difference between three-dimensional objects that roll, stack, or slide.	**Math Online** Concepts in Motion
4 Lesson 10-3		Identify and describe common two-dimensional and three-dimensional figures.	Does not color square figure.	Math Adventures

Finding Figures

Identifying Figures

You Will Need

Play with a partner. Take turns.
- One player uses red counters. The other player uses yellow.
- Roll the [5].
- Find a figure with that many sides.
- If a 5 is rolled, the next player takes a turn.
- Cover the figure with your counter.
- Each figure can be covered by only one player. If there is no figure for you to cover, the other player takes a turn.
- When the board is covered, count to see who has the most figures covered.

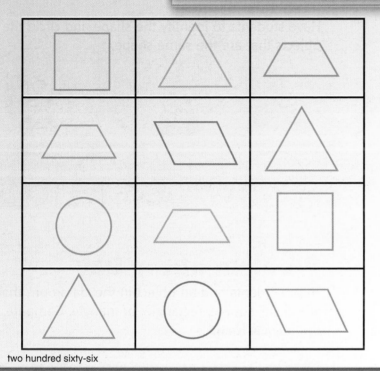

266 two hundred sixty-six

Copyright © Macmillan/McGraw-Hill, a division of The McGraw-Hill Companies, Inc.

Finding Figures

Math Concept:
Identifying Figures

Manipulatives: number cubes, 12 counters (red), 12 counters (yellow)

Introduce the game on page 268 to students to play as a class, in small groups, or at a learning workstation to review concepts introduced in this chapter.

Instructions

- Assign each student a color.

- Students play in pairs, taking turns rolling the number cube.

- Players find figures of given sides corresponding to the number on the cube. After a roll of 3, for example, a student would cover a triangle because it has 3 sides.

- A player skips a turn if there are no figures with sides corresponding to the number that is rolled.

- Players count their color counters when the board is covered. The player with the most counters wins.

Extend the Game

Have students create their own game board with drawings of various figures.

Differentiated Practice

Use these leveled suggestions to differentiate the game for all learners.

Level	Assignment
BL Below/Approaching Level	Work with students to count the sides of each figure before they play. Put small sticky notes on the game board with the numbers for extra support.
OL On Level	Have students play the game with the rules as written.
AL Above/Beyond Level	Encourage students to create a game board by cutting pictures from magazines of objects containing various shapes. Students can play with this new game board.

Lesson Planner

Objective

Determine figures missing in the design, and draw the figures to complete the design.

Resources

Materials: crayons, paper

Manipulatives: pattern blocks

Literature Connection: *Shape Space* by Cathryn Falwell

Teacher Technology

🔵 TeacherWorks

📖 **Real-World Problem-Solving Library**
Math and Science: *Playground Shapes*
Use these leveled books to reinforce and extend problem-solving skills and strategies.

Leveled for:

OL On Level
ELL Sheltered English
SP Spanish

For additional support, see the Real-World Problem Solving Teacher Guide.

On-level title is available in classroom Big Book.

Daily Routine

Use these suggestions before beginning the lesson on p. 267

5-Minute Check

(Reviews Lesson 10-5)
Have students to identify the shape and circle the objects that are the same shape.

Problem of the Day 📖

Have students find an object in the classroom that is a circle, square, rectangle, or triangle. Compare the objects found.

LINE UP Provide some simple puzzles that need to be completed. Give each student a puzzle piece. Have students place their piece in the puzzle, then line up.

Differentiated Instruction

Small Group Options

Option 1 — Below/Approaching Level (BL)

KINESTHETIC, LOGICAL

Materials: pattern blocks

Have students work in pairs.

Each partner takes a turn making a pattern out of the pattern blocks; patterns must be three units long.

When the pattern is finished, the partner uses the remaining pattern blocks to extend the pattern.

The students should each take 3 turns making a variety of patterns with the pattern blocks.

Option 2 — English Language Learners (ELL)

INTRAPERSONAL

Materials: pictures of houses, transparency, overhead, dry erase marker, crayons

Core Vocabulary: circle, square, triangle

Common Use Verb: outline

See Math This strategy helps students identify shapes.
- Show the house transparency. Put a clear sheet on top and outline the shapes in the house.
- Take off the original picture. Discuss the shapes you outlined. Have students outline shapes on their own house picture.

Independent Work Options

Option 1 — Early Finishers (AL) (OL)

LOGICAL

Materials: two scenes of the same pictures, crayons

- Show two simple pictures of the same scene, but have the second picture missing some elements of the first picture.
- Tell students to study the two pictures of the same scene.
- Ask them to draw the missing elements into the second picture.

Option 2 — Student Technology

Math Online ▷ macmillanmh.com

Math Adventures

Option 3 — Learning Station: Social Studies (p. 251H)

Direct students to the Social Studies Learning Station for opportunities to explore and extend the lesson concept.

Leveled Lesson Resources

Reteach (pp. 26–27) (BL)

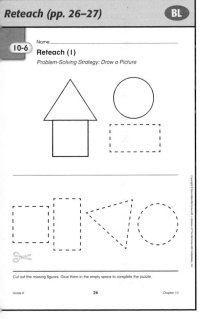

10-6 Reteach (1)
Problem-Solving Strategy: Draw a Picture

Cut out the missing figures. Glue them in the empty space to complete the puzzle.

Grade K   26   Chapter 10

Skills Practice (p. 28) (OL)

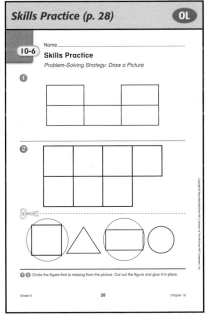

10-6 Skills Practice
Problem-Solving Strategy: Draw a Picture

1
2

Circle the figure that is missing from the picture. Cut out the figure and glue it in place.

Grade K   28   Chapter 10

Enrich (p. 30) (AL)

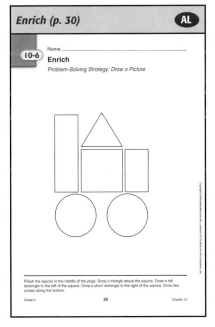

10-6 Enrich
Problem-Solving Strategy: Draw a Picture

Finish the square in the middle of the page. Draw a triangle above the square. Draw a tall rectangle to the left of the square. Draw a short rectangle to the right of the square. Draw two circles along the bottom.

Grade K   30   Chapter 10

Homework Practice (p. 29) (OL)

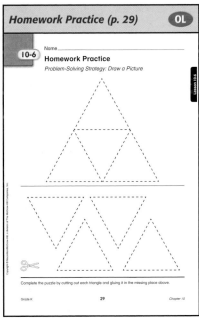

10-6 Homework Practice
Problem-Solving Strategy: Draw a Picture

Complete the puzzle by cutting out each triangle and gluing it in the missing place above.

Grade K   29   Chapter 10

① Introduce

Circle Time

Activity Choice 1 • Literature

Shape Space by Cathryn Falwell

- Read the book aloud and discuss, focusing on patterns made with two-dimensional figures.

- Review four two-dimensional figures: square, rectangle, circle, triangle.

- Create a pattern using two of the the four two-dimensional figures. Have students draw the next figure in the pattern.

- Have students work in pairs to create patterns using the two-dimensional figures. Have them draw the pattern they created.

Activity Choice 2 • Hands-On

Materials: crayons, paper, pattern blocks

- Give each student a piece of paper with a hexagon on it that is the size of the pattern block.

- **What are some ways you can cover the hexagon with pattern blocks?** Sample answers: 1 hexagon, 2 trapezoids, 6 triangles, 1 trapezoid with 3 triangles

- Have students trace several hexagons and draw the lines needed to show how to fill it.

② Teach

Understand Review what students know and what they need to find for each problem.

Plan Have students discuss their strategy for solving the problems.

Solve Guide students to draw a picture in order to solve the problems. Have students use pattern blocks to find the missing figures in each design. Then have students draw pictures to represent the missing figures.

Check Have students look back at the problem to be sure that the answers fit what they already know about the problem. Students should check to make sure each drawing matches the pattern block that could fit in the missing figure area. Discuss with students that mathematical statements can be true or false. Students need to check to make sure their answers are true statements.

ⒷⓁ Alternate Teaching Strategy

If ▶ students have trouble using logic to reason through problems . . .

Then ▶ use one of these reteach options.

1 🄲🅁🄼 **Daily Reteach Worksheet** (pp. 26-27)

2 Use Pattern Blocks Build a picture using pattern blocks. Have students copy the picture.

- Tell students to cover their eyes. Remove one block.

- Tell them to open their eyes, and fill in the missing piece by drawing a picture of the pattern block.

- Repeat the activity, removing more pieces each time.

⚠ **COMMON ERROR!**

Students may start to fill in the holes of a picture with small pieces first. Encourage students to try larger pieces first, then use the smaller pieces to complete it.

Name _____

Problem-Solving Strategy
Draw a Picture

What is missing?

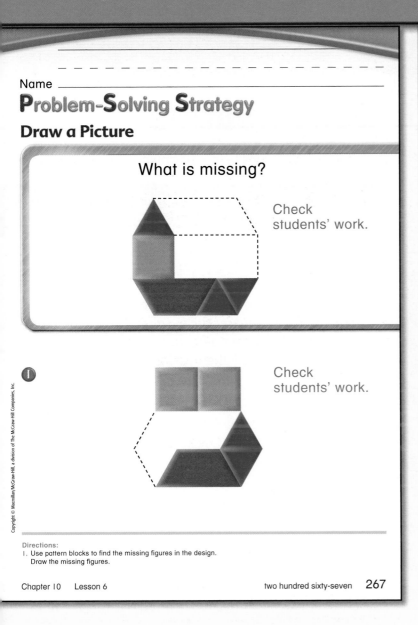

Check students' work.

Check students' work.

①

②

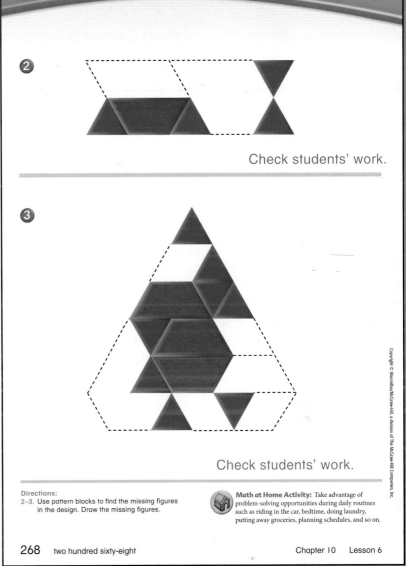

Check students' work.

③

Check students' work.

Directions:
1. Use pattern blocks to find the missing figures in the design. Draw the missing figures.

Directions:
2–3. Use pattern blocks to find the missing figures in the design. Draw the missing figures.

Math at Home Activity: Take advantage of problem-solving opportunities during daily routines such as riding in the car, bedtime, doing laundry, putting away groceries, planning schedules, and so on.

Chapter 10   Lesson 6   two hundred sixty-seven **267**

268   two hundred sixty-eight   Chapter 10   Lesson 6

③ Practice

Guided Practice

- Direct students to p. 267.
- Ask students what figures they see in Exercise 1.
- Have students explain what figures they think should be used to fill in the white space.
- Have students use pattern blocks to fill in the white space.
- Tell them to draw the lines to show which pattern blocks they used.

Independent Practice

Have students turn to p. 268 and work independently on the exercises.

④ Assess

✓ Formative Assessment

- Create a picture made of pattern blocks. Show some of the figures, but omit 3–5 figures.
- Have students use pattern blocks to figure out and draw the missing figures.

Quick Check — Are students still struggling to determine figures missing in the design?

If Yes → Small Group Options (p. 267B)
If No → Independent Work Options (p. 267B)
        [CRM] Skills Practice Worksheet (p. 28)
        [CRM] Enrich Worksheet (p. 30)

Lesson 10-6 Problem-Solving Strategy **268**

Lesson Planner

Objective
Identify things divided into equal parts or halves.

Vocabulary
equal parts, half

Resources
Materials: construction paper squares, circles, triangles
Manipulatives: geometric solids
Literature Connection: *Captain Invincible and the Space Shapes* by Stuart J. Murphy
Alternate Lesson: Adapt *Pattern Block Puzzles* on page 349 of *Math Their Way* to provide practice with fractions.
Teacher Technology
  TeacherWorks

Focus on Math Background

In this lesson, kindergarteners begin to identify equal parts in relation to a whole. Students' future work with fractions and decimals is contingent upon the ability to understand and describe part-to-whole relationships, such as how one red pattern block (the trapezoid) is half of a yellow block (the hexagon). Moreover, the geometrical figures (pattern blocks) used in this lesson are symmetrically designed to show these types of proportional relationships.

Daily Routine

Use these suggestions before beginning the lesson on p. 269.

5-Minute Check
(Reviews Lesson 10-6)
Show students an AB pattern such as circle, square, circle, square, circle, square. Then continue the pattern with some figures missing. Ask students to identify the missing figures.

Problem of the Day
Have students draw a design using two-dimensional figures. Check students work.

LINE UP Show students pictures of items divided into equal and unequal parts. Have students say "equal" or "not equal" to describe the parts and then line up

Building Math Vocabulary

- Show students a construction paper circle. Fold it in **half** and show students the two **equal parts**.

- Fold the circle in half again to make four equal parts. **How many equal parts are there now?** four

- Fold the circle again so that the fold makes parts that are not equal.

- **Are the parts of this circle equal?** no **Why not?** They are not the same size.

- **When do you need to divide something into equal parts?** Sample answer: when you are sharing and you want everyone to have the same size

- Repeat this activity using other figures.

Differentiated Instruction

Small Group Options

Option 1
Below/Approaching Level BL   SPATIAL

Materials: pattern blocks

Have small groups of students find a yellow hexagon.

Ask students to find another pattern block shape that can cover the hexagon in equal parts. Have students tell how many of the same blocks are needed to cover the hexagon.

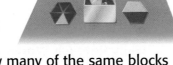

Have students repeat by covering other shapes.

Option 2
English Language Learners ELL   VISUAL/SPATIAL, LOGICAL

Materials: die-cut capital letters that have been cut into symmetrical halves

Core Vocabulary: equal parts, find, half of a letter

Common Use Verb: match

Do Math This strategy helps students understand equal parts. Fold a piece of paper in half. Say: "Both sides are the same. They are **equal parts**." Repeat for capital A.

Give each student half of a letter. Ask: " Can you find the equal part?" Allow students to move around the room to match their half.

Independent Work Options

Option 1
Early Finishers   LINGUISTIC

Materials: fraction cards showing equal and unequal parts

- Mix up the fraction cards and place them facedown on a table.
- Have student pairs place the cards that show equal parts in one pile and those that do not show equal parts in another pile.

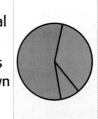
Not Equal

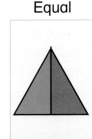
Equal

Option 2
Student Technology

Math Online ▷ macmillanmh.com

Math Adventures

Option 3
Learning Station: Art (p. 251G)

Direct students to the Art Learning Station for opportunities to explore and extend the lesson concept.

Leveled Lesson Resources
Additional support for English Language Learners can be found in the ELL Guide (p. 127). ELL

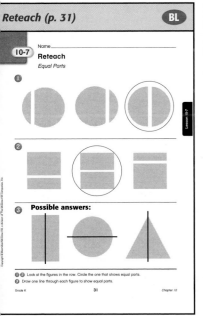

Reteach (p. 31) BL

10-7 Reteach
Equal Parts

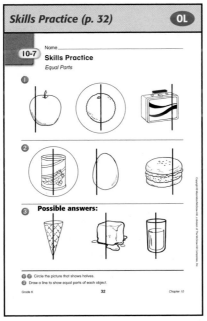

Skills Practice (p. 32) OL

10-7 Skills Practice
Equal Parts

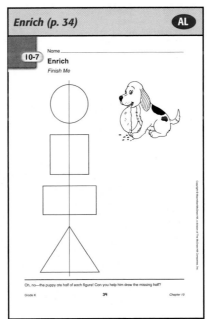

Enrich (p. 34) AL

10-7 Enrich
Finish Me

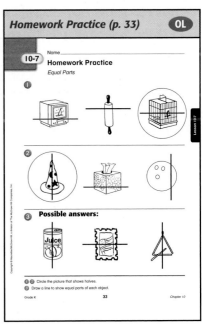

Homework Practice (p. 33) OL

10-7 Homework Practice
Equal Parts

① Introduce

Circle Time

Activity Choice 1 • Literature

Captain Invincible and the Space Shapes by Stuart J. Murphy

- Read the book, identifying pyramid, cube, sphere, cone, cylinder, and rectangular prism.
- Discuss common attributes such as size, shape, roundness, or number of corners.
- Using three-dimensional figures, students work with a partner to discuss common attributes.
- Create a T-chart classifying two-dimensional figures by an attribute, such as corners/no corners, square faces/no square faces.

Activity Choice 2 • Hands-On

- Lead students in a discussion about sharing. Guide them to say that when they share, they usually want to have **equal parts**.
- Show students a sandwich in the shape of a square.
- **How might you share this sandwich with a friend?** Split it so each person has the same amount.
- **What are some ways you could divide, or split, the sandwich into equal parts?** Cut an up-and-down line down the middle; cut a sideways line across the middle.
- Invite a volunteer to come to the front of the room to show how to split the square in **half.**
- **Is there another way to show two equal parts?** Yes; cut a diagonal line.
- Draw additional squares on the chalkboard so that students can draw all possible ways to show two equal parts.
- Tell students that when something has two equal parts each part is called a half.

② Teach

- Call students' attention to the top of p. 269.
- **How are the muffins the same and different?** They are all muffins. One is split in equal parts and the others are not.
- **Which muffin is circled?** the one with equal parts
- **How can you tell the parts are equal?** The parts on either side of the line are the same size and figure.

ⓑⓛ Alternate Teaching Strategy

If students have trouble understanding equal parts . . .

Then use one of these reteach options.

1. ⓒⓡⓜ **Daily Reteach Worksheet** (p. 31)

2. **Make Equal Parts** Provide construction paper figures (squares, circles, triangles) for each student to use.
   - Have students begin this activity with the square.
   - **How can we divide this square into two equal parts?** Fold it in half.
   - Model how to fold the square in half. Ask students to open the square to show two equal parts.
   - Continue this activity using the other construction paper shapes.
   - **How do you know that each part is half of the whole?** The two parts are exactly the same size, when you put the two parts together they make the whole shape.

⚠ COMMON ERROR!

Some students may have difficulty differentiating which shape is divided into equal parts. Help them look at each part of a shape to determine if the parts are equal or unequal in size.

Name _____

Equal Parts

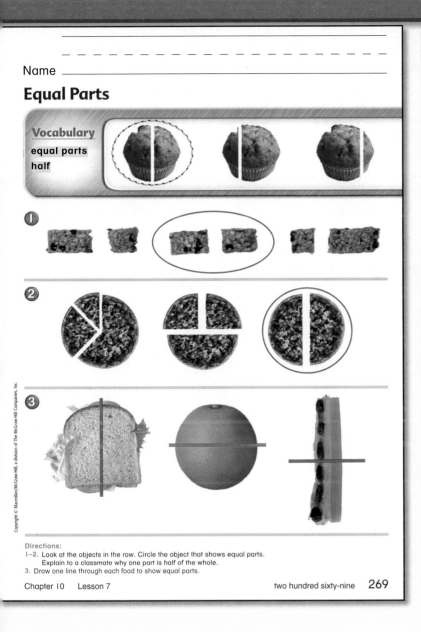

Vocabulary
equal parts
half

①

②

③

Directions:
1–2. Look at the objects in the row. Circle the object that shows equal parts.
Explain to a classmate why one part is half of the whole.
3. Draw one line through each food to show equal parts.

Chapter 10   Lesson 7

two hundred sixty-nine   **269**

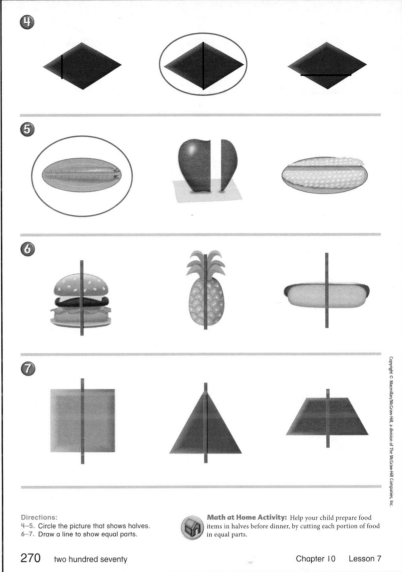

④

⑤

⑥

⑦

Directions:
4–5. Circle the picture that shows halves.
6–7. Draw a line to show equal parts.

 **Math at Home Activity:** Help your child prepare food items in halves before dinner, by cutting each portion of food in equal parts.

270   two hundred seventy

Chapter 10   Lesson 7

---

③ Practice

Guided Practice

• Direct students to Exercises 1 and 2 on p. 269.
• **Which picture shows crackers with two equal parts?** the middle one **How can you tell?** They are the same size and shape; one part is not larger than the other part.
• **Which picture shows two halves of the whole pizza?** the last one **How can you tell?** They are the same size and shape; one part is not larger than the other parts.
• Help them circle the object that shows equal parts.
• Explain the directions for Exercise 3.

Independent Practice

Have students turn to p. 270. Explain the directions and have students work independently on the exercises.

④ Assess

✓ Formative Assessment

Show students a picture of a hamburger.

• **What lines can be drawn to show equal parts?** Sample answers: a horizontal or vertical line through the middle

• **Why is part of the hamburger half of the whole?** There are two parts that are the same size.

Quick Check	Are students still struggling with equal parts?

If Yes → Small Group Options (p. 269B)

If No → Independent Work Options (p. 269B)

CRM Skills Practice Worksheet (p. 32)

CRM Enrich Worksheet (p. 34)

Lesson 10-7 Equal Parts   **270**

Two-Dimensional Figures In Position

Lesson Planner

Objective

Explore the attributes of two-dimensional figures in different forms and orientations.

Review Vocabulary

two-dimensional figure

Resources

Materials: paper figures, drawing paper, pencils
Manipulatives: pattern blocks
Literature Connection: *When a Line Bends . . . A Shape Begins* by Rhonda Gowler Greene
Alternate Lesson: Use *IMPACT Mathematics*: Unit G to provide practice with exploring attributes of two-dimensional figures.
Teacher Technology
  ○ TeacherWorks

Focus on Math Background

This lesson focuses on two-dimensional figures in position. Based on their work in the previous lessons, students now have a general understanding of and the vocabulary for basic two-dimensional figures: circles, triangles, and rectangles (including squares). In this lesson, students will explore geometrical figures in position and discover that no matter their spatial position, a figure remains the same figure. This will lay the foundation for more formal experiences to create mathematical arguments and proofs that describe geometry.

Daily Routine

Use these suggestions before beginning the lesson on p. 271.

5-Minute Check

(Reviews Lesson 10-6)
Give students pictures of objects that clearly show triangles and circles. Have students identify the shapes and then sort the pictures.

Problem of the Day

Show a square. Rotate the square to stand on its corner. Is the square still a square? Why or why not? Sample answer: Yes; it still has four equal sides and four corners. Repeat with other shapes.

LINE UP Have students line up if they can show circles on their clothing. Continue with other figures such as triangles, squares, and rectangles until all students have lined up.

Review Math Vocabulary

Materials: paper figures, paper bag

- Review two-dimensional figure names with students. Put the figures into a paper bag.
- Have students take turns pulling a figure from the bag.
- Ask them to name and describe the figure, including the number of sides and corners.
- Turn the figure. Ask if it is still the same figure.

Visual Vocabulary Card

Use Visual Vocabulary Card 36 to reinforce the vocabulary reviewed in this lesson. (The Define/Example/Ask routine is printed on the back of each card.)

Differentiated Instruction

Small Group Options

Option 1   KINESTHETIC

Below/Approaching Level **BL**

Materials: masking tape

Put tape on the floor to make a square, circle, rectangle, and triangle.

Play a game of Simon Says. Use commands such as "Simon says walk on the edge of the circle; Simon says go inside the square and jump; Simon says stand next to the triangle."

Option 2   INTRAPERSONAL, INTERPERSONAL

English Language Learners **ELL**

Materials: sand tub, spray bottle to wet the sand

Core Vocabulary: will it be, imagine, change the position

Common Use Verb: press

See Math This strategy explores position and two- and three-dimensional figures.

Give one student a sand tub and the other student a rectangular prism, cone, or a pyramid.

Model pressing the figure in the sand. Identify the figures made and explore if changing the position pressed changes the result. Discuss and repeat as time permits.

Independent Work Options

Option 1   VISUAL

Early Finishers **OL** **AL**

Materials: figure stickers, paper, crayons

- Give students three stickers that are the same figure.
- Have students put the stickers randomly on a sheet of paper.
- Have students draw around the figures to create pictures. Point out that the figure did not change its name as they drew around it.

Option 2

Student Technology

Math Online macmillanmh.com

Option 3

Learning Station: Health (p. 251G)

Direct students to the Art Learning Station for opportunities to explore and extend the lesson concept.

Leveled Lesson Resources
Additional support for English Language Learners can be found in the ELL Guide (p. 7). **ELL**

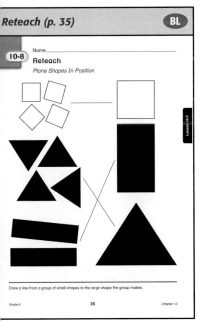

Reteach (p. 35) **BL**

10-8 Reteach
Plane Shapes In Position

Draw a line from a group of small shapes to the large shape the group makes.

Grade K   35   Chapter 10

Skills Practice (p. 36) **OL**

10-8 Skills Practice
Plane Shapes In Position

Color the small shapes. Cut them out. Use only one shape on each part of the clock. Glue them onto the clock. The first triangle has been placed for you.

Grade K   36   Chapter 10

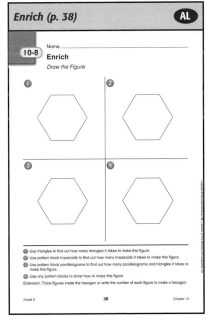

Enrich (p. 38) **AL**

10-8 Enrich
Draw the Figure

1. Use triangles to find out how many triangles it takes to make this figure.
2. Use pattern block trapezoids to find out how many trapezoids it takes to make this figure.
3. Use pattern block parallelograms to find out how many parallelograms and triangles it takes to make this figure.
4. Use any pattern blocks to show how to make this figure.

Extension: Trace figures inside the hexagon or write the number of each figure to make a hexagon.

Grade K   38   Chapter 10

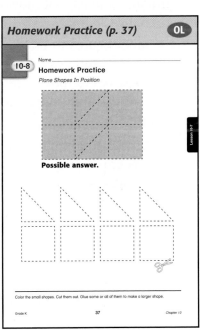

Homework Practice (p. 37) **OL**

10-8 Homework Practice
Plane Shapes In Position

Possible answer.

Color the small shapes. Cut them out. Glue some or all of them to make a larger shape.

Grade K   37   Chapter 10

1 Introduce

Circle Time

Activity Choice 1 • Literature

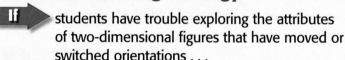

When A Line Bends . . . A Shape Begins by Rhonda Gowler Greene

• Read the book aloud, identifying squares, rectangles, circles, and triangles by their attributes. Discuss their movements within the illustrations.

• Have students explore the movement of squares, rectangles, circles, and triangles in the room.

• Have students work with partners and demonstrate the movement of two-dimensional figures using cut-out figures.

Activity Choice 2 • Hands-On

Materials: paper figures

• Gather students in a circle.

• Hold up and name various figures. Put the figures on the floor.

• Tell students that the figures have moved.

• **Have the figures changed?** no

• Point to various figures and ask what figure it is now.

• Have students pass figures around the circle, move them around the room, and so on. Remind students that moving figures does not change them.

• Use paper figures to build larger figures such as four squares to make a larger square or six squares to make a rectangle.

• Tell students that smaller figures can be used to make larger figures.

• Distribute paper figures and have students create larger figures from smaller figures.

2 Teach

Direct students to the top of p. 271.

• Give square and triangle pattern blocks to each student.

• Using an overhead projector, play with pattern blocks, having students follow your directions in how you move the blocks around. Ask students to identify the figure after each position change. Allow students to do the same process on the overhead.

• Guide students in laying pattern blocks on top of the triangles and squares at the top of the page.

BL Alternate Teaching Strategy

If students have trouble exploring the attributes of two-dimensional figures that have moved or switched orientations . . .

Then use one of these reteach options.

1 CRM **Daily Reteach Worksheet** (p. 35)

2 **Trace Figures** Give each student a pattern block, drawing paper, and a pencil.

• Have students put a pattern block on the paper, then trace around the block.

• Tell students to keep the block on the paper and slide the block to another place on the paper.

• Have them retrace the block and then lift the block. Point out that the tracings are the same and the block is the same.

 COMMON ERROR!

Students may think that moving a figure changes it. Point out the results of the tracing activity. Give students blocks to manipulate and compare.

Name _____

Two-Dimensional Figures in Position

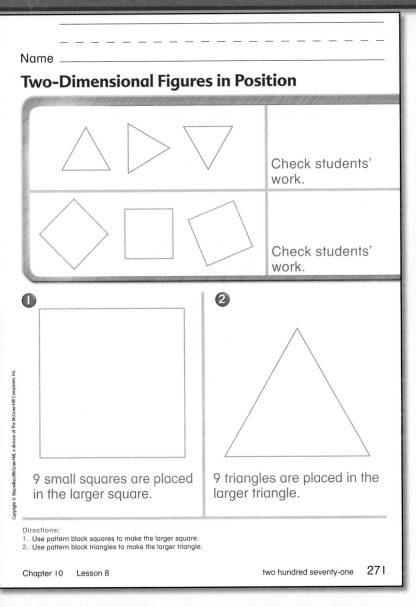

Check students' work.

Check students' work.

① 9 small squares are placed in the larger square.

② 9 triangles are placed in the larger triangle.

Directions:
1. Use pattern block squares to make the larger square.
2. Use pattern block triangles to make the larger triangle.

Chapter 10   Lesson 8   two hundred seventy-one   **271**

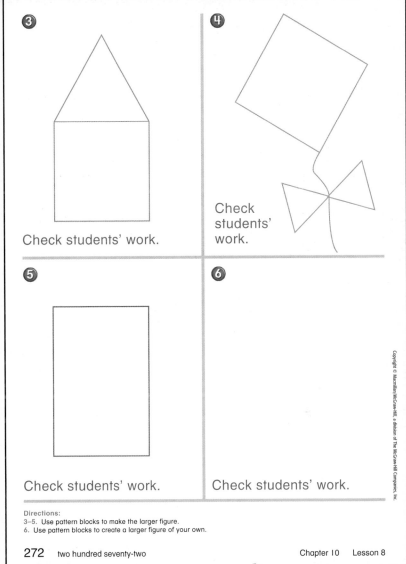

③ Check students' work.

④ Check students' work.

⑤ Check students' work.

⑥ Check students' work.

Directions:
3–5. Use pattern blocks to make the larger figure.
6. Use pattern blocks to create a larger figure of your own.

272   two hundred seventy-two   Chapter 10   Lesson 8

③ Practice

Guided Practice

- Direct students to p. 271.
- Ask students to name the figure in Exercise 1.
- Give each student nine 1-inch squares. Guide students to discover how many smaller squares make up the larger square.
- **How can the nine squares be positioned to fit into the larger square?** Put the nine squares together with three across and three down.
- Repeat the activity with triangles in Exercise 2, using five 1-inch triangles on the bottom, three 1-inch triangles in the middle, and one 1-inch triangle on the top, to make a large triangle.

Independent Practice

Have students turn to p. 272 and work independently on the exercises after directions are explained.

④ Assess

Formative Assessment

- Show students a figure. Ask them to name and describe the figure. Move the figure.
- **How has the figure changed?** The figure has not changed. Have students describe the figure.
- Give students smaller figures to create a large figure.

Quick Check

Are students still struggling to describe two-dimensional figures in different forms and orientations?

If Yes → Small Group Options (p. 271B)

If No → Independent Work Options (p. 271B)
- CRM Skills Practice Worksheet (p. 36)
- CRM Enrich Worksheet (p. 38)

Lesson 10-8 Two-Dimensional Figures In Position   **272**

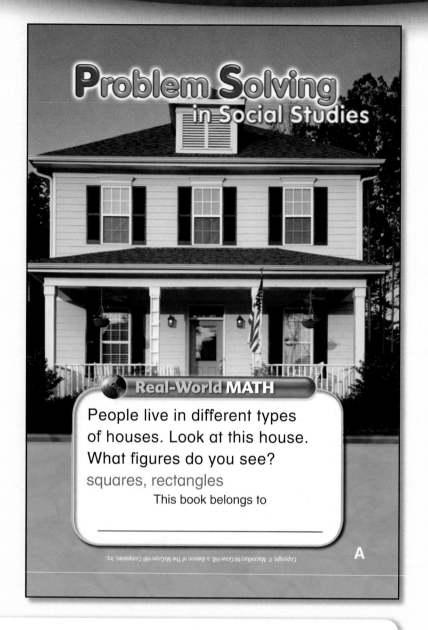

Problem Solving
in Social Studies

Real-World MATH

People live in different types of houses. Look at this house. What figures do you see?

squares, rectangles

This book belongs to

_____

A

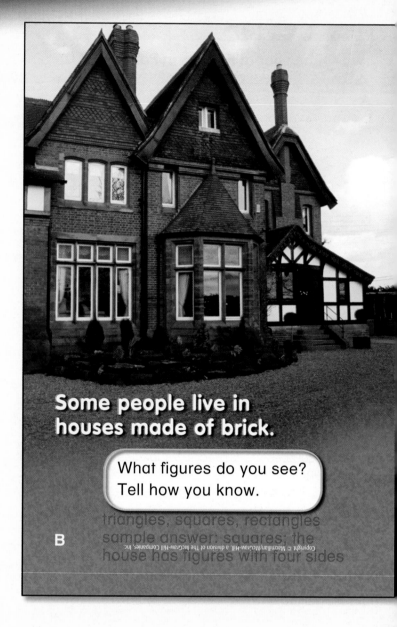

Some people live in houses made of brick.

What figures do you see? Tell how you know.

triangles, squares, rectangles sample answer: squares; the house has figures with four sides

B

Lesson Planner

Objective
Identify and describe the shapes in different types of homes.

National Standard
Understand the physical and human characteristics of places.

Vocabulary
shape, circle, triangle, square, rectangle, corner, side, round, cube, sphere, cylinder

Activate Prior Knowledge

Before you turn students' attention to the pages, discuss homes.

- **What kinds of homes do you know about? How are homes different in different places in the world?** Answers will vary. Prompt discussion on different types of homes and where they are found, such as huts, igloos, cabins, houses, and so on.

- **How is your home different from some of the homes we talked about? How is it the same?** Answers will vary. Students may mention that homes have doors and windows, places to sleep and eat, and so on. Students may mention homes such as houses, condominiums, townhouses, apartments, and so on.

Some people live in houses made of logs.

What figures do you see?
Tell how you know.

circles, rectangles, squares;
sample answer: rectangles; I see a
figure with four corners.

C

Some people live in houses with pointed roofs.

Home is different for everyone.
What figures do you see?

D   squares, rectangles, triangles

FOLD DOWN

Create the Book

Guide students to create their book.

- Have them fold the page in half.

- Ask them to write their name on page A.

- Explain that page A is the front cover and page D is the back cover. If necessary, have them practice flipping through the book in order.

- Guide them in reading the information and word problems on each of the pages.

Use the Student Pages

Have students work individually or in pairs to solve the word problems on pages B–D.

Page B Students can trace shapes with their fingers or use paper cutouts of circles, triangles, and other shapes to compare to the shapes in the building.

Page C Students should notice shapes including circles and rectangles.

Page D Students will notice triangles in the photograph. Ask them what shapes they can find in their own homes.

If necessary, review the problem-solving strategies suggested in Lesson 10-6, p. 267.

WRITING IN ▶ MATH Have students draw pictures with shapes for others to identify. For example, they may draw a bus with circles for wheels and squares for windows.

FOLDABLES® **Dinah Zike's Foldables**

If students have not completed their Foldables, guide them to create and fill in the appropriate information using the instructions on pp. 251 and 265.

You may choose to use the Foldable to help students review the concepts presented in this chapter and as a tool for studying for the Chapter Review/Test.

 Chapter 10 Project

Lead a discussion on the results of the completed chapter project with the class.

Vocabulary Review

Review chapter vocabulary using one of the following options.

- **Visual Vocabulary Cards** (6, 8, 9, 10, 11, 34, 36, 40, 41, 48)
- **eGlossary** at macmillanmh.com

Data-Driven Decision Making

Based on the results of the Chapter Review/Test, use the following to review concepts that continue to present students with problems.

Exercises	State/Local Standards	What's the Math?	Error Analysis	Resources for Review
1 Lesson 10-1		Identify common objects and describe three-dimensional figures.	Does not know word "sphere." Confuses circle and sphere.	CRM Chapter 10 Resource Masters (Reteach Worksheets)
2 Lesson 10-6		Identify and describe common figures. Identify and extend simple patterns by referring to these figures.	Does not recognize what piece of pattern is missing. Circles both answers.	**Math Online** Concepts in Motion
3–4 Lesson 10-7		Identify equal parts and objects cut in half.	Does not recognize equal parts. Circles or objects not divided in half.	Math Adventures

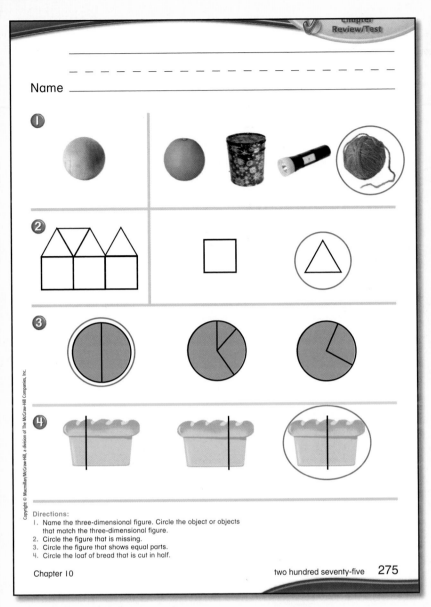

Name _____

Directions:
1. Name the three-dimensional figure. Circle the object or objects that match the three-dimensional figure.
2. Circle the figure that is missing.
3. Circle the figure that shows equal parts.
4. Circle the loaf of bread that is cut in half.

Spiral Review Chapters 1–10

Name _____

Directions:
1. Circle the rubber band that is the longest. Mark an X on the rubber band that is the shortest.
2. Count the cars. Write how many.
3. Circle April 9th. Place an X on the first Thursday in April. Write how many days there are in April.

Summative Assessment

Use these alternate leveled chapter tests to differentiate assessment for the specific needs of your students.

Leveled Chapter 10 Tests			
Form	**Type**	**Level**	**CRM Pages**
1	Multiple Choice	BL	42–43
2A	Multiple Choice	OL	44–45
2C	Multiple Choice	OL	46–47
2D	Free Response	AL	48–49

BL = below/approaching grade level
OL = on grade level
AL = above/beyond grade level

Spiral Review

Reviews Chapters 1 to 10

Objective: Review and assess mastery of skills and concepts from previous chapters.

Resources for Review

Based on student results, refer to these lessons for remediation.

- **Exercise 1: Lesson 7-1** (p. 179)
- **Exercise 2: Lesson 8-1** (p. 205)
- **Exercise 3: Lesson 9-4** (p. 235)

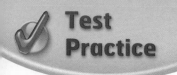

Test Practice

Chapters 1–10

 Formative Assessment

- You can use Student Edition pp. 275–276 to benchmark student progress.

Additional practice pages can be found in Chapter 10 Resource Masters

[CRM] **Chapter 10 Resource Masters**
   Cumlative Test Practice

- Multiple Choice format (pp. 42–47)
- Free Response format (pp. 48–49)

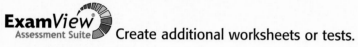 Create additional worksheets or tests.

Math Online > For additional practice with the **NCTM Focal Points and Focal Connections**, visit

macmillanmh.com.

Test-Taking Tips

For the Teacher

- Preview the test or each section of a test with students before they begin working.

For the Student

- Tell students to stay focused on their test and do not worry if classmates finish before them.

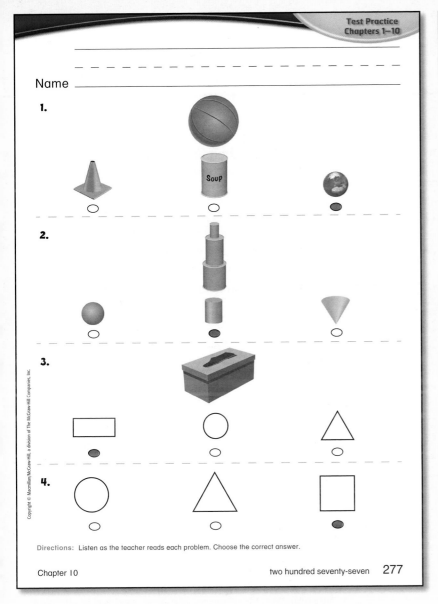

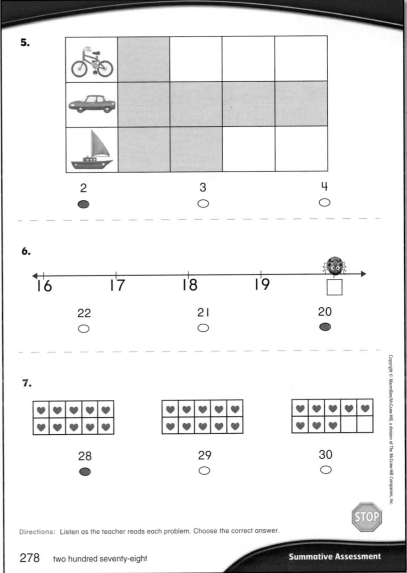

Name

1.

2.

3.

4.

Directions: Listen as the teacher reads each problem. Choose the correct answer.

Chapter 10   two hundred seventy-seven   **277**

5.

| 2 | 3 | 4 |

6.

| 22 | 21 | 20 |

7.

| 28 | 29 | 30 |

Directions: Listen as the teacher reads each problem. Choose the correct answer.

278   two hundred seventy-eight   **Summative Assessment**

Test Directions for Teachers

Read the following directions to students before they begin. Then read each question followed by a pause to allow students time to work and choose an answer. The first test item can be worked on as a class example.

- **Write your name at the top of the page.**
- **I am going to read each question to you. Listen carefully to the entire question before you choose an answer.**

1. Look at the figure. It is a sphere. Find the figure that matches the shape of the basketball. Mark the figure that matches the shape of the basketball.

2. Look at the canned goods. Find the same solid figure that stacks. Mark the solid figure that stacks like the canned goods.

3. Look at the shoebox. Find the figure that is the flat surface of the shoebox. Mark the figure that is the flat surface of the shoebox.

4. Look at the figures. Find the figure that has 4 corners. Mark the figure that has 4 corners.

- **Turn the page over.**

5. Look at the graph. Find the number that shows how many sailboats. Mark that number.

6. Look at the number line. Count on to find the number that is missing. Find the number that is missing. Mark the number.

7. Count the hearts in the ten-frames. Find the number that tells how many hearts. Mark the number.

Chapter Overview

Chapter-at-a-Glance

In Chapter 11, students use concrete objects to solve addition problems.

Model Addition

BIG Idea At this point in the curriculum, kindergarteners have worked extensively with numbers through 30. Comfort with these numbers will help students immensely as they begin their first steps toward addition. In this chapter, students begin to add by combining concrete objects to model simple addition stories and problems. Students are also given ample opportunity to discover all the ways to combine numbers to sums up to nine.

Algebra Students prepare for Algebra through mathematical sentences. Students discover that there are many ways to combine numbers for a particular sum. Lessons 11-4, 11-5, 11-6, 11-7, 11-8

GK-FP1 *Number and Operations:* **Representing, comparing, and ordering whole numbers and joining and separating sets**

Children use numbers, including written numerals, to represent quantities and to solve quantitative problems, such as counting objects in a set, creating a set with a given number of objects, comparing and ordering sets or numerals by using both cardinal and ordinal meanings, and modeling simple joining and separating situations with objects. They choose, combine, and apply effective strategies for answering quantitative questions, including quickly recognizing the number in a small set, counting and producing sets of given sizes, counting the number in combined sets, and counting backward.

Skills Trace
Vertical Alignment

PreKindergarten

In PreK, students learned to:
- Recognize and describe the concept of zero (meaning there are none).
- Combine, separate, and name "how many" concrete objects.

Kindergarten

During this chapter, students learn to:
- Model addition as combining sets and adding to sets.
- Use concrete objects to solve addition problems.
- Use concrete objects to show different ways to solve to nine.

After this chapter, students will learn to:
- Use concrete objects to determine the answers to addition and subtraction problems (for two numbers that are each less than 10).

First Grade

In first grade, students will learn to:
- Model and solve addition problems.
- Write addition sentences.
- Use strategies and skills to solve problems.

Backmapping and Vertical Alignment
McGraw-Hill's *Math Connects* program was conceived and developed with the final results in mind: student success in Algebra 1 and beyond. The authors, using the **NCTM Focal Points and Focal Connections** as their guide, developed this brand new series by backmapping from Algebra 1 concepts, and vertically aligning the topics so that they build upon prior skills and concepts and serve as a foundation for future topics.

Math Vocabulary

The following math vocabulary words for Chapter 11 are listed in the glossary of the **Student Edition.** You can find interactive definitions in 13 languages in the **eGlossary** at macmillanmh.com.

add to join together sets to find the total (at this level, also referred to as "join," "in all," or "put together"). (p. 283)

plus sign (p. 291)
$$5 + 2 = 7$$
$$\uparrow$$
$$\text{plus}$$

in all to join together sets to find the total. (p. 283)

join adding sets together. (p.287)

Visual Vocabulary Cards Use Visual Vocabulary Card 1 to introduce and reinforce that vocabulary in this chapter. (The Define/Example/Ask routine is printed on the back of each card.)

Chapter Planner

Suggested Pacing		
Instruction	Review and Assessment	TOTAL
9 days	2 days	**11 days**

✓ **Diagnostic Assessment**
Are You Ready? (p. 270)

	Lesson 11-1 — Pacing: 1 day	**Lesson 11-2** — Pacing: 1 day	**Lesson 11-3** — Pacing: 1 day
Lesson/ Objective	**Addition Stories** (pp. 283–286) **Objective:** Model addition as combining sets and adding to sets.	**Use Objects to Add** (pp. 287–288) **Objective:** Use concrete objects to solve addition problems.	**Addition Sign** (pp. 291–292) **Objective:** Use the plus symbol (+) to show addition.
State/Local Standards			
Math Vocabulary	**in all**, **add**	**join**	**plus sign**
Lesson Resources	**Materials** stuffed animals, 2 baskets, yarn or a hula hoop, large paper, markers, crayons, cup **Manipulatives** two-colored counters, connecting cubes **Other Resources** CRM Leveled Worksheets (pp. 6–9) Daily Reteach Problem of the Day	**Materials** basket, stuffed animals, number cards, books, paper, crayons **Manipulatives** color tiles, connecting cubes **Other Resources** CRM Leveled Worksheets (pp. 10–13) Daily Reteach Problem of the Day	**Manipulatives** connecting cubes **Other Resources** CRM Leveled Worksheets (pp. 14–17) Daily Reteach Problem of the Day
Technology Math Online	Math Adventures	Math Adventures Concepts in Motion	
Reaching All Learners	English Learners, p. 283B **ELL** Gifted and Talented, p. 283B **AL** Early Finishers, p. 283B **OL** **AL**	English Learners, p. 287B **ELL** Below Level, p. 287B **BL** Early Finishers, p. 287B **OL** **AL**	English Learners, p. 291B **ELL** Below Level, p. 291B **BL** Early Finishers, p. 291B **OL** **AL**
Alternate Lesson	*Math Their Way*, pp. 188–189 *IMPACT Mathematics:* Unit B, C	*Math Their Way*, p. 180 *IMPACT Mathematics:* Unit B, C	*Math Their Way*, pp. 183–185

✓ **Formative Assessment**
Mid-Chapter Check (p. 289)

Game Time: How Many In All? (p. 290)

Lesson 11-4	Pacing: 1 day		

Lesson 11-4 — Pacing: 1 day

Ways to Make 4 and 5
(pp. 293–296)

Objective: Use concrete objects and pictures to show ways to make 4 and 5.

Materials
paper, cups, pencils, classroom items

Manipulatives
connecting cubes, two-colored counters

Other Resources
CRM Leveled Worksheets (pp. 18–21)
Daily Reteach
Problem of the Day

Math Adventures

English Learners, p. 293B **ELL**
Below Level, p. 293B **BL**
Early Finishers, p. 293B **OL** **AL**

Math Their Way, pp. 183–185

Lesson 11-5 — Pacing: 1 day

Ways to Make 6
(pp. 297–298)

Objective: Use concrete objects and pictures to show ways to make 6.

Materials
egg cartons, cups, paper, pencil, string

Manipulatives
connecting cubes, two-colored counters, attribute buttons, number cubes

Other Resources
CRM Leveled Worksheets (pp. 22–25)
Daily Reteach
Problem of the Day

Math Adventures

Concepts in Motion

English Learners, p. 297B **ELL**
Below Level, p. 297B **BL**
Early Finishers, p. 297B **OL** **AL**

Lesson 11-6 — Pacing: 1 day

Ways to Make 7
(pp. 299–300)

Objective: Use concrete objects and pictures to show ways to make 7.

Materials
jacks, double-six dominoes, paper, pencils

Manipulatives
pattern blocks, two-colored counters, color tiles

Other Resources
CRM Leveled Worksheets (pp. 26–29)
Daily Reteach
Problem of the Day

English Learners, p. 299B **ELL**
Below Level, p. 299B **BL**
Early Finishers, p. 299B **OL** **AL**

Right-column labels
- Lesson/Objective
- State/Local Standards
- Math Vocabulary
- Lesson Resources
- Technology — Math Online
- Reaching All Learners
- Alternate Lesson

KEY

BL Below/Approaching Level	**OL** On Level
AL Above/Beyond Level	**ELL** English Learners
SE Student Edition	**TE** Teacher Edition
CRM Chapter 1 Resource Masters	**CD-Rom**
Transparency	Flip Chart
Real-World Problem Solving Library	

Chapter Planner

	Lesson 11-7 **Pacing:** 1 day	Lesson 11-8 **Pacing:** 1 day	Lesson 11-9 **Pacing:** 1 day
Lesson/ Objective	**Ways to Make 8** (pp. 301–302) **Objective:** Use concrete objects and pictures to show ways to make 8.	**Ways to Make 9** (pp. 303–304) **Objective:** Use concrete objects and pictures to show ways to make 9.	**Problem-Solving Strategy Act It Out** (pp. 305–306) **Objective:** Use concrete objects to solve addition problems.
State/Local Standards			
Math Vocabulary			
Lesson Resources	**Materials** dominoes, paper, pencils, drawing paper, markers **Manipulatives** color tiles, connecting cubes **Other Resources** CRM Leveled Worksheets (pp. 30–33) Daily Reteach Problem of the Day	**Materials** paper, chart paper, markers, dominoes **Manipulatives** connecting cubes, counters, 0–5 spinner **Other Resources** CRM Leveled Worksheets (pp. 34–37) Daily Reteach Problem of the Day	**Materials** number strips, string **Manipulatives** connecting cubes, attribute buttons **Other Resources** CRM Leveled Worksheets (pp. 38–42) Daily Reteach Problem of the Day *Animals on the Farm*
Technology Math Online	Concepts in Motion	Concepts in Motion	
Reaching All Learners	English Learners, p. 301B ELL Below Level, p. 301B BL Early Finishers, p. 301B OL AL	English Learners, p. 303B ELL Below Level, p. 303B BL Early Finishers, p. 303B OL AL	English Learners, p. 305B ELL Below Level, p. 305B BL Early Finishers, p. 305B OL AL
Alternate Lesson	*Math Their Way*, p. 190		

Problem Solving: Science (p. 307)

Summative Assessment
✓ • Chapter Review/Test (p. 309)
• Test Practice (p. 311)

Assessment Options

Diagnostic Assessment

SE *Option 1:* Are You Ready? (p. 280)
Option 2: Online Quiz macmillanmh.com
CRM *Option 3:* Diagnostic Test (p. 44)

Formative Assessment

TE Alternate Teaching Strategies (every lesson)
SE Talk About It (every lesson)
SE Writing in Math (every lesson)
TE Line Up (every lesson)
SE Mid-Chapter Check (p. 289)
CRM Mid-Chapter Test (p. 45)

Summative Assessment

SE Chapter Review/Test (p. 309)
SE Test Practice (p. 311)
CRM Leveled Chapter Tests (pp. 50–57)
CRM Cumulative Test Practice (pp. 58–59)
CRM Listening Assessment (pp. 48–49)
CRM Oral Assessment (pp. 46–47)
● Exam*View*® Assessment Suite
Ａ Advance Tracker

McGraw Hill Professional Development

Targeted professional development has been articulated throughout **McGraw-Hill's** *Math Connects* program. The **McGraw-Hill Professional Development Video Library** provides short videos that support the **NCTM Focal Points and Focal Connections**. For more information, visit macmillanmh.com.

| Model Lessons | Instructional Strategies |

Assessment Tips

As students work on their addition problems, take time to observe their understanding of putting two sets together to come up with the total.

- Record individual student observations on an address label.
- Make sure address labels are dated.
- Adhere the label to the inside cover of a student's file folder.
- You will be able to chart progress over time.

Teacher Notes

Learning Stations
Cross-Curricular Links

Art

  individual | SPATIAL

Story Paintings

- Paint an addition story.
- Hang your painting. Tell your number story.

Teacher Note: Tell students to wait to hang their picture until the paint is dry. After all students' paintings are hung, have each student find their own painting. Encourage students to look at other students' work and tell the story they painted. Ask students to identify any paintings that represent the same number story.

Materials:
- painting paper
- tempera paint
- paint brushes
- water

Reading

  small group | VISUAL

Choo Choo

- Pretend you are on a train.
- Take turns as riders or workers.
- Draw a picture to show the train ride.

Teacher Note: Have suggestions for the students of numbers to use to tell about people on the train; for example, five and four or two and six. Students can act out five people and four more people getting on the train or two workers getting off the train and six more workers getting off the train. Then ask how many got off in all. Tell students to act out the train ride and then draw a picture to show it.

Materials:
- paper
- pencils
- chairs

Technology

 individual | VISUAL

Addition

 Math Tool Chest: Counters/Addition

- Choose the Counters button. Choose the Addition work mat.
- Use counters to create addition stories. Add the numbers.
- Enter your answer. Check to see if you are right.

Teacher Note: Have students use the counters to enter any number of objects into columns A and B. Then have them click on the dump truck to add the numbers. Students can enter their answer by clicking on the question mark button. Then, they may click on the star button to see if they are correct. Provide a list of addition problems or have students develop their own problems and justify their thinking by showing the problems using Math Tool Chest.

Materials:
- Math Tool Chest: Counters tool

Music

 pairs | **LOGICAL**

Musical Mystery

- Draw an addition story. Use musical objects.
- Draw another addition story. Show the first number. Show how many in all.
- Share your stories with a partner.
- Have your partner find the answer.

Teacher Note: When students are finished with their first musical mystery situation, have them create new mysteries to solve. You may want to create musical notes on cardstock for students to use. If possible, allow students to take turns playing the instruments used in their stories.

Materials:
- paper
- crayons

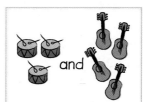

Science

 individual | **SPATIAL**

Number Rainbow

- Draw a rainbow using 11 squares.
- Write 0 to 10 on the squares.
- Roll two number cubes. How many in all?
- Color that number square on the rainbow.
- Do it again.

Teacher Note: Help students form an arch/rainbow shape with the 11 squares. Tell them that each number cube is 0 to 5 so the total will never be more than 10. Have students continue to roll the number cube and color the totals until all squares are colored, as time permits. Discuss numbers and when they might occur in nature.

Materials:
- two 0–5 number cubes
- connecting cubes
- crayons
- paper

Calendar Time

How Many Students in All?

Ask students the following questions and have them write a number sentence for each one. Add or adapt questions to fit your class.

- Today is Tuesday. There are ten girls and 8 boys here today. How many students are here in all?
- Yesterday there were 9 girls and 10 boys here. How many students were there in all?

Teacher Note: Encourage students to come up with their own attendance questions for the class.

Introduce the Chapter

 Real World: Making 5

Share with students that they are going to learn about addition. Explain that when you add something, you join sets of objects together.

Ask students to answer the following questions. Use your finger or student volunteers to model each one.

- **If I show four fingers on my left hand and one finger on my right hand, how many fingers am I showing in all?** five

- **If I have three brothers and two sisters, how many brothers and sisters do I have in all?** five

Use the Student Page

Have students turn to p. 279. Guide students to discuss the images on the page and answer the Explore questions.

Key Vocabulary

Introduce the key vocabulary in the chapter using the routine below.

Define: When asked how many you have in all, you combine all that you have by adding them.

Example: I have two dogs and three cats; I have five pets in all.

Ask: Why would you want to know how many of something you have in all?

Diagnostic Assessment

Check for students' prerequisite skills before beginning the chapter.

- **Option 1: *Are You Ready for Chapter 11?***

  SE Student Edition, p. 280

- **Option 2: *Online Assessment Quiz***

  Math Online ⟩ macmillanmh.com

- **Option 3: *Diagnostic Test***

  CRM Chapter 1 Resource Masters, p. 44

RTI (Response to Intervention)

Apply the Results Based on the results of the diagnostic assessment on p. 280, use the chart on the next page to address individual needs before and during the chapter.

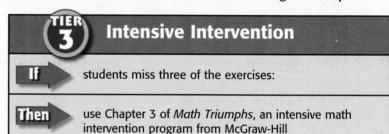

TIER 3	Intensive Intervention
If	students miss three of the exercises:
Then	use Chapter 3 of *Math Triumphs*, an intensive math intervention program from McGraw-Hill

---

FOLDABLES Study Organizer **Dinah Zike's Foldables**

Guide students to create a Bound Book Foldable graphic organizer to make a giant addition journal.

1. Fold two sheets of paper like a hamburger. Place the papers on top of each other, leaving $\frac{1}{16}$ inch between the "mountain tops".

2. Mark both folds 1 inch from the outer edges. On one of the folded sheets, cut from the top and bottom edge to the marked spot on both sides.

3. On the second folded sheet, start at one of the marked spots and cut the fold between the two marks.

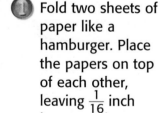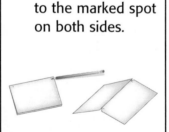

4. Take the cut sheet from step 2 and fold it like a burrito. Place the burrito through the slit in the other sheet, then open the burrito. Fold the bound pages in half to form an eight-page book.

5. Fold the bound pages in half to form an eight-page book. On page 1 use pictures to model addition and combining sets.

When to Use It *Lessons 11-1, 11-2, 11-4, 11-5, and 11-6 (Additional instructions for using the Foldable with these lessons are found on pp. 289 and 309.)*

▶ Key Vocabulary
in all
add
join

Explore
How many birds are red? 4
How many birds are yellow? 1
How many birds are on the branch? 5

Chapter 11   two hundred seventy-nine   279

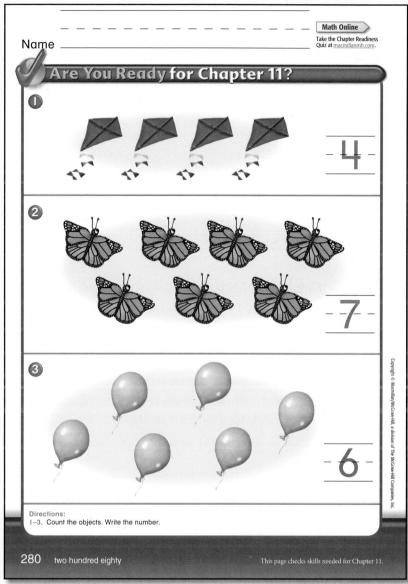

Name _____

Math Online ▶
Take the Chapter Readiness
Quiz at macmillanmh.com.

✓ Are You Ready for Chapter 11?

① [kites] 4

② [butterflies] 7

③ [balloons] 6

Directions:
1–3. Count the objects. Write the number.

280   two hundred eighty   This page checks skills needed for Chapter 11.

RTI (Response to Intervention)

TIER 2 Strategic Intervention below/approaching grade level	TIER 1 On-Level	Above/Beyond Level
If ▶ students miss two in: **Exercises 1–3**	**If** ▶ students miss one in: **Exercises 1–3**	**If** ▶ students miss none: **Exercises 1–3**
Then ▶ choose a resource:	**Then** ▶ choose a resource:	**Then** ▶ choose a resource:
CRM Chapter 4 Resource Masters (Reteach Worksheets) Math Online ▶ Concepts in Motion	TE Learning Stations (pp. 279G–279H) TE Chapter Project (p. 281) CRM Game: Hop On Math Adventures My Math Zone Chapter 10	TE Learning Stations (pp. 279G–279H) TE Chapter Project (p. 281) Real-World Problem Solving: *Animals on the Farm* My Math Zone Chapters 10 and 11 Math Online ▶ Game

WRITING IN ►MATH

Starting the Chapter

Ask students to choose a traceable object, trace it four times in their Math Journal, and then write the number four. Ask them to trace the object again one, two, three, four, five, or six times and have them write that number. Ask students to circle the tracings. Help them write the word *join* on the page. At the end of the lesson allow students to go back and count the tracings to see how many in all.

✓ Chapter 11 Project

Collections Poster

Have students make a collections poster showing different ways to make 10.

- Students will show five collections of objects on a poster.

- Each collection will be divided into two sets that, when combined, make 10.

- Under each collection, students will write the appropriate numbers, for example, four and six is 10.

- Students explain one of their collections to the class.

Chapter 11 Literature List

Lesson	Book Title	Author
11-1	The Crayon Counting Book	Pam Munoz Ryan and Jerry Pallotta
11-2	Ten Puppies	Lynn Reiser
11-3	Quack and Count	Keith Baker
11-4	Animals on Board	Stuart J. Murphy
11-5	Quack and Count	Keith Baker
11-6	Quack and Count	Keith Baker
11-7	Domino Addition	Lynette Long
11-8	Domino Addition	Lynette Long
11-9	Little Quack	Lauren Thompson
Any	The Napping House	Audrey Wood

THE NAPPING HOUSE
by AUDREY WOOD
Illustrated by DON WOOD

ELL National ESL Standards Alignment for Chapter 11			
Lesson, Page	ESL Standard	Modality	Level
11-1, p. 283B	Goal 1, Standard 3, c	Auditory	Beginning
11-2, p. 287B	Goal 1, Standard 1, k	Auditory	Intermediate
11-3, p. 291B	Goal 1, Standard 3, c	Visual/Spatial, Intrapersonal	Intermediate
11-4, p. 293B	Goal 1, Standard 3, j	Kinesthetic	Beginning
11-5, p. 297B	Goal 2, Standard 1, a	Visual	Advanced
11-6, p. 299B	Goal 1, Standard 2, d	Auditory/Visual	Beginning
11-7, p. 301B	Goal 1, Standard 3, b	Visual	Intermediate
11-8, p. 303B	Goal 1, Standard 3, g	Auditory, Visual	Beginning
11-9, p. 305B	Goal 2, Standard 2, f	Social, Linguistic	Advanced

The National ESL Standards can be found in the Teacher Reference Handbook.

MATH at HOME

Dear Family,

Today my class started Chapter 11, **Model Addition**. In this chapter, I will use objects to help me add. Here is an activity we can do and a list of books we can read together.

Love, _____

Activity

Have your child count out pieces of cereal to represent their age. Then have them count out pieces to show the age of a younger sibling, cousin or friend. Have them add the cereal pieces together to find out how many they have in all.

Key Vocabulary

in all to join together groups to find the total

add to join together

3 birds   2 more join

5 birds in all

Math Online Click on the eGlossary link at macmillanmh.com to find out more about these words. There are 13 languages.

Books to Read

Quack and Count
by Keith Baker
Harcourt Children's Books, 2004.

Domino Addition
by Lynette Long
Charlesbridge Publishing, Inc, 1996.

The Napping House
by Audrey Wood
Harcourt Children's Books, 2000.

two hundred eighty-one   281

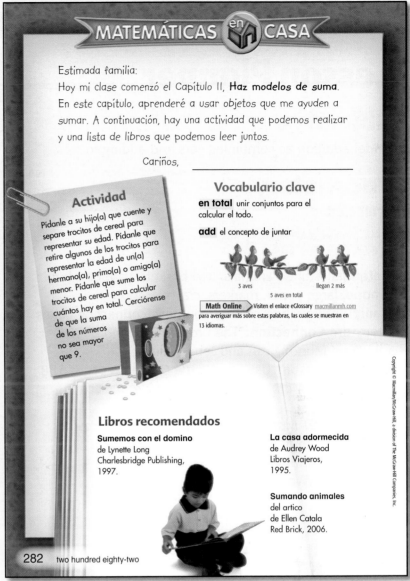

MATEMÁTICAS en CASA

Estimada familia:

Hoy mi clase comenzó el Capítulo 11, **Haz modelos de suma**. En este capítulo, aprenderé a usar objetos que me ayuden a sumar. A continuación, hay una actividad que podemos realizar y una lista de libros que podemos leer juntos.

Cariños, _____

Actividad

Pídanle a su hijo(a) que cuente y separe trocitos de cereal para representar su edad. Pídanle que retire algunos de los trocitos para representar la edad de un(a) hermano(a), primo(a) o amigo(a) menor. Pídanle que sume los trocitos de cereal para calcular cuántos hay en total. Cerciórense de que la suma de los números no sea mayor que 9.

Vocabulario clave

en total unir conjuntos para el calcular el todo

add el concepto de juntar

3 aves   llegan 2 más

5 aves en total

Math Online Visiten el enlace eGlossary macmillanmh.com para averiguar más sobre estas palabras, las cuales se muestran en 13 idiomas.

Libros recomendados

Sumemos con el domino
de Lynette Long
Charlesbridge Publishing, 1997.

La casa adormecida
de Audrey Wood
Libros Viajeros, 1995.

Sumando animales
del artico
de Ellen Catala
Red Brick, 2006.

282   two hundred eighty-two

MATH at HOME

- Read the Math at Home letter on p. 281 with the class and have each student sign it.

- Send home copies of the Math at Home letter with each student.

- Use the Spanish letter on p. 282 for students with Spanish-speaking parents or guardians.

Read-Aloud Anthology

For an optional reading activity to introduce this chapter's math concepts, see the Read Aloud Anthology on p. TR33.

Lesson Planner

Objective
Model addition as combining sets and adding to sets.

Vocabulary
in all, **add**

Resources
Materials: stuffed animals, two baskets, yarn or a hula hoop, large paper, markers, crayons, cup

Manipulatives: two-colored counters, connecting cubes

Literature Connection: The *Crayon Counting Book* by Pam Muñoz Ryan and Jerry Pallotta

Alternate Lesson: Use *The Whale Game* on pages 188 and 189 of *Math Their Way* to provide practice in combining sets.
Use *IMPACT Mathematics*: Unit B and C to provide practice with adding sets.

Teacher Technology
💿 TeacherWorks

Focus on Math Background

Students come to school with explicit ideas about joining, such as from family events where family members join others for meals or special occasions. Students join their classmates in line, at recess, and in the media center. The concept of joining a number of objects, animals, or people with another set of objects, animals, or people comes readily to students. Recording the number sentence to go with the addition story is an essential operational concept.

Composing numbers is at the core as a foundational skill for solving equations and applying many geometric formulas.

Daily Routine

Use these suggestions before beginning the lesson on p. 283.

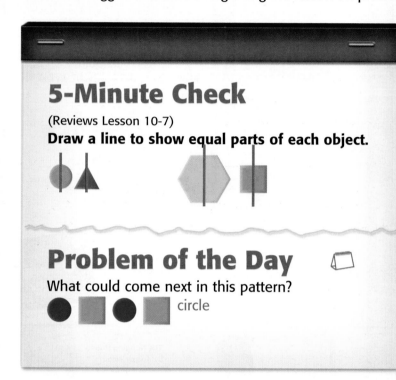

5-Minute Check
(Reviews Lesson 10-7)
Draw a line to show equal parts of each object.

Problem of the Day
What could come next in this pattern?
● ■ ● ■ circle

LINE UP Ask students to get in line in sets of five. Have three students get in line and then add two more; then have four students get in line and add one more. Repeat the activity, using sets of four.

▷ Building Math Vocabulary

- Gather students in a circle and sing *Here We Are Together.* Have two students join hands. Explain that they were each one, and joined to make two.

- **Add** other students to the first two and record how the number of students **in all** increases.

- Count the students. If any students are absent, discuss. If they were not absent, ask how many students would there be in all.

Visual Vocabulary Cards

Use Visual Vocabulary Card 1 to reinforce the vocabulary introduced in this lesson. (The Define/Example/Ask routine is printed on the back of each card.)

add

Differentiated Instruction

Small Group Options

Option 1
Gifted and Talented (AL)   LOGICAL

Have students create a book showing an addition story problem about cats and dogs.

On page 1, students draw how many cats there are.

On page 2, students draw how many dogs there are.

On page 3, students draw how many cats and dogs in all.

Option 2
English Language Learners (ELL)   AUDITORY

Materials: song lyrics written out

Core Vocabulary: some, sum, adding up

Common Use Verb: share

Hear Math This strategy introduces new vocabulary.

• Sing to the tune of "Mr. Golden Sun."

Oh, Mr. Sum, Sum, adding up is fun, please share some with me. Oh, Mr. Sum, Sum, adding up is fun. How many do you see? I see three and I see four. When we share some we will have some more. Please share some with, please share some with, please share some with me.

Independent Work Options

Option 1
Early Finishers (OL) (AL)   KINESTHETIC

Materials: connecting cubes, list of addition sentences

• Have students use connecting cubes to model addition sentences.

• Have students create their own addition story and then model it with their cubes.

• Challenge them to tell their story to a partner about a train and have the partner model the story with cubes.

Option 2
Student Technology

Math Online > macmillanmh.com

Math Adventures

Option 3
Learning Station: Art (p. 279G)

Direct students to the Art Learning Station for opportunities to explore and extend the lesson concept.

Leveled Lesson Resources

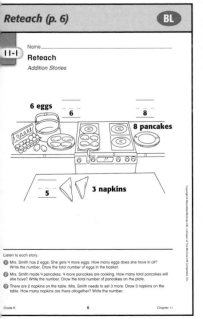

Reteach (p. 6) (BL)

Skills Practice (p. 7) (OL)

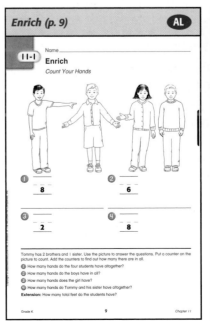

Enrich (p. 9) (AL)

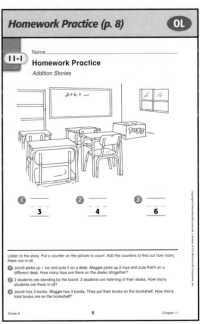

Homework Practice (p. 8) (OL)

① Introduce

Circle Time

Activity Choice 1 • Literature

The Crayon Counting Book by
Pam Muñoz Ryan and Jerry Pallotta

- Read the story and emphasize that the number of crayons is getting bigger because more crayons are being **added**.

- After the story model addition problems using some crayons. For example, "I have one black and one red and one blue. How many crayons do I have **in all**?" Tell many stories until the students are comfortable answering your stories. Have a few students model telling their own story.

- Have students pair up and tell each other addition stories using their own crayons. Monitor the students and clarify any misunderstanding.

Activity Choice 2 • Hands-On

Materials: yarn or a hula hoop, two-colored counters, large paper, markers, stuffed animals, 2 baskets

- Place a large circle of yarn or a hula hoop on the floor and ask a student volunteer to stand inside the circle. Tell this story: ***John (use student's name) is in the kitchen getting ready for supper. His mother, grandmother, and brother come into the kitchen.***

- Have three students join the students standing in the circle.

- **How many people are in the kitchen in all?** four

- Continue the concept with stuffed animals and two baskets. Make up addition stories using three or fewer animals from each basket. For example, tell a story about an animal rescue. Take two animals from one basket and three animals from another basket and join them together.

- Have students create their own stories for others to act out or model.

② Teach

- Direct students to the top of p. 283.
- Identify the picture and discuss ant hills.
- Distribute connecting cubes to students.
- Tell this story: *Two red ants are climbing up the hill. Three purple ants follow them.*
- **How many ants are there in all?** five ants
- Have students use their cubes to model the story.

> ⚠️ **COMMON ERROR!**
> Students may have difficulty relating the math concepts. Help them associate everyday words with math words. For example, *in all* means to show objects together in one group.

Name _____

Addition Stories

Vocabulary
in all
add

Check students' use of counters to model addition.

Check students' use of counters to model addition.

Directions:
1. Listen to the story. Use counters to model the addition stories. Tell how many in all.

2 Check students' use of counters to model addition.

Directions:
2. Listen to the story. Use counters to model the addition story. Tell how many in all.

GO on

BL Alternate Teaching Strategy

If students have trouble modeling addition . . .

Then use one of these reteach options.

1 CRM **Daily Reteach Worksheet** (p. 6)

2 Use Manipulatives Use two-colored counters to model joining addition stories.

- Start with five two-colored counters in a cup to shake and spill compositions of five.
- Each time, ask a student to say the number story as you record it on the chalkboard or recording sheet.
- Increase the number of counters to 10 as student comprehension increases.

③ Practice

Guided Practice

- Direct students to p. 283. Have students identify the picture and discuss picnics in the park.

- **Three red plates were set on the table for lunch. Three yellow plates were also set on the table. How many plates in all?** six plates

- Have students use counters to model the story.

Independent Practice

Have students turn to p. 284. Read this or stories like it and have students model with counters.

- **Three children were swinging on the swings. Two more children were also swinging. How many children were swinging in all?** five

- Tell students other addition stories about the park. Use zero if students are ready.

③ Check students' use of cubes to model addition.

Directions:
3. Create an addition story. Model it using cubes. Trace the cubes used. Tell how many in all.

④ Check students' use of cubes to model addition.

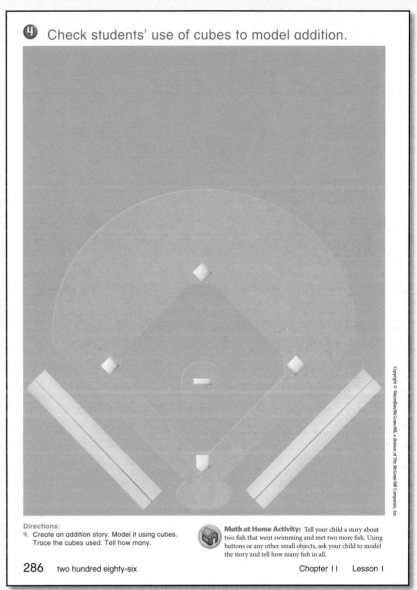

Directions:
4. Create an addition story. Model it using cubes. Trace the cubes used. Tell how many.

 Math at Home Activity: Tell your child a story about two fish that went swimming and met two more fish. Using buttons or any other small objects, ask your child to model the story and tell how many fish in all.

④ **Assess**

✓ **Formative Assessment**

Give students counters to model the following stories:

- **One dog is on the path. Three more dogs come on the path. How many dogs in all?** four

- **There are four children playing ball. One more child begins playing ball. How many children in all?** five

Quick Check	Are students still struggling to model addition?

If Yes → Small Group Options (p. 283B)

If No → Independent Work Options (p. 283B)
      [CRM] Skills Practice Worksheet (p. 7)
      [CRM] Enrich Worksheet (p. 9)

Use Objects to Add

Lesson Planner

Objective

Use concrete objects to solve addition problems.

Vocabulary

join

Resources

Materials: basket, stuffed animals, number cards, books, paper, crayons

Manipulatives: color tiles, connecting cubes

Literature Connection: *Ten Puppies* by Lynn Reiser

Alternate Lesson: Use *The Hand Game* on page 180 of *Math Their Way* to provide practice adding concrete objects.

Use *IMPACT Mathematics*: Unit B and C to provide practice with solving addition problems.

Teacher Technology

  TeacherWorks • Concepts in Motion

Focus on Math Background

Providing a setting for joining or addition stories helps students see real-world connections for their stories as well as providing a context for the language of addition: *joining, altogether, in all, a total of,* and so on.

As students compose numbers, they begin to see how to decompose them as well. This inverse process is foundational for algebra and other areas of mathematics where working with equations is essential.

Daily Routine

Use these suggestions before beginning the lesson on p. 287.

5-Minute Check

(Reviews Lesson 11-1)

1. I pick three flowers. Then I pick two flowers. How many flowers do I have in all? five

2. I use one crayon. Then I use four crayons. How many crayons did I use in all? five

3. I eat two apple slices. Then I eat two more apple slices. How many apple slices have I eaten in all? four

Problem of the Day

Use counters to show how many there will be in all if the two groups come together. five

LINE UP Ask students to pretend they are animals in a pond. Touch five students on their head and ask the "frogs" to hop into the line, then ask two more "frogs" to jump into the line. Count how many frogs in all. Repeat with other animals.

Building Math Vocabulary

- Use pattern blocks to create several joining stories.

- For example: There are three squares. Two triangles **join** them. How many shapes in all?

- Give pattern blocks to students, and have them create their own joining stories.

Differentiated Instruction

Small Group Options

Option 1 — Below/Approaching Level BL
SPATIAL

Materials: masking tape, red and blue crayons, poster board

- Use masking tape to make a ten-frame on a poster board. Place two red crayons and one blue crayon near the ten-frame.

- **How many red crayons? Blue crayons?** two; one Let a student place the crayons in the ten-frame.

- **How many crayons in the ten-frame in all?** three

- Continue with other combinations.

Option 2 — English Language Learners ELL
AUDITORY

Materials: toys
Core Vocabulary: say/said, see/saw, What happened?
Common Use Verb: give/gave

Hear Math This strategy teaches irregular past tense.
- Allow students to play with toys. Catch them sharing, and use it to verbalize an addition story using vocabulary.
- Ask students to reenact the story.
- Discuss as time permits.

Independent Work Options

Option 1 — Early Finishers OL AL
SPATIAL

Materials: attribute buttons

- Give each student seven buttons.
- Ask them to divide their buttons into two separate piles of buttons.
- Have them draw a picture of how many buttons they have in all.
- Have students repeat the activity with different amounts of buttons: nine, 10, 12.

Option 2 — Student Technology

Math Online ▷ macmillanmh.com

Math Adventures

Option 3 — Learning Station: Technology (p. 279G)

Direct students to the Technology Learning Station for opportunities to explore and extend the lesson concept.

Leveled Lesson Resources
Additional support for English Language Learners can be found in the ELL Guide (p. 87). ELL

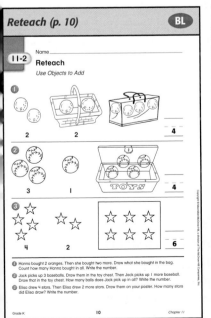

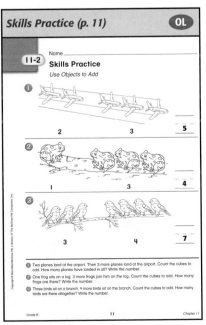

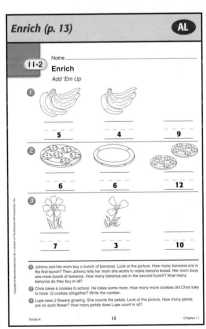

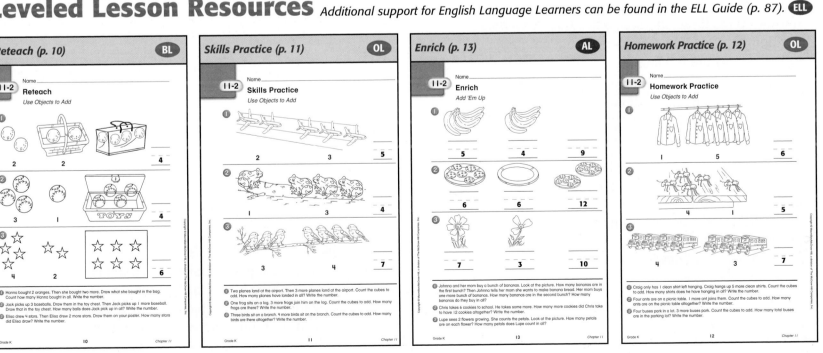

① Introduce

ⓒircle Time

Activity Choice 1 • Literature

Ten Puppies by Lynn Reiser

Materials: color tiles, paper, crayons

- Each student needs 10 color tiles.

- As the story is read, have students show different arrangements of 10. For example, on the first page with nine and one, students should have a set of nine and a set of one.

- Continue through the story and let students model each combination of 10.

- After the story, have students use their tiles to model different combinations of 10 and draw their own pictures (pumpkins, cats, trees, flowers, and so on) to show the combinations. Make a class book of their artwork.

Activity Choice 2 • Hands-On

Materials: number cards; six library books; bags of three, four, and five cubes

- Tell this addition story and ask volunteers to **join** books together to model adding.

- **Our library has three new books. If we put four more new books in the library how many new books will we have in all?** seven

- Present the addition story again using books and number cards three and four. Ask students to hold the number card that corresponds to the number of books they are holding.

- Ask students to count how many in all. Hold up the number seven card to show how many in all.

- Give students one bag of cubes and number cards. Have pairs model an addition story.

- Present other addition stories when students are ready. You may choose to use zero or larger numbers such as seven, eight, and nine. For example: **I have two pennies. I found some more. Now I have seven pennies. How many pennies did I find?** five

② Teach

- Direct students to the top of p. 287.

- Distribute connecting cubes to students.

- Tell a joining addition story, such as: **Three red parrots landed on a branch. Two red parrots joined them. Now how many parrots are there in all?** five

- Have students model the story with connecting cubes.

- Guide them in counting and writing the number five.

- If needed, present other addition stories for practice.

ⒷⓁ Alternate Teaching Strategy

If ▶ students have trouble modeling addition . . .

Then ▶ use one of these reteach options.

1 CRM **Daily Reteach Worksheet** (p. 10)

2 Model Addition Model an addition story with overhead manipulatives.

- Tell simple joining addition stories. Model the stories using overhead manipulatives.

- Have students follow along, using their own manipulatives on a WorkMat 7.

> ⚠ **COMMON ERROR!**
> When using manipulatives, students sometimes forget to clear their mats before starting a new problem. Remind students to start each problem with an empty mat.

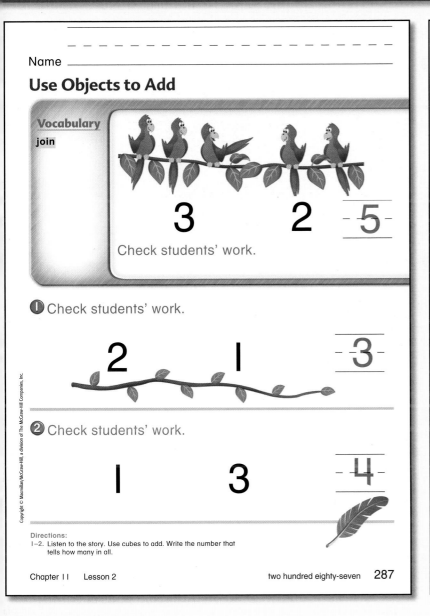

Name _____

Use Objects to Add

Vocabulary
join

3   2   -5-

Check students' work.

❶ Check students' work.

2   1   -3-

❷ Check students' work.

1   3   -4-

Directions:
1–2. Listen to the story. Use cubes to add. Write the number that tells how many in all.

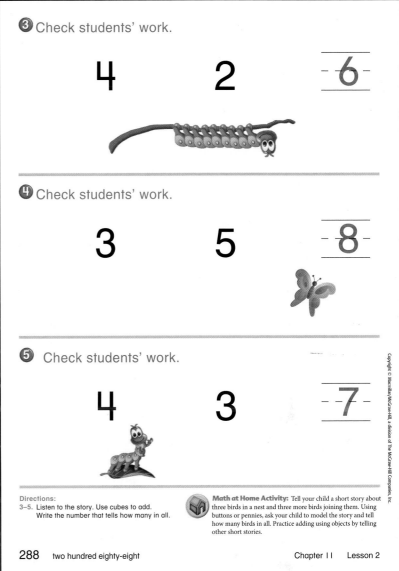

❸ Check students' work.

4   2   -6-

❹ Check students' work.

3   5   -8-

❺ Check students' work.

4   3   -7-

Directions:
3–5. Listen to the story. Use cubes to add.
Write the number that tells how many in all.

Math at Home Activity: Tell your child a short story about three birds in a nest and three more birds joining them. Using buttons or pennies, ask your child to model the story and tell how many birds in all. Practice adding using objects by telling other short stories.

❸ Practice

Guided Practice

- Have students use cubes to model stories on p. 287.

1. **Two bird nests are in a tree. One more nest is built in the tree. How many nests in all?** three
2. **A mother bird lays one egg in a nest. Then she lays three more. How many eggs in all?** four

Independent Practice

Have students turn to p. 288 and model these stories.

3. **Four green grasshoppers are on a branch. Two green grasshoppers joined them. How many grasshoppers are on the branch?** six
4. **Three ladybugs are looking for some friends. They find five ladybugs to join them. How many ladybugs in all?** eight
5. **Four crickets are taking a nap. Three crickets come join them for a nap. How many are napping?** seven

❹ Assess

✓ Formative Assessment

- Use connecting cubes to represent animals: three frogs and one frog. Use a blue piece of paper for a pond.
- Have students create joining addition stories and write the number of animals in all.

Quick Check   Are students still struggling to solve addition problems using objects?

If Yes → Small Group Options (p. 287B)

If No → Independent Work Options (p. 287B)
    CRM Skills Practice Worksheet (p. 11)
    CRM Enrich Worksheet (p. 13)

Lesson 11-2 Use Objects to Add   **288**

Lessons 11-1 to 11-2

✓ Formative Assessment

Use the Mid-Chapter Check to assess students' progress in the first half of the chapter.
Read the following addition stories:

1. **There are two fish swimming in the lake. Three more came to join them. How many fish are there in all?** five
2. **There are four sailboats on the lake. Two more sailboats join them. How many sailboats are there in all?** six
3. **There is one seagull flying in the air. Along come six more seagulls flying in the air. How many seagulls are flying in all?** seven

ExamView® Assessment Suite Customize and create multiple versions of your Mid-Chapter Check and the test answer keys.

FOLDABLES® Dinah Zike's Foldables

Use these lesson suggestions for incorporating the Foldables during the chapter.

Lesson 11-1 On the first page of the addition journal, use pictures to model addition and combining sets. Guide students to use proper terminology as they describe simple addition problems.

Lesson 11-2 Use large paper clips to form and solve addition problems and then tape them onto the second page of the journal.

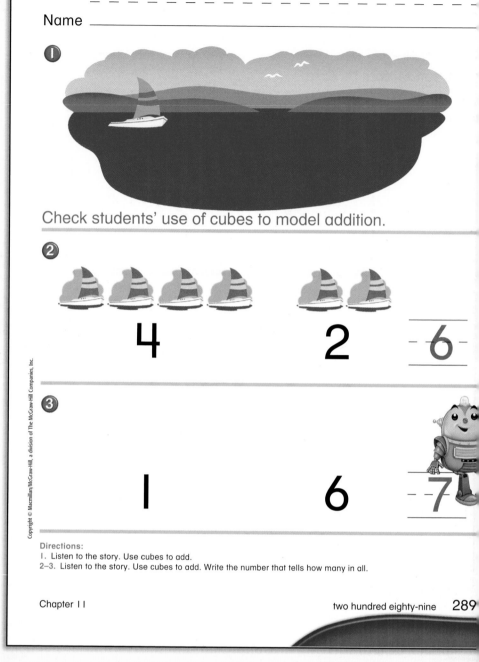

Name _____

Check students' use of cubes to model addition.

Directions:
1. Listen to the story. Use cubes to add.
2–3. Listen to the story. Use cubes to add. Write the number that tells how many in all.

Chapter 11   two hundred eighty-nine   289

Data-Driven Decision Making

Based on the results of the Mid-Chapter Check, use the following resources to review concepts that continue to give students problems.

Exercises	State/Local Standards	What's the Math?	Error Analysis	Resources for Review
1 Lesson 11-1		Understand simple addition problems.	Does not listen carefully. Does not choose correct number of cubes as story proceeds.	**CRM** Chapter 11 Resource Masters (Reteach Worksheets) **Math Online** Concepts in Motion Math Adventures
2–3 Lesson 11-2		Use concrete objects to determine the answers to addition problems.	Does not listen carefully. Does not add correctly. Does not write correct number.	

How Many In All?

Adding

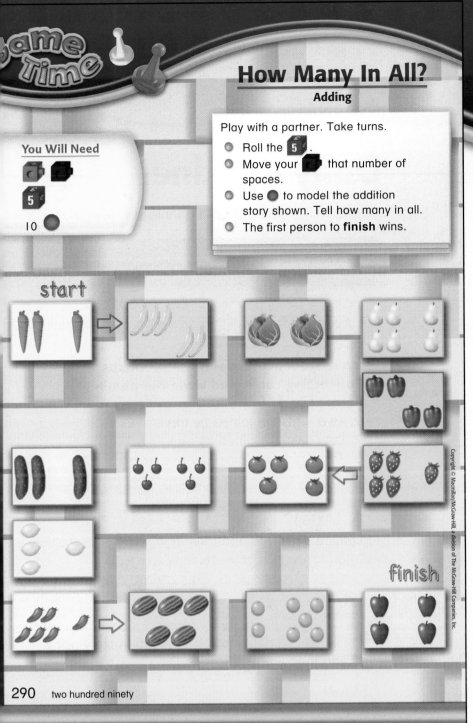

How Many In All?

Math Concept:
Adding

Manipulatives: number cubes, connecting cubes, two-colored counters

Introduce the game on p. 290 to your students to play in pairs to review concepts introduced in this chapter.

Instructions

- Give each student a different color connecting cube to use as a game piece, and put a pile of two-colored counters on the table.
- Students take turns rolling the number cube and moving their pieces along the path.
- For each square they land on, students use counters from the pile to model the addition story shown.
- The first person to finish wins.

Extend the Game

After modeling the addition story shown, have students create another story that results in the same sum.

Differentiated Practice

Use these leveled suggestions to differentiate the game for all learners.

Level	Assignment
BL Below/Approaching Level	Have students work with an older student or parent volunteer to guide addition modeling.
OL On Level	Have students play the game with the rules as written.
AL Above/Beyond Level	Have students write the numbers used to add for each square.

Lesson Planner

Objective

Use the plus symbol (+) to show addition.

Vocabulary

plus sign (+)

Resources

Manipulatives: connecting cubes

Alternate Lesson: Adapt *Jewels* on page 239 of *Math Their Way* to provide practice in using the plus symbol to show addition.

Literature Connection: *Quack and Count* by Keith Baker

Teacher Technology

⊙ TeacherWorks

Focus on Math Background

In this lesson, kindergarteners will begin to use the plus sign to represent situations in which they count and combine sets with concrete objects. By first grade, the students will eventually connect the [+] symbol with the informal experiences they have had in kindergarten combining and joining sets to the formal operation of addition. The use of symbols to represent mathematical operations is a cornerstone of algebraic reasoning.

Daily Routine

Use these suggestions before beginning the lesson on p. 291.

5-Minute Check

(Reviews Lesson 11-2)

Have students model these problems with connecting cubes and write the number sentences.

1. Two birds are joined by three bees. $2 + 3 = 5$

2. Four cats are joined by one dog. $4 + 1 = 5$

3. Three girls are joined by two boys. $3 + 2 = 5$

Problem of the Day

Draw a picture to add three and four and write the total. Check students' drawings.

LINE UP As you prepare for recess, lunch, or dismissal, ask students to say an addition story using "plus" and then line up.

▷ Building Math Vocabulary

- Write 2 + 3 on the chalkboard.
- Draw a picture of a set of two ducks and a set of three ducks to illustrate this problem.
- **What would we do if we wanted to find out how many ducks there are in all?** Sample answers: Add them; count them.
- Point to the **plus sign (+)**. Share with students that the plus sign (+) is a symbol to show addition. **What are we doing with the two and three?** adding them together to get a total

Differentiated Instruction

Small Group Options

Option 1

Below/Approaching Level BL
KINESTHETIC

Materials: modeling clay, spinners, connecting cubes

- Have students make a large plus symbol out of clay.
- Ask students to spin the spinner for the first number in the addition problem.
- Have students put that number of cubes in the front of the plus sign.
- Students spin again and put cubes after.
- Have students say the total and how they figured it out.

Option 2

English Language Learners ELL
VISUAL/SPATIAL, INTRAPERSONAL

Core Vocabulary: other ways, plus (+), say the same thing
Common Use Verb: means

See Math This strategy connects words, symbols, and concepts.

- Write and model: "Three plus two is the same as five." Say: "There are other ways to say the same thing." Model changing from words to numbers and symbols and manipulatives.

Independent Work Options

Option 1

Early Finishers OL AL
LINGUISTIC

Materials: addition facts written on index cards, two-colored counters

- Have students take turns choosing an addition fact card and saying the problem aloud.
- Ask students to work together to show the addition fact using 2-colored counters.
- Have students find and say the answer to the problem by counting all the counters.

Option 2

Student Technology

Math Online > macmillanmh.com

Option 3

Learning Station: Art (p. 279G)

Direct students to the Art Learning Station for opportunities to explore and extend the lesson concept.

Leveled Lesson Resources

Reteach (p. 14) BL

Skills Practice (p. 15) OL

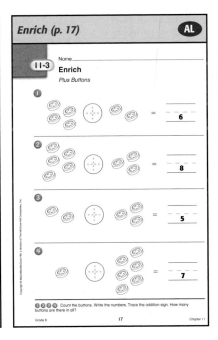

Enrich (p. 17) AL

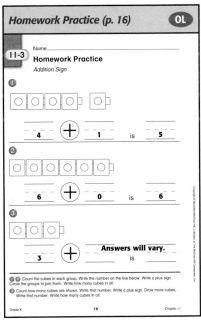

Homework Practice (p. 16) OL

1 Introduce

⏰ircle Time

Activity Choice 1 • Literature

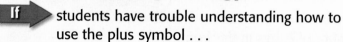

Quack and Count
by Keith Baker

- Each student will need 7 objects and a **plus sign** (+).

- As the book is read, have students raise their hands when they hear the word *plus*.

- Reread the first page. Write the math sentence on the board (6 + 1 = 7) while repeating the words. Explain that symbols are a quick way to write math words. Students then group individual objects and attempt to say and/or demonstrate their own sentence.

- Continue modeling the process as students arrange their objects and orally respond.

Activity Choice 2• Hands-On

- Invite five students to stand in front of the class—three to your left and two to your right.

- Ask the seated students to tell how many students are on each side of you. **How can we find how many students are standing in all?** Answers will vary. Sample answers: Join the two sets; count them; add the two parts. Record the number sentence on the chalkboard.

- Have the two sets of students stand together. **How many students are there in all?** five

- Erase the word "and" and write a plus sign (+). Identify the "+" by calling it a plus sign.

- Repeat the addition story of three students plus two students is five students.

- Have students say "three, plus two is five".

- Write "3 and 2" on the chalkboard as you say it aloud. Tell students the plus sign shows us to add or join sets together.

2 Teach

- Direct students to the top of p. 291.

- Have them identify the bear on the swing set and the bears on the jungle gym.

- Guide students to suggest that they add the sets to find out how many bears there are in all.

- Have students circle both sets to make sure students understand that the sets are joined together.

- **What does the plus sign show?** It shows that sets are being joined.

- Have students write numbers of bears being combined and the total number of bears beneath the picture.

BL Alternate Teaching Strategy

If students have trouble understanding how to use the plus symbol . . .

Then use one of these reteach options.

1 CRM **Daily Reteach Worksheet** (p. 14)

2 **Use the Plus Sign** Provide each student with a handful of connecting cubes. Ask students to make one train of two cubes and another train of two cubes.

- **What could we do if we wanted to find out how many cubes there are in all?** Add the trains together or count all the cubes.

- Have students join the trains together and tell them this is just like using the plus sign. **How many cubes in all?** four

- Write 2 + 2 is 4 on the chalkboard to illustrate what the students just did.

- Continue to add other cube trains together as time allows.

- If cubes do not convey the concept, have students act out the addition story using themselves as actors in the story.

> ⚠️ **COMMON ERROR!**
>
> Some students may have difficulty associating the plus sign with joining sets. Help them understand the plus sign by saying an addition number sentence and modeling it using classroom objects. When combining the sets of objects have each student hold up a paper plus sign to show that the objects are being joined together to find the total.

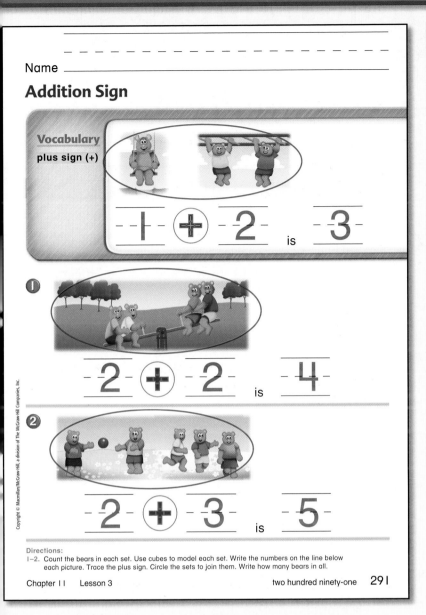

Name _____

Addition Sign

Vocabulary
plus sign (+)

$-1 - (+) - 2$ is -3

①

$-2 - (+) - 2$ is -4

②

$-2 - (+) - 3$ is -5

Directions:
1–2. Count the bears in each set. Use cubes to model each set. Write the numbers on the line below each picture. Trace the plus sign. Circle the sets to join them. Write how many bears in all.

Chapter 11   Lesson 3   two hundred ninety-one   291

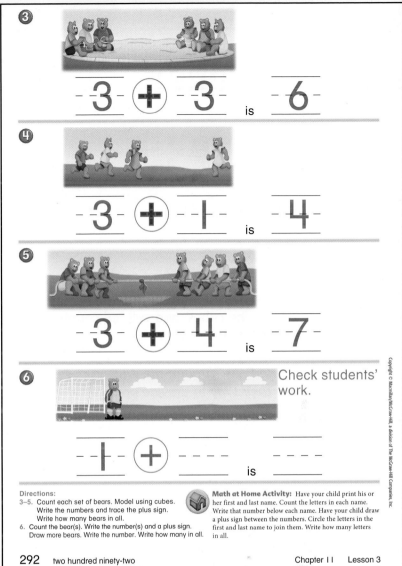

③

$-3 - (+) - 3$ is -6

④

$-3 - (+) - 1$ is -4

⑤

$-3 - (+) - 4$ is -7

⑥

Check students' work.

$-1 - (+) - $ is $-$

Directions:
3–5. Count each set of bears. Model using cubes. Write the numbers and trace the plus sign. Write how many bears in all.
6. Count the bear(s). Write the number(s) and a plus sign. Draw more bears. Write the number. Write how many in all.

 Math at Home Activity: Have your child print his or her first and last name. Count the letters in each name. Write that number below each name. Have your child draw a plus sign between the numbers. Circle the letters in the first and last name to join them. Write how many letters in all.

292   two hundred ninety-two   Chapter 11   Lesson 3

③ Practice

Guided Practice

- Direct students to p. 291.
- Have students count the number of bears in each set and write the number below each picture.
- Tell students to model each exercise using cubes.
- Make sure students understand that they use an addition sign to show joining by tracing each addition sign and circling that group of bears.
- Have students write the total number of bears.

Independent Practice

Have students turn to p. 292. Explain the directions. Have students work independently on the exercises.

④ Assess

✓ Formative Assessment

- Show students two sets of items and ask them to write a number to represent each set and use a sign to join the two sets. Sample answer: 3 + 4
- Have students tell how many in all and write the number.

Quick Check | **Are students still struggling to use the plus symbol?**

If Yes → Small Group Options (p. 291B)

If No → Independent Work Options (p. 291B)

CRM Skills Practice Worksheet (p. 15)

CRM Enrich Worksheet (p. 17)

Lesson 11–3 Addition Sign   **292**

Lesson Planner _____

Objective

Use concrete objects and pictures to show ways to make 4 and 5.

Review Vocabulary

add

Resources

Materials: paper, cups, classroom items, pencils
Manipulatives: connecting cubes, two-colored counters
Literature Connection: *Animals on Board*
  by Stuart J. Murphy
Alternate Lesson: Use *Peek Through the Wall* on pages
  183–185 of *Math Their Way* to provide practice in
  different ways to make 5 using addition.
Teacher Technology
  ⊙ TeacherWorks

Focus on Math Background

Looking at situations where groups work together (a band, a team, a family) provides a context for addition stories as well as the concept of how many in all (the total or sum). You may wish to use examples, such as three boys and two girls make a total of five students in the family or on a sports team. Focusing on groups helps students look at how the group number is composed.

Daily Routine _____

Use these suggestions before beginning the lesson on p. 293.

5-Minute Check

(Reviews Lesson 11-3)
Use the plus sign to show 3 and 2 added together.
3 + 2

Problem of the Day

There are three students on the swings and two students on the slides. How many students in all are playing? five

LINE UP Have students put themselves in sets of five to get in line. For each set, discuss how many boys and how many girls, for a total of five.

Review Math Vocabulary

Materials: rhythm instrument
Have one student join another student to begin a marching band. (Use rhythm instruments if they are available.) Point out that the second student has joined the first student.

* As more students are invited to join the band one-by-one, focus on the concepts of "**add**" and "in all" for the number of students in the marching band.

* You may wish to change the setting to a school parade if musical instruments are not available.

Differentiated Instruction

Small Group Options

Option 1
Below/Approaching Level (BL)　　KINESTHETIC

Materials: paper with a row of four and five squares, crayons

- Have students model joining, by using a strip of graph paper. Have students color four squares, using two colors. (For example, color one square red and three squares yellow.)
- Have students use two colors to make four color strips to create a different combination. Repeat for five.

Option 2
English Language Learners (ELL)　　KINESTHETIC

Materials: 1 x 4 grid, 2 color counters
Core Vocabulary: in the square, combinations, have you tried
Common Use Verb: try/tried

Do Math This strategy shows combinations of 4 and 5.

- Give students a 1 x 4 grid and 4 counters.
- Allow students to experiment with materials.
- Ask a student how many red cubes and yellow cubes are in the squares. Write the number sentence for it.
- Repeat with other combinations. Discuss results.

Independent Work Options

Option 1
Early Finishers (OL) (AL)　　VISUAL

Materials: paper, crayons

- Have students trace their hands on a piece of paper.
- Have them draw finger puppets on some of their fingers.
- Have students write the number that represents how many fingers they have in all, by combining fingers with puppets and fingers without them.
- Ask them how it would have changed if they had drawn a different number of puppets.

Option 2
Student Technology

Math Online　macmillanmh.com

Math Adventures

Option 3
Learning Stations: Music (p. 279G)

Direct students to the Music Learning Station for more opportunities to explore and extend the lesson concept.

Leveled Lesson Resources
Additional support for English Language Learners can be found in the ELL Guide (p. 89). (ELL)

Reteach (p. 18) (BL)	Skills Practice (p. 19) (OL)	Enrich (p. 21) (AL)	Homework Practice (p. 20) (OL)
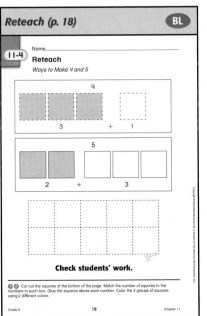	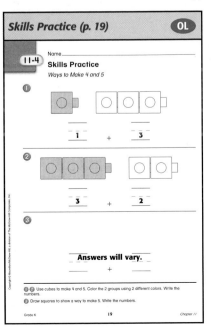	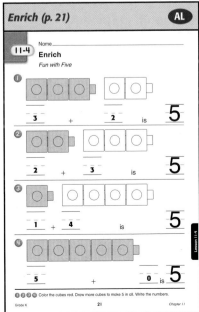	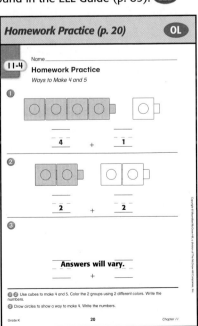

1 Introduce

Circle Time

Activity Choice 1 • Literature

Animals on Board
by Stuart J. Murphy

Materials: connecting cubes

- Give each student two colors of connecting cubes.

- Read the story. Students show the first truck's number (three) with one colored (red) cube. They show the second truck's number (two) in another color. They join the cubes to find the total cubes for both trucks.

- Have students count their cubes to verify that they match the problem in the book.

- Repeat the process for each new set of two trucks.

- After reading the story, have students model all the ways to **add** two colors to make five. Record results on paper.

- Discuss zero as a way to make four and/or five and be sure students include zero and five and five and zero on their papers.

- Early finishers can find combinations that make a total of four.

Activity Choice 2 • Hands-On

- Send students on a classroom scavenger hunt for four each of the same items, such as crayons, lunch boxes, paper clips, manipulatives, and so on.

- Show students four items that you found and create an addition story about them. Then ask students to create their own addition stories about their items.

- As a class, discuss all the ways to join numbers to make four (zero and four, four and zero, one and three, three and one, two and two).

- Repeat the activity, using five items.

- When finished, make a "Ways to Make" chart of all the ways to make four and five. Model four and zero as a way to make four if class is ready.

2 Teach

- Direct students to the top of p. 293.

- Have them use cubes to model the examples shown.

- Have students write the numbers that tell how many cubes are shown.

> **! COMMON ERROR!**
>
> Students may see only one way to make four or five. Have them explore different situations so that they understand there are several ways to make each number.

Ways to Make 4 and 5

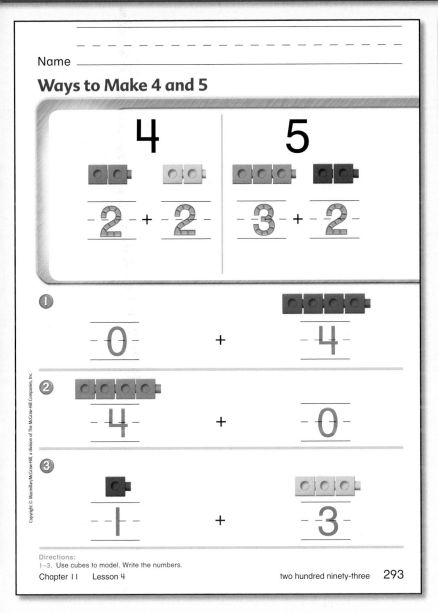

Directions:
1–3. Use cubes to model. Write the numbers.
Chapter 11   Lesson 4   two hundred ninety-three   293

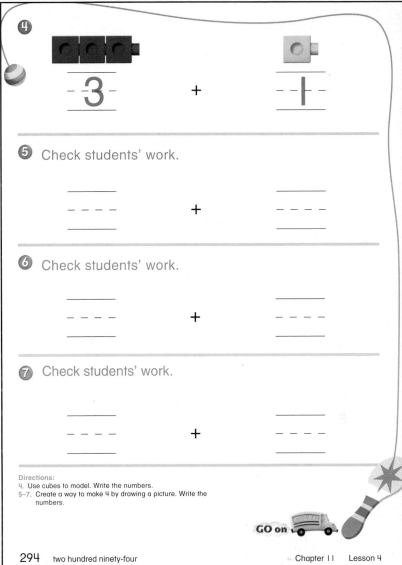

⑤ Check students' work.

_____   +   _____

⑥ Check students' work.

_____   +   _____

⑦ Check students' work.

_____   +   _____

Directions:
4. Use cubes to model. Write the numbers.
5–7. Create a way to make 4 by drawing a picture. Write the numbers.

GO on

294   two hundred ninety-four   Chapter 11   Lesson 4

BL Alternate Teaching Strategy

If ▶ students have trouble modeling addition . . .

Then ▶ use one of these reteach options.

1 CRM **Daily Reteach Worksheet** (p. 18)

2 **Use Counters to Add** Use counters to model adding to make four and five.

- Give each student a cup, four two-colored counters, pencil, and paper.
- Have students put their counters in the cup, shake, and spill them onto the desk.
- Students write the addition sentence that shows how many red plus how many yellow makes a total of four.
- Repeat several times. Discuss the number combinations for four.
- Repeat the activity, using five counters.

③ Practice

Guided Practice

• Direct students to p. 293.

• For Exercises 1–3 have students use cubes to model three ways to make four and write numbers to show each way.

Independent Practice

Have students turn to p. 294. Explain the directions and then have students work independently on the exercises on pages 294–296.

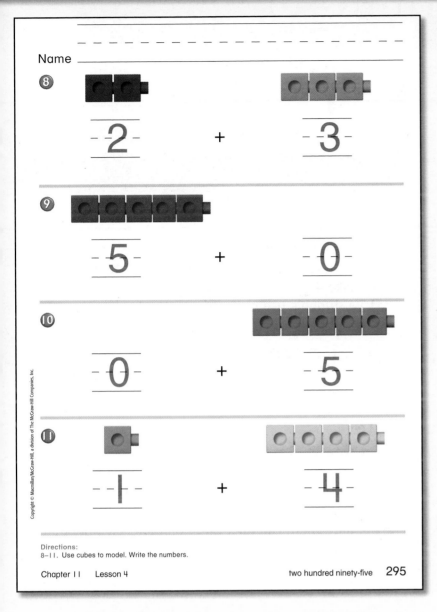

Name _____

⑧   __2__   +   __3__

⑨   __5__   +   __0__

⑩   __0__   +   __5__

⑪   __1__   +   __4__

Directions:
8–11. Use cubes to model. Write the numbers.

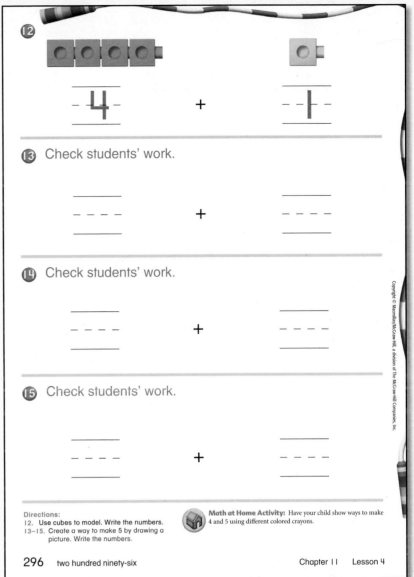

⑫   __4__   +   __1__

⑬   Check students' work.

    _____   +   _____

⑭   Check students' work.

    _____   +   _____

⑮   Check students' work.

    _____   +   _____

Directions:
12. Use cubes to model. Write the numbers.
13–15. Create a way to make 5 by drawing a picture. Write the numbers.

 **Math at Home Activity:** Have your child show ways to make 4 and 5 using different colored crayons.

④ Assess

✓ Formative Assessment

- Have students choose classroom objects to make their own compositions of numbers four and five. Have students write numbers to show the way they made four and five.

- Have students explain their work.

Quick Check   **Are students still struggling with ways to make 4 and 5?**

If Yes → Small Group Options (p. 279B)

If No → Independent Work Options (p. 279B)

    CRM   Skills Practice Worksheet (p. 19)

    CRM   Enrich Worksheet (p. 21)

Lesson Planner

Objective

Students will use concrete objects and pictures to show different ways to make 6.

Review Vocabulary

six

Resources

Materials: egg cartons, cups, paper, pencils, string

Manipulatives: two-colored counters, 0–5 number cubes, attribute buttons, connecting cubes

Literature Connection: *Quack and Count* by Keith Baker

Teacher Technology

⊙ TeacherWorks • Concepts in Motion

Daily Routine

Use these suggestions before beginning the lesson on p. 297.

5-Minute Check

(Reviews Lesson 11-4)

Have students use connecting cubes to show ways to make 4. $0 + 4, 1 + 3, 2 + 2, 3 + 1, 4 + 0$

Have students use connecting cubes to show ways to make 5. $0 + 5, 1 + 4, 2 + 3, 3 + 2, 4 + 1, 5 + 0$

Problem of the Day

Two students are sitting at a table. Three more sit down. How many students are sitting at the table in all? 5

LINE UP Have students form sets of six. Have each set divide into two smaller sets. As the smaller sets line up, have them call their other part and say how they make six in all.

▷ Review Math Vocabulary

Materials: 0–5 number cube

- Have a volunteer roll a 0–5 number cube. Record the number.
- Ask how many more do you need to add or join to make **six**. Record how to make six.
- Repeat the activity with other volunteers and record how to make six. Show the seven ways: $0 + 6, 1 + 5, 2 + 4, 3 + 3, 4 + 2, 5 + 1, 6 + 0$.

Differentiated Instruction

Small Group Options

Option 1 — Gifted and Talented (AL)
KINESTHETIC

Materials: brown lunch bags, classroom objects, crayons

- Have students collect six items and put them in a bag.
- On the front of their bags, have students write a number less than or the same as (equal to) that number of items.
- On the bottom of the bag, have students write the number that they would need to add to the bag to make six.
- Have students justify their thinking by modeling the addition problem with the objects and explaining it to a friend.

Option 2 — English Language Learners (ELL)
VISUAL

Materials: paper with ladybug outline, counters
Core Vocabulary: our ladybugs, dots, on either side
Common Use Verb: should have
See Math This strategy improves number understanding.

- Say: "**Our ladybugs *should have*** six dots."
- Model placing 3 on one side of the line. Repeat for the other sie.
- Allow students to experiment with counters. Emphasize that dots can go on either side of the line.

Independent Work Options

Option 1 — Early Finishers (AL) (OL)
SPATIAL

Materials: pattern blocks, paper, crayons

- Have students choose two styles of pattern blocks for a total of six.
- Ask them to create a picture using their blocks.
- Have students trace their blocks on a piece of paper.
- Have them color their pictures.
- **How did you make 6?** Sample answer: 1 + 5 is 6

Option 2 — Student Technology

Math Online ▷ macmillanmh.com

Math Adventures

Option 3 — Learning Station: Reading (p. 279G)

Direct students to the Reading Learning Station for opportunities to explore and extend the lesson concept.

Leveled Lesson Resources

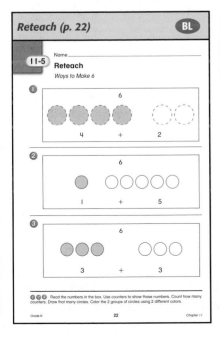

Reteach (p. 22) **BL**

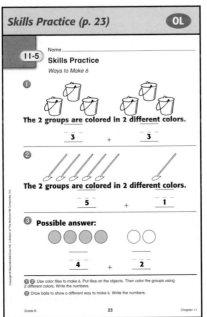

Skills Practice (p. 23) **OL**

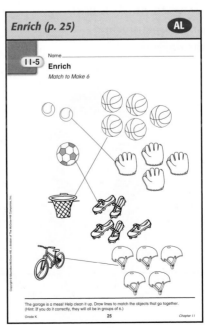

Enrich (p. 25) **AL**

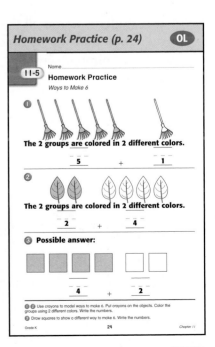

Homework Practice (p. 24) **OL**

1 Introduce

Circle Time

Activity Choice 1 • Literature

Quack and Count by Keith Baker

- Read the book to students.
- Turn to the page and illustrations showing the ducks splash and dive.
- Ask students what other ways they could see six ducks come together. You might use the illustration to point out three ducks meeting three ducks, or one duck meeting five ducks.
- Ask students to think of different combinations of the six ducks meeting (for example, 4 + 2).

Activity Choice 2 • Hands-On

Materials: egg cartons, cups, two-colored counters, paper, pencils

- Cut egg cartons in half so that each half has six holders.
- Give each student half of an egg carton, a cup, and six counters.
- Have students put the counters in the cup, shake and spill the counters, then place the counters in the six holders.
- **How many of each color counter do you have in your cup?** Sample answers: 3 red and 3 yellow, 4 red and 2 yellow
- Have students name all the ways to make 6 and justify their thinking by drawing a picture and writing a number sentence for each way to make 6.

2 Teach

Direct students to the top of p. 297.

- Have them identify the number of counters in each group.
- Have students write the number in each group below it.
- **How did you make 6?** 5 + 1 is 6
- Repeat the activity with the second example.

BL Alternate Teaching Strategy

If students have trouble with making 6 . . .

Then use one of these reteach options.

1. CRM **Daily Reteach Worksheet** (p. 22)
2. **Play a Game** Have pairs take turns rolling two 0–5 number cubes.
   - Have players who roll two numbers that make six get one point.
   - Have pairs roll ten times. Say that the winner has the most points.

! **COMMON ERROR!**
Students may not understand that a set of 0 is a set. Reinforce that 0 is an important number.

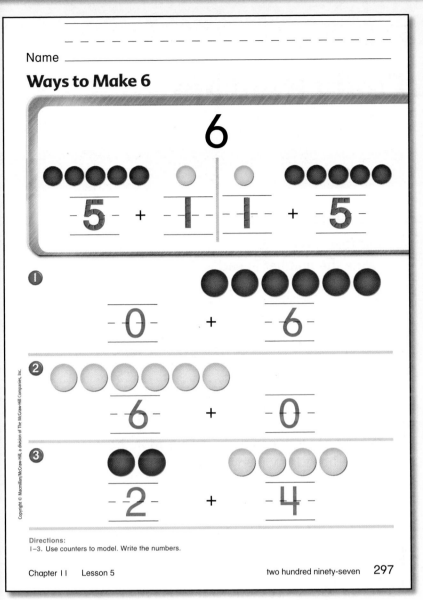

Name _____

Ways to Make 6

6

5 + | | + 5

1
0 + 6

2
6 + 0

3
2 + 4

Directions:
1–3. Use counters to model. Write the numbers.

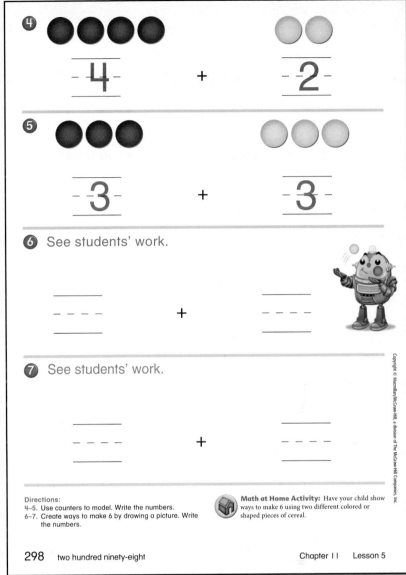

4
4 + 2

5
3 + 3

6 See students' work.

_____ + _____

7 See students' work.

_____ + _____

Directions:
4–5. Use counters to model. Write the numbers.
6–7. Create ways to make 6 by drawing a picture. Write the numbers.

Math at Home Activity: Have your child show ways to make 6 using two different colored or shaped pieces of cereal.

3 Practice

Guided Practice

- Direct students to p. 297.
- Have students identify how many counters are in each group in Exercise 1.
- Have them write the numbers below the counters.
- Ask students to identify how many counters there are in all.
- Repeat the activity with Exercises 2 and 3.

Independent Practice

Have students turn to p. 298 and work independently on the exercises.

4 Assess

Formative Assessment

- Have students string together four attribute buttons. **How many more buttons do you need to have six in all?**
- Repeat the activity with other combinations that make six.

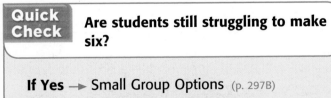

Quick Check   **Are students still struggling to make six?**

If Yes → Small Group Options (p. 297B)
If No → Independent Work Options (p. 297B)
          CRM Skills Practice Worksheet (p. 23)
          CRM Enrich Worksheet (p. 25)

Lesson 11-5 Ways to Make 6   **298**

Ways to Make 7

Lesson Planner _____

Objective

Students will use concrete objects and pictures to show different ways to make 7.

Review Vocabulary

seven

Resources

Materials: jacks, double-six dominoes, paper, pencils
Manipulatives: pattern blocks, two-colored counters, color tiles
Literature Connection: *Quack and Count* by Keith Baker
Teacher Technology
 💿 TeacherWorks

Daily Routine _____

Use these suggestions before beginning the lesson on p. 299.

5-Minute Check

(Reviews Lesson 11-5)

Write the number in each group and tell how many in all.

Problem of the Day 📖

A boat has two people in it. Four more people get in the boat. How many people in all are in the boat? 6

LINE UP Have students roll a number cube. Roll a number cube and call out the number. Have students line up if both numbers make 7. Repeat until all are in line.

▷ Review Math Vocabulary

- Have four students hold hands to form a circle.
- **How many more students need to join to make seven?** 3
- Ask three students to join the circle. Have students repeat that when three joins four, there are seven in all.
- Repeat the activity with other combinations that make seven, such as 0 + 7, 1 + 6, 2 + 5, 4 + 3, and so on.

Differentiated Instruction

Small Group Options

 1 **Gifted and Talented** **AL** LOGICAL

Materials: paper, pencils, number cube

- Each pair of students will need a piece of paper, a pencil and a number cube.
- Each student will take turns rolling the cube.
- Once the cube stops on a number, the students decide how many they need to add to the number to get to seven.
- Each partner should take three turns each solving to 7.

 2 **English Language Learners** **ELL** AUDITORY/VISUAL

Materials: overhead counters
Core Vocabulary: they do, for sure, see
Common Use Verb: make

Talk Math This strategy vocalizes combinations of seven.
- Sing and model to the tune of "Mr. Golden Sun."
  Oh, Mr. Sum, Sum, seven can be fun. Please make seven with me. (*chorus)
  Oh, Mr. Sum, Sum, seven can be fun. How many do you see?
  I see 5 and I see 2. These 2 numbers make 7, they do. (*)
  I see 3 and I see 4. These 2 numbers make 7, for sure. (*)
  I see 6 and I see 1. These 2 numbers make 7, its fun! (*)

Independent Work Options

1 **Early Finishers** **AL** **OL** KINESTHETIC

Materials: construction paper, stickers

- Have students fold a sheet of paper in half and write 7 at the top.
- Have them choose 7 stickers.
- Tell them to put some stickers on one side of the paper, and the rest on the other side.
- Have them write the number of stickers on each side with a plus sign in the middle.
- **How did you make seven?** Sample answer: 6 + 1 is 7.

2 **Student Technology**

Math Online ▷ macmillanmh.com

3 **Option 3 Learning Station: Science** (p. 279H)

Direct students to the Science Learning Station for opportunities to explore and extend the lesson concept.

Leveled Lesson Resources

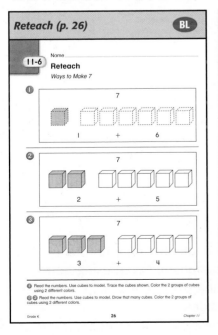

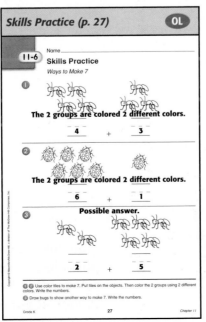

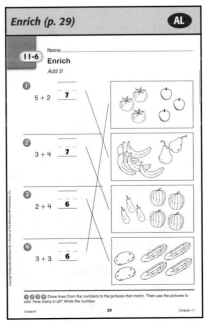

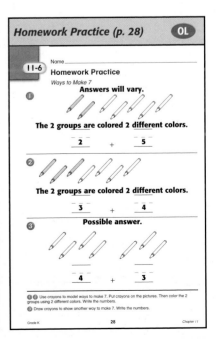

① Introduce

ⓒircle Time

Activity Choice 1 • Literature

Quack and Count
by Keith Baker

- Reread the book to students.
- Emphasize pages showing illustrations of ducks jumping into the pond to join the swimming ducks.
- Have students work in groups. Ask them to use color tiles or another manipulative to show you various ways to make **seven**.
- Discuss with the class how the illustrations in the book helped them devise ways to make seven.

Activity Choice 2 • Hands-On

Materials: pattern blocks

- Have each student create a picture using seven pattern blocks of two different shapes.
- Have students describe what their picture is and how they made it.
- **How did you make seven?** Sample answer: 3 + 4 is 7
- Have students form pairs and repeat the activity. Have partners check each other's work.

② Teach

- Direct students to the top of p. 299.
- Discuss the game of jacks. Pass jacks around for students to see.
- Have students identify the number of jacks in each set.
- Have them write the number in each set below it.
- **How did you make seven?** 3 + 4 is 7
- Repeat the activity for the second example.

ⒷⓁ Alternate Teaching Strategy

If students have trouble with making 7 . . .

Then use one of these reteach options.

1 🖳 **Daily Reteach Worksheet** (p. 26)

2 **Play a Game** Give each student seven double-six dominoes.

- Have them turn over all dominoes that add up to seven.
- Tell them that for each turned domino, they get a point.
- Say that they also get a point if they can say how to make seven from their dominoes, both turned over and not turned over.
- Explain that the first player with seven points wins.

> **⚠ COMMON ERROR!**
>
> Students may not take the time to look for all possible combinations of seven using both sides of the double-six dominoes. Remind them to look at both sides.

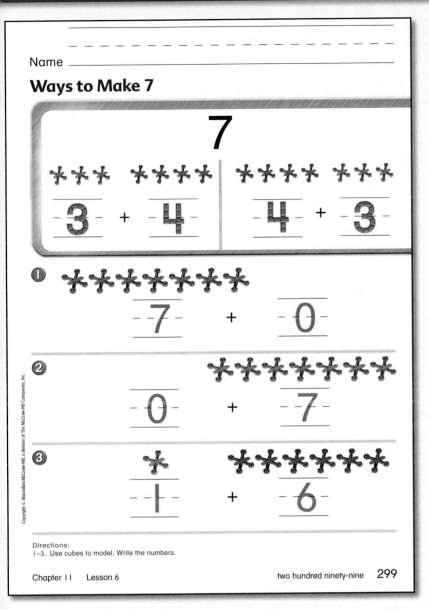

Name _____

Ways to Make 7

7

*** **** | **** ***
-3- + -4- | -4- + -3-

① ********
-7- + -0-

② ********
-0- + -7-

③ * ******
-1- + -6-

Directions:
1–3. Use cubes to model. Write the numbers.

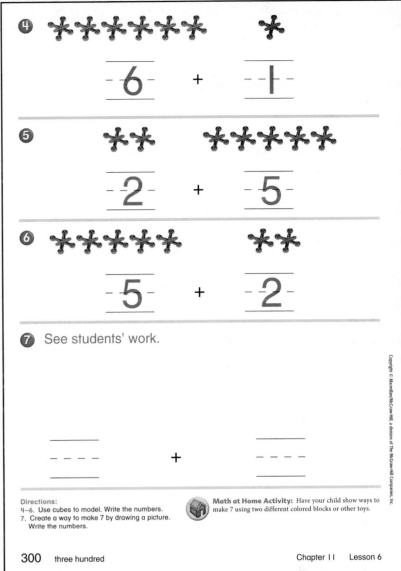

④ ****** *
-6- + -1-

⑤ ** *****
-2- + -5-

⑥ ***** **
-5- + -2-

⑦ See students' work.

_____ + _____

Directions:
4–6. Use cubes to model. Write the numbers.
7. Create a way to make 7 by drawing a picture. Write the numbers.

Math at Home Activity: Have your child show ways to make 7 using two different colored blocks or other toys.

③ Practice

Guided Practice

- Direct students to p. 299.
- Have students identify how many jacks are in each set in Exercise 1.
- Have them write the numbers below the jacks.
- Ask them to identify how many they have in all.
- Repeat the activity with Exercises 2 and 3.

Independent Practice

Have students turn to p. 300 and work independently on the exercises.

④ Assess

Formative Assessment

- Have students use a set of seven two-colored counters to show a way to make seven. **How did you make seven?** Sample answer: 2 + 5 is 7.
- **What is another way you can show how to make seven?** 5 + 2 is 7.
- Have them write both ways on paper.

Quick Check **Are students still struggling to make 7?**

If Yes → Small Group Options (p. 299B)
If No → Independent Work Options (p. 299B)
    CRM Skills Practice Worksheet (p. 27)
    CRM Enrich Worksheet (p. 29)

Lesson Planner

Objective

Students will use concrete objects and pictures to show different ways to make 8.

Review Vocabulary

count, eight

Resources

Materials: pencils, paper, drawing paper, markers

Manipulatives: connecting cubes, color tiles

Literature Connection: *Domino Addition* by Lynette Long

Teacher Technology

💿 TeacherWorks • Concepts In Motion

Daily Routine

Use these suggestions before beginning the lesson on p. 301

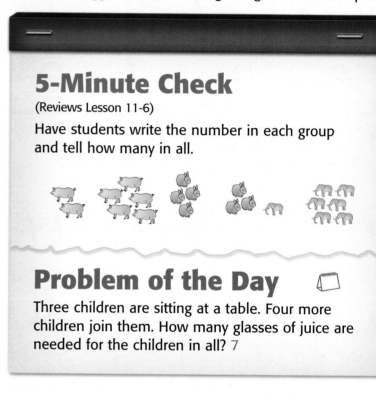

5-Minute Check

(Reviews Lesson 11-6)

Have students write the number in each group and tell how many in all.

Problem of the Day 📖

Three children are sitting at a table. Four more children join them. How many glasses of juice are needed for the children in all? 7

🔼 **LINE UP** Give half the students eight counters each. Have them share with students who did not get counters. Have each pair line up, saying how many counters each has and that they join or add to eight.

▷ Review Math Vocabulary

- Have students work in pairs.
- Give each pair **eight** two-color counters.
- Have each pair use the two-color counters to make eight.

Differentiated Instruction

Small Group Options

Option 1 **Below/Approiaching Level** BL

KINESTHETIC

Materials: large paper clips

- Have students form pairs. Give each pair a pile of paper clips. Have the first partner hook one to seven large paper clips together to form a chain.
- Have the second partner finish the chain by hooking the number of paper clips to total eight.
- Have students count each paper clip aloud to check that there are eight paper clips in all.
- Have students take turns going first.

Option 2 **English Language Learners** ELL

VISUAL

Materials: 8 fish and 1 boat for each pair, paper
Core Vocabulary: boat, fish, sea
Common Use Verb: see
Hear Math This strategy helps understand homonym vocabulary and ways to make eight.

- Model placing fish in the boat and on paper. Write "see" and "sea," pointing to your eyes, then to the correct area.
- Ask: "How many **fish** do you **see** in the **sea**? How many **fish** do you **see** in the **boat**?"

Independent Work Options

Option 1 **Early Finishers** AL OL

KINESTHETIC

Materials: craft sticks, markers, glue, construction paper

- Have students take eight craft sticks.
- Tell them to color some of the sticks red and the rest blue.
- Have them glue their craft sticks on paper to make a picture.
- Have students write how they made eight with their craft sticks.

Option 2 **Student Technology**

Math Online ⟩ macmillanmh.com

Option 3 **Learning Station: Music** (p. 279H)

Direct students to the Music Learning Station for opportunities to explore and extend the lesson concept.

Leveled Lesson Resources

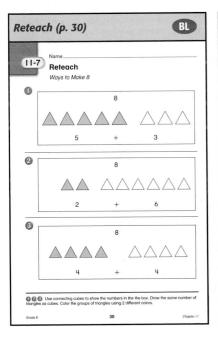

Reteach (p. 30) BL

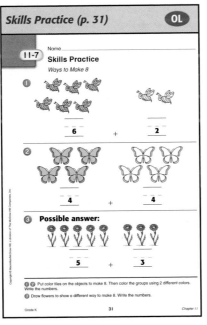

Skills Practice (p. 31) OL

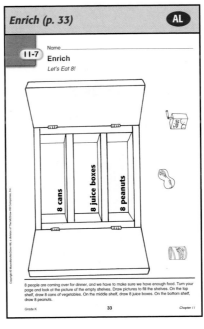

Enrich (p. 33) AL

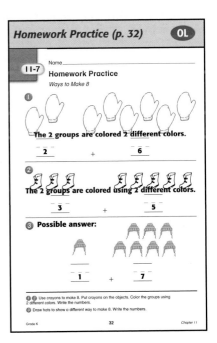

Homework Practice (p. 32) OL

① Introduce

ⓒircle Time

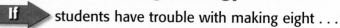

Activity Choice 1 • Literature

Domino Addition by Lynette Long

- Turn to the last page of the book, which shows all the dominoes. Ask the class to help you **count eight** dominoes.

- Pass out to each group of students sets of dominoes. There should be at least eight dominoes per group.

- Ask them to arrange dominoes to show you different ways to make eight.

Activity Choice 2 • Hands-On

Materials: connecting cubes

- Have students make trains of one color using one to seven connecting cubes.

- Have them choose another color and add cubes so that the train is eight cubes in all.

- Ask students to identify how they made eight using their trains.

- Have students form pairs. Have the first partner make a train using one to seven connecting cubes.

- Have the second partner add enough cubes so that the train is eight cubes in all.

- Have the first partner say the addition story.

- Repeat the pair activity, having pairs trade tasks.

② Teach

- Direct students to the top of p. 301.

- Have students identify the number of color tiles in each set. Have them write the number in each set below it.

- **How did you make eight?** 2 + 6 is 8.

- Repeat the activity with the second example.

BL Alternate Teaching Strategy

If ▶ students have trouble with making eight . . .

Then ▶ use one of these reteach options.

1. CRM **Daily Reteach Worksheet** (p. 30)

2. **Make Trains** Give each student eight connecting cubes.
   - Have them connect some of the cubes to make a train.
   - Have them add more cubes to the train to make eight in all.
   - Have students write how they made eight for the train on a separate sheet of paper.

⚠ COMMON ERROR!

When combining two sets, students may start counting the second group with the total from the first group. Remind them to start with the next number.

Ways to Make 8

Directions:
1-3. Use color tiles to model. Write the numbers.

Directions:
4-7. Use color tiles to model. Write the numbers.

 Math at Home Activity: Have your child show ways to make 8 using two different shapes of pasta.

---

3 Practice

Guided Practice

- Direct students to p. 301.
- Have students identify how many color tiles are in each group in Exercise 1.
- Have them write the numbers below the color tile.
- Ask students to identify how many they made in all.
- Repeat the activity with Exercises 2 and 3.

Independent Practice

Have students turn to p. 302 and work independently on the exercises.

4 Assess

Formative Assessment

- Ask students to draw a picture showing eight people sitting in chairs at a round table.
- Have them say how many boys and how many girls they drew to make eight in all.

Quick Check Are students still struggling to make eight?

If Yes → Small Group Options (p. 301B)

If No → Independent Work Options (p. 301B)
　　CRM Skills Practice Worksheet (p. 31)
　　CRM Enrich Worksheet (p. 33)

Lesson 11-7 Ways to Make 8　**302**

Ways to Make 9

Lesson Planner

Objective

Students will use concrete objects and pictures to show different ways to make 9.

Review Vocabulary

nine

Resources

Materials: paper, chart paper, markers, dominoes
Manipulatives: connecting cubes, counters, 0–5 spinner
Literature Connection: *Domino Addition* by Lynette Long
Teacher Technology
  TeacherWorks • Concepts In Motion

Daily Routine

Use these suggestions before beginning the lesson on p. 303.

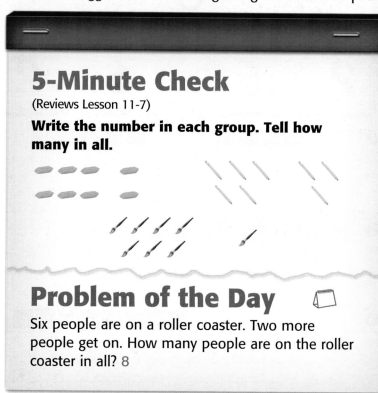

5-Minute Check
(Reviews Lesson 11-7)

Write the number in each group. Tell how many in all.

Problem of the Day

Six people are on a roller coaster. Two more people get on. How many people are on the roller coaster in all? 8

LINE UP Have students count the number of letters in their names. Ask them to join with another student to make nine letters in all. Have pairs line up. Have remaining students tell how many more they need to make nine before lining up.

Review Math Vocabulary

Materials: classroom objects, chart paper, marker

- Have students gather **nine** classroom objects that are the same.

- Have them make up and tell a story about how to make nine using their objects. Encourage them to use *in all, add,* or *join.*

- Record the ways they make nine on chart paper, such as 1 + 8, 2 + 7, 3 + 6, and so on.

Differentiated Instruction

Small Group Options

Option 1
Below/Approaching Level BL LOGICAL

Materials: nine two-colored counters, cup, paper, pencil

- Have pairs of students count out nine counters.
- Have students take turns putting all nine counters in the cup, shaking them, then tossing them out on the table.
- Have students write an addition problem from the counters by writing how many of one color plus how many of the second color equals the total of nine.
- Have students take nine turns each, duplicating any addition problems.

Option 2
English Language Learners ELL AUDITORY, VISUAL

Materials: posted song lyrics (see below)
Core Vocabulary: really fun, too, also new
Common Use Verb: can split
Talk Math This strategy uses music to model number 9.
- Post lyrics, sing, and model to the tune of "Twinkle, Twinkle Little Star."

What ways can you make or find, ways to make the number 9. Nine can split by 7 and 2, 6 and 3 will work for you. 5 and 4 is also new, 8 and 1 can make 9 too. Number 9 is really fun, now I think our song is done.

Independent Work Options

Option 1
Early Finishers AL OL SPATIAL

Materials: construction paper, markers, pre-cut paper figures, glue

- Fold a piece of paper in half horizontally to create a card. On the front write *How many*?
- Give each student a card. Tell them to choose nine of one figure.
- Have them glue some of the figures on the inside front page, then write how many are on that page.
- Have them glue the rest of the figures on the inside second page, then write how many are on that page.
- Tell them to write *9 in all* on the back.

Option 2
Student Technology

Math Online ⟩ macmillanmh.com

Option 3
Learning Station: Science (p. 279H)

Direct students to the Science Learning Station for opportunities to explore and extend the lesson concept.

Leveled Lesson Resources

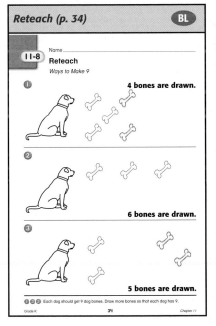

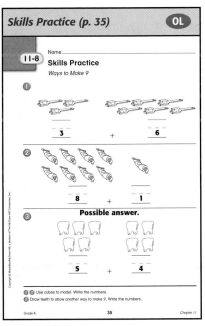

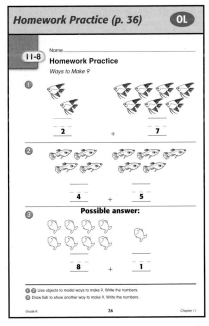

1 Introduce

Circle Time

Activity Choice 1 • Literature

Domino Addition by Lynette Long

- Turn to the last page of the book, which shows all the dominoes. Ask the class to help you count up to **nine** dominoes.

- Once again, distribute dominoes to each grouping of students. They should have at least nine dominoes per group.

- Ask them to arrange dominoes to show you different ways to make eight and nine.

- Afterward, call nine volunteers up to the front of the class. Have the other students pair them off in order to show different ways to demonstrate making nine.

- To review the chapter, repeat this activity. Use a set number of volunteers to show ways to make four, five, six, seven, eight, and nine.

Activity Choice 2 • Hands-On

Materials: paper, connecting cubes, chart paper, markers

- Fold a piece of paper in half.

- Have students form pairs. Give each pair a piece of folded paper, nine connecting cubes, a sheet of chart paper, and a marker.

- Have pairs make two towers from their cubes and lay each tower on half of the paper.

- **How did you make nine?** Sample answer: 3 + 6 is 9.

- Have them record their addition story on chart paper.

- Have pairs repeat the activity, finding a new way to make nine.

2 Teach

- Direct students to the top of p. 303.
- Have students identify the number of marbles in each set.
- Have students write the number in each set below it.
- **How did you make nine?** 3 + 6 is 9.
- Repeat the activity for the second example.

BL Alternate Teaching Strategy

If students have trouble with making 9 . . .

Then use one of these reteach options.

1 CRM **Daily Reteach Worksheet** (p. 34)

2 **Use Counters and Spinners** Give each student 9 counters.

- Have each student spin a 0–5 spinner to get a number 0–5.

- Have students form a group of that number with their counters. Tell them to use the remaining counters to make a second group.

- **How did you make nine?** Sample answer: 4 + 5

- Repeat the activity as time permits.

! COMMON ERROR!

Students may struggle with different ways to make nine. Point out that 3 + 6 and 6 + 3 both make 9, so they only have to remember one pair of numbers for two ways.

Ways to Make 9

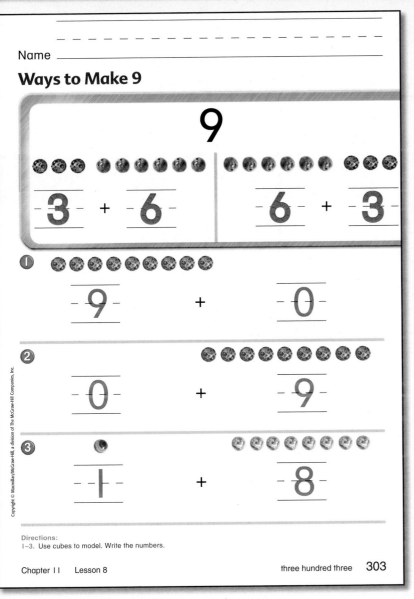

9

3 + 6   6 + 3

① 9 + 0

② 0 + 9

③ 1 + 8

Directions:
1–3. Use cubes to model. Write the numbers.

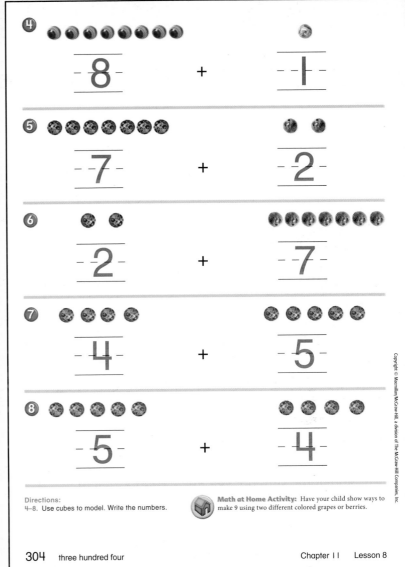

④ 8 + 1

⑤ 7 + 2

⑥ 2 + 7

⑦ 4 + 5

⑧ 5 + 4

Directions:
4–8. Use cubes to model. Write the numbers.

Math at Home Activity: Have your child show ways to make 9 using two different colored grapes or berries.

③ Practice

Guided Practice

- Direct students to p. 303.
- Have them identify how many marbles are in each set in Exercise 1.
- Have them write the numbers below the marbles.
- Ask them to identify how many they made in all.
- Repeat the activity with Exercises 2 and 3.

Independent Practice

Have students turn to p. 304 and work independently on the exercises.

④ Assess

Formative Assessment

- **Which picture shows how to make nine?** 6 balloons and 3 balloons

Quick Check   Are students still struggling to make nine?

If Yes → Small Group Options (p. 303B)

If No → Independent Work Options (p. 303B)

CRM Skills Practice Worksheet (p. 35)

CRM Enrich Worksheet (p. 37)

Lesson 11-8 Ways to Make 9   **304**

Problem-Solving Strategy
Act It Out

Lesson Planner

Objective

Use concrete objects to solve addition problems.

Resources

Materials: number strips, string
Manipulatives: connecting cubes, attribute buttons
Literature Connection: *Little Quack*
  by Lauren Thompson
Teacher Technology
  ⊙ TeacherWorks
  📖 **Real-World Problem Solving Library**
  Math and Social Studies: *Animals on the Farm*
  Use these leveled readers to reinforce and extend
  problem-solving skills and strategies.
  Leveled for:
  OL On Level
  ELL Sheltered English
  SP Spanish

For additional support, see Real-World Problem
Solving Teacher Guide.

*On-leveled title is available in
classroom Big Book.*

Daily Routine

Use these suggestions before beginning the lesson on p. 305.

5-Minute Check

(Reviews Lesson 11-8)
Write number sentences showing two different
ways to make nine. Sample answers: 4 + 5, 3 + 6

Problem of the Day 📖

A set of three students were playing soccer. Four
more students joined them. How many more
would they need to have nine players? They would
need two more.

LINE UP Have six students get in line. Ask how many
more you would need to make nine. Have three
students join them. Repeat for other combinations of nine
until all students are in line.

Differentiated Instruction

Small Group Options

Option 1
Gifted and Talented (AL)   KINESTHETIC

- Have students in small groups create and model addition stories with their fingers.
- Each student in the group thinks of an addition story that can be shown with 10 fingers. Without talking, the student shows the other students in the group the addition story, using both hands. Another student in the group writes the numbers in the addition story on paper, and a third student writes the answer.
- Have students check each other's work and then switch roles and repeat the activity.

Option 2
English Language Learners (ELL)   SOCIAL, LINGUISTIC

Materials: camera
Core Vocabulary: arms, legs, eyes
Common Use Verb: figure out

See Math This strategy helps students act out story problems.
- Prompt students to form a group and figure out how many arms there are.
- Write a story problem as the group acts out how they counted their arms. Repeat with legs and eyes.

Independent Work Options

Option 1
Early Finishers (OL) (AL)   KINESTHETIC

Materials: magazines, scissors, glue, construction paper, crayons
- Have students cut out pictures that have multiple objects, up to 9.
- Glue the pictures onto construction paper.
- Have the students write a number sentence that matches the picture.

Option 2
Student Technology

Math Online macmillanmh.com

Option 3
Learning Station: Reading (p. 279G)

Direct students to the Reading Learning Station for opportunities to explore and extend the lesson concept.

Leveled Lesson Resources

Reteach (pp. 38–39) (BL)

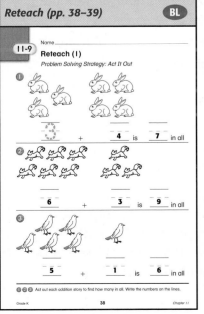

Skills Practice (p. 40) (OL)

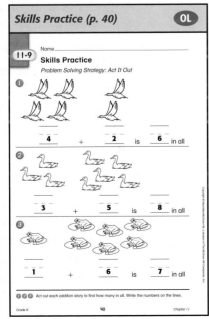

Enrich (p. 42) (AL)

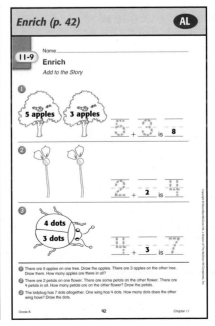

Homework Practice (p. 41) (OL)

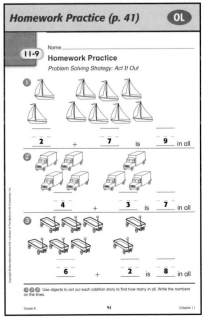

① Introduce

Circle Time

Activity Choice 1 • Literature

Little Quack by Lauren Thompson

Materials: strips that match the purple strips in the book

- Select six students (Mama Duck and five ducklings) to act out the story.
- Give sets of the remaining students number strips replicating the ones in the book (duck and duck is two).
- As the book is read, the actors demonstrate the story, and the other students hold up the correct number strip to match the story action.
- Quickly compare the strips to the actors and to the story.
- Continue "quack-u-lating" to five.

Activity Choice 2 • Hands-On

Materials: connecting cubes

- Have each student pick up five cubes of one color and four of another color.
- **How many cubes do you have in all?** nine
- After each problem, write on the chalkboard "___ and ___ is ___ in all," filling in the blanks.
- Have each student pick up three cubes.
- **If you want to have eight cubes in all, how many more do you need?** five more
- Continue with similar problems for totals up to nine.

② Teach

Understand Review what students know and what they need to find for each problem.

Plan Have students discuss their strategy for solving the problems.

Solve Guide students to act it out to solve the problems. Have students physically act out the addition problems in order to find the answers.

Check Have students look back at the problem to be sure that the answers fit what they already know about the problem.

Read the following stories aloud. Use student volunteers to act out each story.

1. **Three soldiers guard the castle. Five more soldiers join them. How many soldiers are guarding the castle in all?** eight

2. **Two alligator are in the water. Three more alligators get in the water. How many alligators are in the water?** five

3. **The king owns five hats. He buys four more. How many hats does he have in all?** nine

BL Alternate Teaching Strategy

If students have trouble solving addition problems . . .

Then use one of these reteach options.

1 CRM **Daily Reteach Worksheet** (pp. 38–39)

2 **Add with Attribute Buttons** Give the students an addition story about buttons.
- Have students string the first number of attribute buttons together.
- Next have them add the next number of buttons.
- Have them count the total to get the answer to the addition story.

> **! COMMON ERROR!**
>
> When using manipulatives to represent people or objects, students may forget what each manipulative represents. Students can choose manipulatives that correlate somehow to what they represent or make a key to help them remember.

Name _____

Problem-Solving Strategy

Act It Out

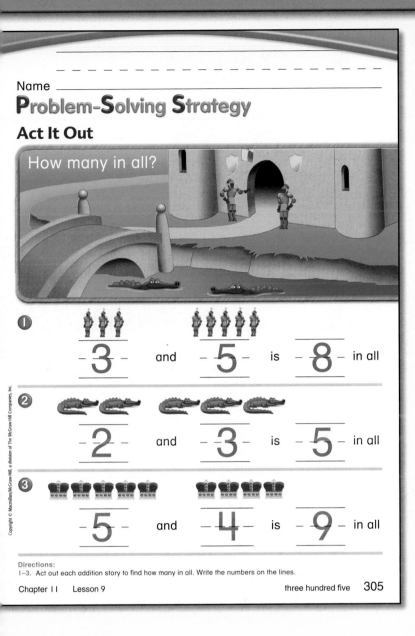

How many in all?

① __3__ and __5__ is __8__ in all

② __2__ and __3__ is __5__ in all

③ __5__ and __4__ is __9__ in all

Directions:
1–3. Act out each addition story to find how many in all. Write the numbers on the lines.

How many in all?

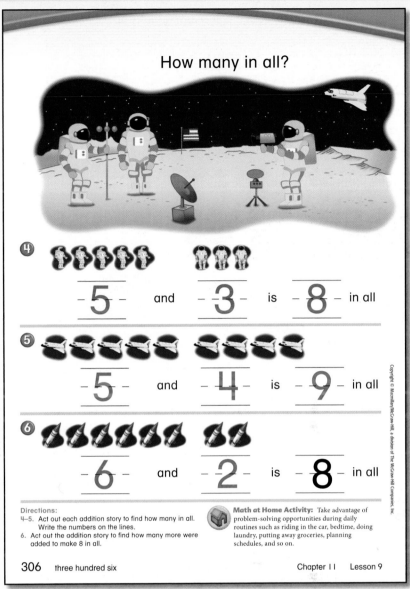

④ __5__ and __3__ is __8__ in all

⑤ __5__ and __4__ is __9__ in all

⑥ __6__ and __2__ is __8__ in all

Directions:
4–5. Act out each addition story to find how many in all.
Write the numbers on the lines.
6. Act out the addition story to find how many more were added to make 8 in all.

Math at Home Activity: Take advantage of problem-solving opportunities during daily routines such as riding in the car, bedtime, doing laundry, putting away groceries, planning schedules, and so on.

---

3 Practice

Guided Practice

Direct students to p 305. Use connecting cubes to model Exercises 1, 2, and 3 as stories from p. 305 are read again. Write answers on the line.

Independent Practice

Have students turn to p. 306 and work independently on the exercises. You will need to read the stories to them.

4. **Five astronauts walked on the moon. Three more walked with them. How many walked in all?** 8
5. **Five space shuttles zoomed through the air. Four more zoomed by. How many in all?** 9
6. **Six rockets land on a planet. More rockets land. Now there are eight rockets. How many more landed?** 2

Ask students to share another approach/strategy that could be used and how it might be used.

4 Assess

Formative Assessment

Read the following story to students. Have students act out the story below and write numbers to show how many in all.

• **Two students went to a party. Seven more students also went. How many students went to the party in all?** 9

Quick Check	**Are students still struggling with acting out addition problems?**

If Yes → Small Group Options (p. 305B)

If No → Independent Work Options (p. 305B)
   CRM Skills Practice Worksheet (p. 40)
   CRM Enrich Worksheet (p. 42)

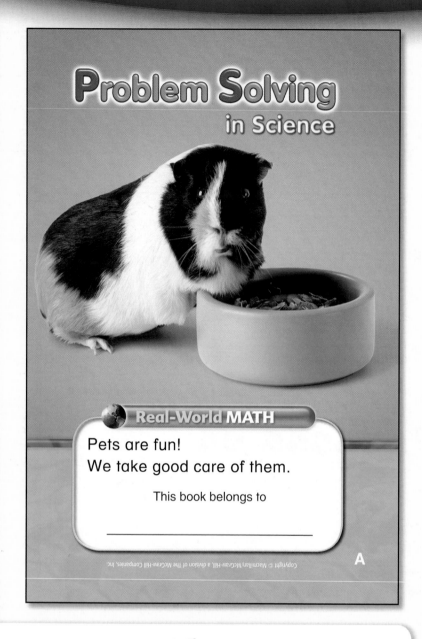

Problem Solving in Science

Real-World MATH

Pets are fun!
We take good care of them.

This book belongs to

_____

A

How many kittens are there in all?

__5__ kittens

B

Lesson Planner

Objective
Make calculations by counting.

National Standard
Students learn about organisms and environments.

Activate Prior Knowledge
Before you turn students' attention to the pages, discuss animals.

- **Who can name some animals?** Sample answers: horses, cows, frogs, rabbits
- **Which animals can be pets?** Sample answers: cats, dogs, hamsters
- **What are some things we can do with our pets?** Sample answers: play, cuddle, walk our pet

How many fish are there total?
___10___ fish

C

How many dogs are there altogether?
___3___ dogs

D

Create the Book

Guide students to create their book.

- Have them fold the page in half.
- Ask them to write their name on page A.
- Explain that page A is the front cover and page D is the back cover. If necessary, have them practice flipping through the book in order.
- Guide them in reading the information and word problems on each of the pages.

Use the Student Pages

Page B Use the picture to help students create an addition sentence. For example, Joey is holding one kitten with three more in the basket. There are four kittens because three and one is four.

Page C Have students create an addition story by, joining the number of fish in the bowl with the number of fish in the tank.

Page D Have students answer how many in all and then ask students to tell how many if three more dogs joined them.

WRITING IN ►MATH Choose an animal. Draw it two times. Choose another animal. Draw it four times. How many animals did you draw in all? Write the number.

 **Dinah Zike's Foldables**

Use these lesson suggestions for incorporating the Foldables during the chapter.

Lesson 11-4 On the third page of the addition journal, use pictures to show different ways to add numbers to make four and five.

Lessons 11-8 On the remaining pages of the addition journal, use pictures of objects that can be taped or glued into the journal to show different ways to add numbers to make nine.

Chapter 11 Project

Collections Poster

Lead a discussion on the results of the completed chapter project with the class.

Vocabulary Review

Review chapter vocabulary using one of the following options.

- **Visual Vocabulary Card** (1)
- **eGlossary** at macmillanmh.com

Data-Driven Decision Making

Based on the results of the Chapter Review/Test, use the following to review concepts that continue to present students with problems.

Exercises	State/Local Standards	What's the Math?	Error Analysis	Resources for Review
1 Lesson 11-6		Use concrete objects to determine the answers to addition problems for numbers up to 7.	Does not write the number that shows the total. Writes wrong numbers.	[CRM] Chapter 11 Resource Masters (Reteach Worksheets) Math Online Concepts in Motion Math Adventures
2–3 Lesson 11-4		Use concrete objects to determine the answers to addition problems for numbers up to 4 or 5.	Writes numbers in wrong spots. Writes wrong numbers.	
4 Lesson 11-8		Use concrete objects to determine the answers to addition problems for numbers up to 9.	Does not draw correct number of objects. Writes wrong numbers for objects drawn.	

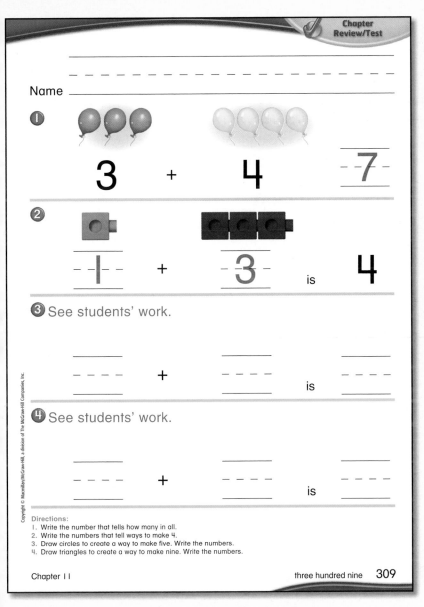

Name _____

① **3** + **4** = **7**

② **1** + **3** is **4**

③ See students' work.

____ + ____ is ____

④ See students' work.

____ + ____ is ____

Directions:
1. Write the number that tells how many in all.
2. Write the numbers that tell ways to make 4.
3. Draw circles to create a way to make five. Write the numbers.
4. Draw triangles to create a way to make nine. Write the numbers.

Chapter 11   three hundred nine 309

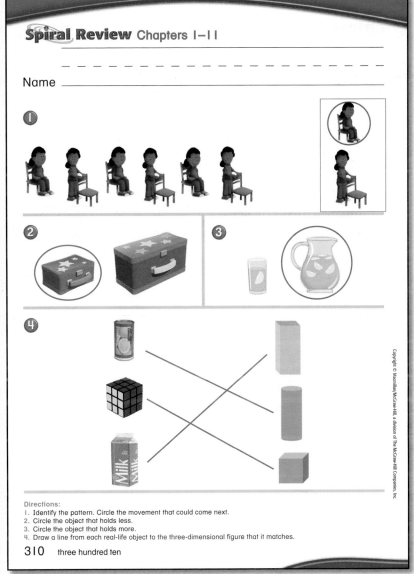

Spiral Review Chapters 1–11

Name _____

①

②   ③

④

Directions:
1. Identify the pattern. Circle the movement that could come next.
2. Circle the object that holds less.
3. Circle the object that holds more.
4. Draw a line from each real-life object to the three-dimensional figure that it matches.

310   three hundred ten

Summative Assessment

Use these alternate leveled chapter tests to differentiate assessment for the specific needs of your students.

Leveled Chapter 11 Tests			
Form	Type	Level	Pages
1	Multiple Choice	BL	52–53
2A	Multiple Choice	OL	54–55
2C	Multiple Choice	OL	56–57
2D	Free Response	AL	58–59

BL = below/approaching grade level
OL = on grade level
AL = above/beyond grade level

Spiral Review

Review Chapters 1 to 11

Review and assess mastery of skills and concepts from previous chapters.

Resources for Review

Based on student results, refer to these lessons for remediation:

- **Exercise 1: Lesson 3-8** (p. 87)
- **Exercises 2–3: Lesson 7-5** (p. 189)
- **Exercise 4: Lesson 10-3** (p. 259)

Test Practice

Chapters 1–11

Formative Assessment

- You can use Student Edition pp. 311–312 to benchmark student progress.

- Additional practice pages can be found in Chapter 11 Resource Masters.

CRM **Chapter 11 Resource Masters**
  Cumulative Test Practice

- Multiple Choice format (pp. 52–57)
- Free Response format (pp. 58–59)

 Create additional practice worksheets or tests.

Test-Taking Tips

For the Teacher

- Make sure each student understands the directions before beginning the test.

For the Student

- Be sure to have an extra pencil ready in case your lead breaks.

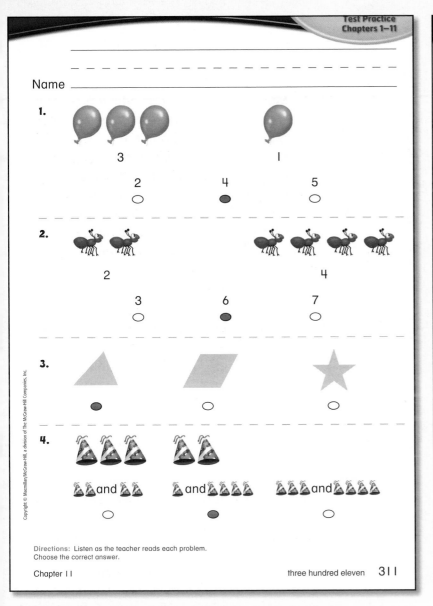

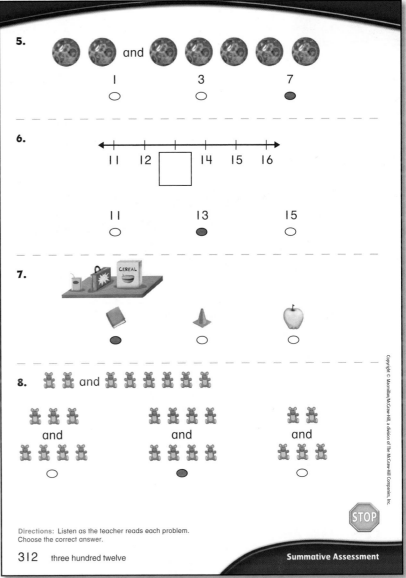

Directions: Listen as the teacher reads each problem. Choose the correct answer.

Chapter 11   three hundred eleven   311

312   three hundred twelve

Directions: Listen as the teacher reads each problem. Choose the correct answer.

Summative Assessment

Test Directions for Teachers

Read the following directions to students before they begin. Then read each question followed by a pause to allow students time to work and choose an answer. The first test item can be worked as a class example.

- **Write your name at the top of the page.**
- **I am going to read each question to you. Listen carefully to the entire question before you choose an answer.**

1. Listen to the story. Molly has 3 balloons. Fran gives Molly 1 balloon. How many balloons in all? Mark the number that tells how many in all.

2. Listen to the story. Hal saw 2 ants in one group on the floor. Then Hal saw 4 ants in another group on the floor. How many ants in all? Mark the number that tells how many ants in all.

3. Look at the shapes. Find the shape that has exactly 3 sides. Mark the shape that has exactly 3 sides.

4. Look at the group of 3 party hats and the group of 2 party hats. Find the group of party hats that is another way to show 5 party hats. Mark the group that shows 5 party hats.

- **Turn the page over.**

5. Listen to the story. Ben has 2 marbles. He finds 5 more marbles. Mark the group that shows the number of marbles Ben has now.

6. Look at the number line. Count on to find the missing number. Mark the number that is missing.

7. Look at the objects on the table. Now look at the objects below the table. Mark the object that has the same shape as the objects on the table.

8. Look at the group of 2 bears and 6 bears. Find the group of bears that is another way to show 8 bears. Mark the group that shows 8 bears.

Chapter Overview

Chapter-at-a-Glance

In Chapter 12, the emphasis is on using concrete objects to solve problems using subtraction. Subtraction will be seen as finding the difference, taking away, or what is left.

Lesson	Math Objective	State/Local Standards
12-1 Subtraction Stories (pp. 317–320)	Model subtraction as taking away from or separating sets of objects.	
12-2 Use Objects to Subtract (pp. 321–322)	Use concrete objects to solve subtraction problems.	
12-3 Subtraction Sign (pp. 323–324)	Use the minus sign(−) to show subtraction.	
12-4 Take Away from 4 and 5 (pp. 325–328)	Use concrete objects and pictures to show ways to subtract from 4 and 5.	
12-5 Take Away from 6 (pp. 331–332)	Use concrete objects and pictures to show ways to subtract from 6.	
12-6 Take Away from 7 (pp. 333–334)	Use concrete objects and pictures to show ways to subtract from 7.	
12-7 Take Away from 8 (pp. 335–336)	Use concrete objects and pictures to show ways to subtract from 8.	
12-8 Take Away from 9 (pp. 337–338)	Use concrete objects and pictures to show ways to subtract from 9.	
12-9 Problem Solving Strategy: Guess and Check (pp. 339–340)	Use the strategy of guess and check to subtract from 7, 8, and 9.	
12-10 Equal Sign (pp. 341–342)	Use the equal sign (=) in addition and subtraction sentences.	

Model Subtraction

BIG Idea Much like the previous addition chapter, students use concrete objects to model and understand subtraction in this chapter. It is essential for students to have extensive experience modeling subtraction before they enter first grade. This work lays the foundation for students to begin using more abstract concepts involving numbers and symbols. In this chapter, students learn to subtract from numbers as big as nine. Phrases such as "take away" and "how many are left" will become commonplace within the classroom.

Algebra Students prepare for Algebra through mathematical sentences. Students discover that there are many ways to subtract numbers from totals to 10.

Lessons 12-4, 12-5, 12-6, 12-7, 12-8

GK-FP1 *Number and Operations:* **Representing, comparing, and ordering whole numbers and joining and separating sets**

Children use numbers, including written numerals, to represent quantities and to solve quantitative problems, such as counting objects in a set, creating a set with a given number of objects, comparing and ordering sets or numerals by using both cardinal and ordinal meanings, and modeling simple joining and separating situations with objects. They choose, combine, and apply effective strategies for answering quantitative questions, including quickly recognizing the number in a small set, counting and producing sets of given sizes, counting the number in combined sets, and counting backward.

Skills Trace
Vertical Alignment

PreKindergarten
During PreK, students learned to:

- Compare the numbers of concrete objects using language (e.g., "same" or "equal," "one more," "more than," or "less than").
- Recognize and describe the concept of zero (meaning there are none).

Kindergarten
During this chapter, students learn to:

- Model subtraction as taking away and finding the difference or what is left.
- Use concrete objects to solve subtraction problems.
- Use concrete objects to show different ways to subtract from numbers to nine.

First Grade
In first grade, students will learn to:

- Model and solve subtraction problems.
- Write subtraction sentences.
- Use strategies and skills to solve problems.
- Use subtraction strategies to 20.

Backmapping and Vertical Alignment
McGraw-Hill's *Math Connects* program was conceived and developed with the final results in mind: student success in Algebra 1 and beyond. The authors, using the **NCTM Focal Points and Focal Connections** as their guide, developed this brand new series by backmapping from Algebra 1 concepts, and vertically aligning the topics so that they build upon prior skills and concepts and serve as a foundation for future topics.

Math Vocabulary

The following math vocabulary words for Chapter 12 are listed in the glossary of the *Student Edition*. You can find interactive definitions in 13 languages in the *eGlossary* at macmillanmh.com.

equal sign = (p. 341)

$$4 + 1 = 5$$
↑
equals

minus sign − (p. 323)

$$5 - 2 = 3$$
↑
minus

subtract the concept of taking away (p. 317)

take away the concept of subtracting from a set (p. 317)

are left the amount that is remaining after a take away problem (p. 317)

Visual Vocabulary Cards Use Visual Vocabulary Card 42 to introduce and reinforce that vocabulary in this chapter. (The Define/Example/Ask routine is printed on the back of each card.)

subtract

Chapter Planner

Suggested Pacing		
Instruction	Review and Assessment	TOTAL
10 days	2 days	**12 days**

Diagnostic Assessment
Are You Ready? (p. 294)

	Lesson 12-1 Pacing: 1 day	**Lesson 12-2** Pacing: 1 day	**Lesson 12-3** Pacing: 1 day
Lesson/Objective	**Subtraction Stories** (pp. 317–320) **Objective:** Model subtraction as taking away from or separating sets of objects.	**Use Objects to Subtract** (pp. 321–322) **Objective:** Use concrete objects to solve subtraction problems.	**Subtraction Sign** (pp. 323–324) **Objective:** Use the minus sign (–) to show subtraction.
State/Local Standards			
Math Vocabulary	**take away, are left, subtract**		**minus sign**
Lesson Resources	**Materials** egg carton **Manipulatives** color tiles, connecting cubes, pattern blocks **Other Resources** CRM Leveled Worksheets (pp. 6–9) Daily Reteach	**Materials** buttons, paper, pencils, crayons **Manipulatives** two-colored counters, color tiles, connecting cubes **Other Resources** CRM Leveled Worksheets (pp. 10–13) Daily Reteach Problem of the Day	**Materials** paper, crayons **Manipulatives** connecting cubes **Other Resources** CRM Leveled Worksheets (pp. 14–17) Daily Reteach Problem of the Day
Technology Math Online	♪ Math Song Track 7 Math Adventures	Math Adventures Concepts in Motion	Math Adventures
Reaching All Learners	English Learners, p. 317B **ELL** Below Level, p. 317B **BL** Early Finishers, p. 317B **OL** **AL**	English Learners, p. 321B **ELL** Below Level, p. 321B **BL** Early Finishers, p. 321B **OL** **AL**	English Learners, p. 323B **ELL** Below Level, p. 323B **BL** Early Finishers, p. 323B **OL** **AL**
Alternate Lesson	*Math Their Way,* pp. 193–194 *IMPACT Mathematics:* Unit D	*Math Their Way,* pp. 193–194 *IMPACT Mathematics:* Unit D	*Math Their Way,* p. 238

KEY

BL Below/Approaching Level	**OL** On Level	**AL** Above/Beyond Level	**ELL** English Learners
SE Student Edition	**TE** Teacher Edition	**CRM** Chapter 1 Resource Masters	CD-Rom
Transparency	Flip Chart	Real-World Problem Solving Library	

Lesson 12-4 Pacing: 1 day	**Lesson 12-5** Pacing: 1 day	**Lesson 12-6** Pacing: 1 day	**Lesson/ Objective**
Take Away from 4 and 5 (pp. 325–328) **Objective:** Use concrete objects and pictures to show ways to subtract from 4 and 5.	**Take Away from 6** (pp. 331–332) **Objective:** Use concrete objects and pictures to show ways to subtract from 6.	**Take Away from 7** (pp. 333–334) **Objective:** Use concrete objects and pictures to show ways to subtract from 7.	
			State/Local Standards
			Math Vocabulary
Materials 0–5 number line made from plastic place mats **Manipulatives** color tiles, connecting cubes **Other Resources** CRM Leveled Worksheets (pp. 18–21) Daily Reteach Problem of the Day	**Materials** bananas, crayons, pencils, drawing paper, blocks, 5" x 8" cards **Manipulatives** yellow connecting cubes, 0–5 number cube, two-colored counters **Other Resources** CRM Leveled Worksheets (pp. 22–25) Daily Reteach Problem of the Day	**Materials** cups, dried beans, pencils, string **Manipulatives** color tiles, attribute buttons **Other Resources** CRM Leveled Worksheets (pp. 26–29) Daily Reteach Problem of the Day	**Lesson Resources**
Math Adventures Concepts in Motion	Math Adventures	Math Adventures	**Technology** Math Online
English Learners, p. 325B ELL Gifted and Talented, p. 325B AL Early Finishers, p. 325B OL AL	English Learners, p. 331B ELL Below Level, p. 331B BL Early Finishers, p. 331B OL AL	English Learners, p. 333B ELL Gifted and Talented, p. 333B AL Early Finishers, p. 333B OL AL	**Reaching All Learners**
			Alternate Lesson

Formative Assessment
Mid-Chapter Check (p. 329)

Game Time: How Many Are Left? (p. 330)

	Lesson 12-7 Pacing: 1 day	**Lesson 12-8** Pacing: 1 day	**Lesson 12-9** Pacing: 1 day
Lesson/ Objective	**Take Away from 8** (pp. 335–336) **Objective:** Use concrete objects and pictures to show ways to subtract from 8.	**Take Away from 9** (pp. 337–338) **Objective:** Use concrete objects and pictures to show ways to subtract from 9.	**Problem Solving Strategy: Guess and Check** (pp. 339–340) **Objective:** Use the strategy of guess and check to subtract from 7, 8, and 9.
State/Local Standards			
Math Vocabulary			
Lesson Resources	**Materials** dry cereal Os, string, pencils, drawing paper, crayons **Manipulatives** color tiles , connecting cubes **Other Resources** CRM Leveled Worksheets (pp. 30–33) 📖 Daily Reteach 🗂 Problem of the Day	**Materials** egg cartons, pencils, crayons, plastic bag, 0–9 spinner **Manipulatives** connecting cubes, two-color counters, number cubes, connecting cubes **Other Resources** CRM Leveled Worksheets (pp. 34–37) 📖 Daily Reteach 🗂 Problem of the Day	**Materials** pencils, poster paper, markers, sticky notes **Manipulatives** connecting cubes, two-color counters **Other Resources** CRM Leveled Worksheets (pp. 38–42) 📖 Daily Reteach 🗂 Problem of the Day 📖 *Pets Find a Home*
Technology Math Online	🌐 Math Adventures	🌐 Math Adventures	
Reaching All Learners	English Learners, p. 335B ELL Gifted and Talented, p. 335B BL Early Finishers, p. 335B OL AL	English Learners, p. 337B ELL Gifted and Talented, p. 337B AL Early Finishers, p. 337B OL AL	English Learners, p. 339B ELL Below Level, p. 339B BL Early Finishers, p. 339B OL AL
Alternate Lesson		*Math Their Way*, pp. 181–182	

Lesson 12-10

Equal Sign
(pp. 341–342)

Objective: Use equal sign (=) in addition and subtraction sentences.

equal sign (=)

Materials
index cards

Manipulatives
connecting cubes, two-colored counters, color tiles

Other Resources
 Leveled Worksheets (pp. 43–46)
Daily Reteach
Problem of the Day

English Learners, p. 341B **ELL**
Below Level, p. 341B **BL**
Early Finishers, p. 341B **OL** **AL**

Math Their Way, p. 237
IMPACT Mathematics: Unit D

Problem Solving: Science
(p. 343)

Summative Assessment
• Chapter Review/Test (p. 345)
• Test Practice (p. 347)

Assessment Options

Diagnostic Assessment
SE *Option 1:* Are You Ready? (p. 314)
   Option 2: Online Quiz (macmillanmh.com)
CRM *Option 3:* Diagnostic Test (p. 48)

Formative Assessment
TE Alternate Teaching Strategies (every lesson)
TE Writing in Math (every lesson)
TE Line Up (every lesson)
SE Mid-Chapter Check (p. 329)
CRM Mid-Chapter Test (p. 49)

Summative Assessment
SE Chapter Review/Test (p. 345)
SE Test Practice (p. 347)
CRM Leveled Chapter Tests (pp. 54–61)
CRM Cumulative Test Practice (p. 62)
CRM Listening Assessment (pp. 52–53)
CRM Oral Assessment (pp. 50–51)
ExamView® Assessment Suite
Advance Tracker

McGraw Hill Professional Development

Targeted professional development has been articulated throughout **McGraw-Hill's *Connects*** program. The **McGraw-Hill Professional Development Video Library** provides short videos that support the **NCTM Focal Points and Focal Connections**. For more information, visit macmillanmh.com.

Model Lessons   Instructional Strategies

CHAPTER 12

Learning Stations
Cross-Curricular Links

---

individual | SPATIAL

Art

Making Patterns

- Start with a row of nine. Color 8 blue.
- Color the rest red.
- In the next row, color 7 blue.
- Use green to color how many are left.
- Do it again with all the rows.

Teacher Note: Provide each student with a piece of paper that has nine rows of nine connected squares; squares should be large enough for students to color. Have students discuss patterns they see. Each new row should have one less square colored with the first color, and one more square colored with the second color. Have students use counters to show each subtraction.

Materials:
- paper
- crayons
- counters

small group | KINESTHETIC

Social Studies

Let's Go Shopping

- Use nine counters to shop.
- Choose an object to buy. Pay for it with counters.
- How many counters do you have left?

Teacher Note: Prepare objects with price tags up to 9. If students are not ready for 9, have them shop with five counters. Make sure each student gets a receipt for their purchase. On their receipt, they can write how many counters they have left.

Materials:
- classroom objects
- tags
- pencils
- counters
- index cards (for receipts)

small group | KINESTHETIC

Health

Healthful Meals

- Take some cards out of the bag. Write how many.
- Choose a partner. Give your partner some cards. Write how many.
- How many are left? Write the number.
- Play again.

Teacher Note: Prepare cards with food pictures. Put nine cards in each bag. Tell students that nine food pictures are in each bag. Allow students to discuss which foods are healthy food choices.

Materials:
- index cards
- pictures of different foods
- bags
- pencils
- paper

Language Arts

pair | LOGICAL

Subtraction Story Book

- Fold a sheet of paper in half.
- Write a "?".
- Draw a group of nine animals or less. Write the number.
- Draw a group of eight animals or less "walking away." Write the number.
- Draw how many animals are left. Write the number.

Teacher Note: Help students describe their subtraction problem by asking what happens next in the pictures. Assist students in folding paper or ordering their drawings on the pages as needed.

5 take away 1 is 4

Materials:
- paper
- crayons

Science

individual | SPATIAL

Seashell Stories

- Roll a number cube.
- Take that many seashells out of your bowl.
- Tell a subtraction story about the seashells.
- Draw your subtraction story.

Teacher Note: Tell students that five to nine seashells are in each bowl. Give each student a bowl. Have students work in pairs. One partner tells the story and the other partner draws the story. Have partners switch roles and repeat the activity.

Materials:
- bowls
- seashells
- 0–5 number cube
- pencils
- paper

Calendar Time

How Many Days Are Left?

Ask students the following questions. Count each result with the class. Add questions or adapt questions to fit your class.
- How many more days are left until (student)'s birthday?
- How many days are left until (a holiday marked on the calendar)?
- How many days are left in the week? month?

Teacher Note: Encourage students to come up with their own calendar questions for the class.

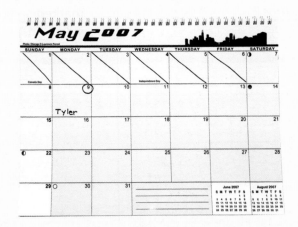

Introduce the Chapter

🌐 Real World: How Many Are Left?

On a plate, there are five carrot sticks. You eat two of them. **How many are left?** three

- Have students model the problem using their fingers.
- Have them pretend to eat two of them.
- Count the three fingers that are left as a class.

Use the Student Page

Have students turn to p. 313. Guide students to discuss the images on the page and answer the Explore questions.

Key Vocabulary

Introduce the key vocabulary in the chapter using the routine below.

Define: When you **subtract**, you are taking something away and finding how many are left.
Example: Take some fruit out of a bowl and count the pieces of fruit left in the bowl.
Ask: What are some ways you subtract in the classroom?

Diagnostic Assessment

Check for students' prerequisite skills before beginning the chapter.

- **Option 1: *Are You Ready for Chapter 12?***
  SE Student Edition, p. 314

- **Option 2: *Online Assessment Quiz***
  Math Online macmillanmh.com

- **Option 3: *Diagnostic Test***
  CRM Chapter 12 Resource Masters, p. 48

RTI (Response to Intervention)

Apply the Results Based on the results of the diagnostic assessment on p. 314, use the chart on the next page to address individual needs before and during the chapter.

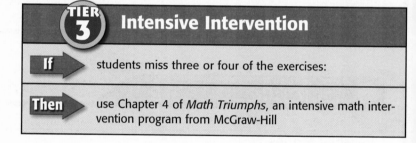

TIER 3 **Intensive Intervention**

If	students miss three or four of the exercises:
Then	use Chapter 4 of *Math Triumphs*, an intensive math intervention program from McGraw-Hill

---

FOLDABLES **Study Organizer**
Dinah Zike's Foldables

Guide students to create a Bound Book Foldable graphic organizer to make a giant subtraction journal.

① Fold two sheets of paper like a hamburger. Place the papers on top of each other, leaving $\frac{1}{16}$ inch between the "mountain tops."

② Mark both folds 1 inch from the outer edges. On one of the folded sheets, cut from the top and bottom edge to the marked spot on both sides.

③ On the second folded sheet, start at one of the marked spots and cut the fold between the two marks.

④ Take the cut sheet from step 2 and fold it like a burrito. Place the burrito through the slit in the other sheet, then open the burrito. Fold the bound pages in half to form an eight-page book.

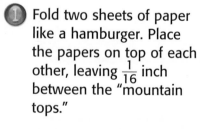
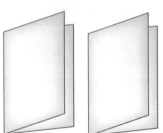
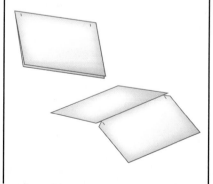
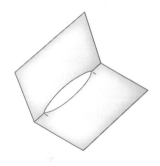
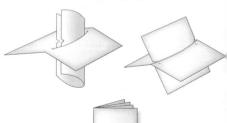

Journal

When to Use It Lessons 12-1, 12-2, 12-4, 12-5, and 12-6 (Additional instructions for using the Foldable with these lessons are found on pp. 329 and 345.)

Copyright © Macmillan/McGraw-Hill, a division of The McGraw-Hill Companies, Inc.

CHAPTER 12 Model Subtraction

Key Vocabulary

take away
are left
subtract

Explore

How many penguins do you see? 5
How many penguins are about to enter the water? 1
How many penguins are still on the ice? 4

Name _____

Are You Ready for Chapter 12?

1. ___7___

   ___5___

2. ___6___

   ___4___

3. ___5___

4. ___4___

Directions:
1–2. Count the objects in each set. Write the number. Circle the set that has two less.
3. Draw five triangles. Write the number.
4. Draw four circles. Write the number.

Copyright © Macmillan/McGraw-Hill, a division of The McGraw-Hill Companies, Inc.

RTI (Response to Intervention)

TIER 2 **Strategic Intervention** below/approaching grade level	TIER 1 **On-Level**	**Above/Beyond Level**
If students miss two in: **Exercises 1–4**	**If** students miss one in: **Exercises 1–4**	**If** students miss none in: **Exercises 1–4**
Then choose a resource:	**Then** choose a resource:	**Then** choose a resource:
CRM Chapter 4 Resource Masters (Reteach Worksheets) Math Online Concepts in Motion	TE Learning Stations (pp. 313G–313H) TE Chapter Project (p. 315) CRM Game: Empty the Orange Basket Math Adventures My Math Zone Chapter 11	TE Learning Stations (pp. 313G–313H) TE Chapter Project (pp. 315) Real-World Problem Solving: *Pets Find a Home* My Math Zone Chapters 11 and 12 Math Online Game

WRITING IN ▶MATH

Starting the Chapter

- Have students write the words *take away* at the top of the journal page.
- Ask students to draw a group of eight marbles. Have them write the number eight below the marbles.
- Ask students to place an X on some of the marbles as if the marbles had rolled away.
- Have students write the number for the Xs they placed. Have students tell how many marbles are left and write that number.
- Allow students to share their marble subtractions.

✓ Chapter 12 Project

Illustrate Subtraction Number Stories

- Throughout the chapter, have students write or tell subtraction number stories using numbers and words, drawings, pictures from magazines, or manipulatives and food items.
- Have students use drawings, magazine clippings, or small food items (cereal, noodles, fish crackers) and manipulatives that can be glued on construction paper to illustrate the subtraction number story (taking away) and the number of items that are left.
- Ask students to share the stories they write with the class.

Chapter 12 Literature List

Lesson	Book Title	Author
12-1	Five Little Ducks	Raffi
12-2	Five Little Monkeys Jumping on the Bed	Eileen Christelow
12-3	Ten Tiny Monsters	Sheila White Shannon
12-4	Five Little Monkeys Sitting in a Tree	Eileen Christelow
12-5	Roll Over! A Counting Song	Merle Peek (Illustrator)
12-6	Roll Over! A Counting Song	Merle Peek (Illustrator)
12-7	Monster Musical Chairs	Stuart J. Murphy
12-8	Monster Musical Chairs	Stuart J. Murphy
12-9	Ten Black Dots	Donald Crews
12-10	Rooster's Off to See the World	Eric Carle
Any	Ten Seeds	Ruth Brown
Any	Ten, Nine, Eight	Molly Bang

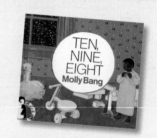

ELL National ESL Standards Alignment for Chapter 1			
Lesson, Page	ESL Standard	Modality	Level
12-1, p. 317B	Goal 1, Standard 2, d	Auditory	Beginning
12-2, p. 321B	Goal 2, Standard 3, k	Kinesthetic	Intermediate
12-3, p. 323B	Goal 1, Standard 3, f	Visual/Spatial, Logical	Intermediate
12-4, p. 325B	Goal 2, Standard 3, c	Visual	Intermediate
12-5, p. 331B	Goal 2, Standard 2, a	Auditory	Beginning
12-6, p. 333B	Goal 1, Standard 3, f	Logical	Intermediate
12-7, p. 335B	Goal 2, Standard 1, f	Logical, Social	Intermediate
12-8, p. 337B	Goal 2, Standard 1, h	Auditory, Kinesthetic	Intermediate
12-9, p. 339B	Goal 2, Standard 2, m	Visual	Advanced
12-10, p. 341B	Goal 2, Standard 1, h	Kinesthetic, Interpersonal	Intermediate

The National ESL Standards can be found in the Teacher Reference Handbook.

- Read the Math at Home letter on p. 315 with the class and have each student sign it.

- Send home copies of the Math at Home letter with each student.

- Use the Spanish letter on p. 316 for students with Spanish-speaking parents or guardians.

Read-Aloud Anthology

For an optional reading activity to introduce this chapter's math concepts, see the Read-Aloud Anthology on p. TR34.

Lesson Planner

Objective

Students will model subtraction as taking away from or separating sets of objects.

Vocabulary

take away, are left, subtract

Resources

Materials: egg carton
Manipulatives: color tiles, connecting cubes, pattern blocks
Literature Connection: *Five Little Ducks* by Raffi
Alternate Lesson: Use *Subtraction Cards* on pages 193 and 194 of *Math Their Way* to provide practice in subtraction.
Use *IMPACT Mathematics*: Unit D to provide practice with subtracting.
Teacher Technology
TeacherWorks Math Song Track 7

Daily Routine

Use these suggestions before beginning the lesson on p. 317.

5-Minute Check

(Reviews Lesson 11-9)

Have students count the number in each set, then write how many in all.

   $3 + 2 = 5$

   $2 + 4 = 6$

Problem of the Day

Model the following problem by drawing birds and crossing them out. Three birds are on a branch. Two birds fly away. How many are on the branch in all? 1

 LINE UP Have two students stand. Subtract one. Have the standing student line up, and the subtracted student line up saying "2 − 1 is 1." Repeat with four subtracting two, until all are in line.

Building Math Vocabulary

Materials: real or plastic apples

- Sing *Five Little Apples in the Grocery Shop*. Discuss what happens to each apple. Use **take away** to explain that the apple is no longer in the shop.
- Act out the story. Tell and show a number story using apples when an apple is bought. Ex: *Five apples are in the grocery shop. One was bought. How many **are left**?* Show 5 take away 1 is four.
- Repeat the activity with four, three, two, and one apple, emphasizing the vocabulary words *take away, are left,* and ***subtract***.

Visual Vocabulary Cards

Use Visual Vocabulary Card 42 to reinforce the vocabulary introduced in this chapter. (The Define /Example/Ask routine is printed on the back of each card.)

subtract

Differentiated Instruction

Small Group Options

Option 1 Gifted and Talented (AL) — LOGICAL

Materials: counters, 1–5 spinner

- Give each small group five counters.
- Model a subtraction problem by having one student spin a 1–5 spinner and remove that number of counters. Have the others say how many are left.
- Repeat using larger numbers of counters, up to 10.
- Explain that 5 – 5 is 0, or use a 1–4 spinner.

Option 2 English Language Learners (ELL) — AUDITORY

Core Vocabulary: take away, I'm hungry, meals
Common Use Verb: eat/ate

Hear Math This strategy uses music to introduce subtraction vocabulary.

- Sing to "Row, Row, Row Your Boat," having students join in:

    Take, take, take away, take away each day,
    When I'm hungry I am sure to eat three meals a day.

- Repeat as time permits.

Independent Work Options

Option 1 Early Finishers (AL) (OL) — SPATIAL

Materials: attribute buttons, string

- Have students string five attribute buttons, then remove some.
- Have them say the number story.
- Repeat the activity having students use attribute buttons to create other number stories about real classroom situations.
- Have students justify their thinking by drawing a picture of their number story and explaining it to a classmate.

Option 2 Student Technology

Math Online ▷  macmillanmh.com

- ♪ Math Song "Ten in the Bed" Track 7
- Math Adventures

Option 3 Learning Station: Science (p. 313H)

Direct students to the Science Learning Station for opportunities to explore and extend the lesson concept.

Leveled Lesson Resources
Additional support for English Language Learners can be found in the ELL Guide (p. 85).

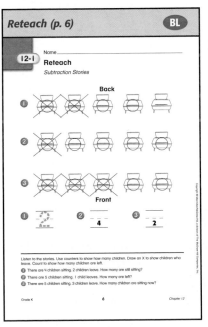

Reteach (p. 6) — BL

12-1 Reteach
Subtraction Stories

Back ... Front

Listen to the stories. Use counters to show how many children. Draw an X to show children who leave. Count to show how many children are left.

Grade K   6   Chapter 12

Skills Practice (p. 7) — OL

12-1 Skills Practice
Subtraction Stories

Listen to the stories. Place counters on the playground to show how many children. Remove counters to show children who leave. Count the counters to show how many are left.

Grade K   7   Chapter 12

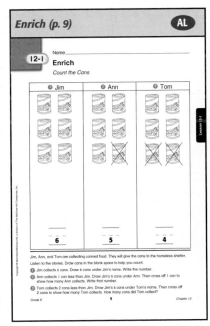

Enrich (p. 9) — AL

12-1 Enrich
Count the Cans

Jim   Ann   Tom

Jim, Ann, and Tom are collecting canned food. They will give the cans to the homeless shelter. Listen to the stories. Draw cans in the blank space to help you count.

Grade K   9   Chapter 12

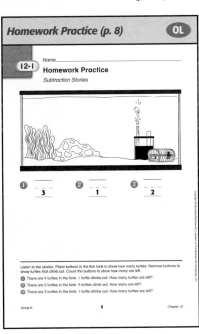

Homework Practice (p. 8) — OL

12-1 Homework Practice
Subtraction Stories

Listen to the stories. Place buttons in the fish tank to show how many turtles. Remove buttons to show turtles that climb out. Count the buttons to show how many are left.

Grade K   8   Chapter 12

① Introduce

Circle Time

Activity Choice 1 • Literature

Five Little Ducks by Raffi

- Get out 5 colored tiles for each student.

- As the story is read have them **take away** one tile and hide it. Ask, "How many **are left**?" After the story collect the tiles.

- Reread the story multiple times and have children act out the story in groups. Pick six students to come up—one mother and five little ducks. As the story is read by the teacher, the students act it out. After a duck disappears, ask the rest of the class, "How many are left?"

Activity Choice 2 • Hands-On

- Have five, six, or seven students line up in front of the class.

- Tap three students on the shoulder and tell them to "run away." Have the class say how many students **are left**.

- Repeat the activity so that every student is allowed to "run away."

- Have students justify their answer by showing the subtraction story with cubes and saying the numbers used.

② Teach

- Direct students to the top of p. 317.

- Identify the conveyor belt and discuss the grocery store check out process.

- Tell subtraction stories using the scene. For example, "Pretend that four boxes of cereal are on the belt. One box is put in a bag. **How many boxes are left on the belt?**" 3

- Have students use concrete objects such as color tiles on the belt to **subtract** and model number stories.

- Observe student understanding of the concept of subtracting from two known sets to get an unknown result. For example: **I had two apples. I lost one apple. How many apples are left?** one

- Once they grasp this concept, tell a subtraction story but reword it such that the result is known but the change is unknown. For example: **I have five oranges. I lost some. Now I have two oranges. How many oranges did I lose?** three

- As the change unknown concept is grasped, tell a subtraction story but reword it such that the start is unknown. For example: **I have some bananas. I bought four more. Now I have eight bananas. How many bananas did I start with?** four

> **⚠ COMMON ERROR!**
>
> Students may have difficulty relating subtraction stories to the math symbols. To help them associate words and symbols, write and say, for example, "are left" or "take away" means "−".

Name _____

Subtraction Stories

Check students' work.

①

Check students' work.

Directions:
1. Listen to the stories. Use color tiles to model the subtraction stories. Tell how many are left.

Chapter 12   Lesson 1

three hundred seventeen   317

---

② Check students' work.

Directions:
2. Listen to the story. Use connecting cubes to model the subtraction stories. Tell how many are left.

GO on

318   three hundred eighteen

Chapter 12   Lesson 1

Guided Practice

- Direct students to p. 317. Model using color tiles to solve the subtraction stories.

- Use color tiles to model stories such as: **Three cans of corn are on the shelf. I put two cans in my cart. How many cans are left on the shelf?** one

---

BL Alternate Teaching Strategy

If students have trouble with subtraction . . .

Then use one of these reteach options.

1 **CRM** **Daily Reteach Worksheet** (p. 6)

2 **Use an Egg Carton** Remove three spaces from an egg carton.

- Put one pattern block in each of the nine remaining spaces.

- Put nine same colored cubes in a cup.

- Shake and roll out some cubes. Remove one block from the egg carton for each cube. Have students say the number story for how many counters are left in the egg carton. Have a volunteer record the number.

- Repeat the procedure.

③ Practice

Independent Practice

- Have students turn to p. 318, look at the picture, and discuss how vegetables and fruits grow in a garden.

- Invite students to use cubes as you tell this subtraction story:

  - **Six carrots were growing in the garden. A rabbit ate three of the carrots. How many carrots are left?** three

- Rephrase the story saying: Six (carrots) take away three (carrots) is three (carrots). Tell more subtraction stories.

- Have students use the scenes on pages 319 and 320 to tell subtraction stories.

- Have students use connecting cubes to model the subtraction stories.

Name _ _ _ _ _ _ _ _ _ _ _ _ _ _ _ _

③

Check students' work.

Directions:
3. Create a subtraction story. Model it using cubes. Trace the cubes used.
   Mark an X on the cubes you take away. Tell your story to a classmate.

Chapter 12   Lesson 1   three hundred nineteen   **319**

---

④

Check students' work.

Directions:
4. Create a subtraction story. Model it using cubes.
   Trace the cubes used. Mark an X on the cubes
   you take away. Tell your story to a classmate.

Math at Home Activity: Tell your child a subtraction story such as four grapes were on a plate. Two grapes were eaten. How many are left? Use cereal or grapes to model the story.

320   three hundred twenty   Chapter 12   Lesson 1

 **Assess**

✓ Formative Assessment

- Show students a subtraction problem such as 6 – 2. Ask them to make up a number story that goes with it.

- **What number story goes with this problem?** Sample answer: Six mice are eating corn. Two mice leave. Four mice are left.

Quick Check   **Are students still struggling to create subtraction stories?**

If Yes → Small Group Options (p. 317B)

If No → Independent Work Options (p. 317B)

   [CRM] Skills Practice Worksheet (p. 7)

   [CRM] Enrich Worksheet (p. 9)

Lesson 12-1 Subtraction Stories   **320**

Lesson Planner

Objective
Use concrete objects to solve subtraction problems.

Review Vocabulary
take away

Resources
Materials: buttons, paper, pencils, crayons
Manipulatives: two-colored counters, color tiles, connecting cubes
Literature Connection: *Five Little Monkeys Jumping on the Bed* by Eileen Christelow
Alternate Lesson: Use *Word Problems Using Children and Props* on page 205 of *Math Their Way* to provide practice subtracting concrete objects.
Use *IMPACT Mathematics*: Unit D to provide practice with using concrete objects to subtract.
Teacher Technology
 ⊙ TeacherWorks • Concepts in Motion

Focus on Math Background

Subtraction as a concept occurs naturally in a classroom and in everyday life. Examples include when students leave a group, note elapsed time such as "there are only five more minutes left," share or give away items, finish tasks in a list or schedule, and so on.

As students become familiar with the process, they readily see subtraction as the inverse of addition. Then they only need reminders to always subtract the smaller amount from the larger amount.

Daily Routine

Use these suggestions before beginning the lesson on p. 321.

5-Minute Check

(Reviews Lesson 12-1)
Model the following problems using concrete objects like counters.

1. I pick five flowers. I give away two. How many flowers do I have left?
three

2. I have five crayons. I give away four. How many crayons do I have left?
one

3. I have four apple slices. I eat two. How many apple slices do I have left? two

Problem of the Day

A girl has nine balloons. She gives five balloons to a friend. How many does she have left? four

LINE UP Have nine students line up. Ask how many should sit so seven students are left. Repeat, changing the numbers who sit down and are left.

▷ Review Math Vocabulary

- Have seven students line up. Then have three sit.
- Have students draw subtraction stories to tell what happened. (Seven **take away** three is four.)
- Repeat this activity with different numbers.
- Emphasize the importance of recording the first number in the group, then the smaller number that is taken away, and finally the number that is left.

Differentiated Instruction

Small Group Options

Option 1 — Below/Approaching Level (BL) SPATIAL

Materials: 0–5 number cube, connecting cubes, markers, drawing paper

- Give students five connecting cubes. Have them draw the cubes, count them, and write the total number.
- Model subtraction by having them toss a number cube and remove that many connecting cubes, cross out that many on their paper, and write the number they took away.
- Have them write how many connecting cubes are left. Repeat.

Option 2 — English Language Learners (ELL) KINESTHETIC

Core Vocabulary: drop out, snap your fingers, no sound

Common Use Verb: take away

Do Math This strategy uses kinesthetic movement and pattern to illustrate subtraction.

- Say: "Tap, Clap," as you perform the motions for this AB pattern three times. Have students join in.
- Say that you will take away "Tap" and leave a space where it was. Perform the pattern: (Space), Clap. Have students join in. Repeat.

Independent Work Options

Option 1 — Early Finishers (OL) (AL) KINESTHETIC

- Give two number cubes to each small group.
- Have two students each roll a number cube and decide the larger number. Have them subtract the smaller number from the larger number to find the subtraction problem answer. Allow students to use counters.
- Have groups take turns up to five times.

Option 2 — Student Technology

Math Online macmillanmh.com

 Math Adventures

Option 3 — Learning Station: Science (p. 313H)

Direct students to the Science Learning Station for opportunities to explore and extend the lesson concept.

Reteach (p. 10) **BL**	Skills Practice (p. 11) **OL**	Enrich (p. 13) **AL**	Homework Practice (p. 12) **OL**
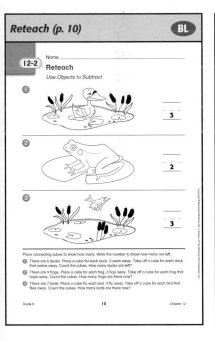	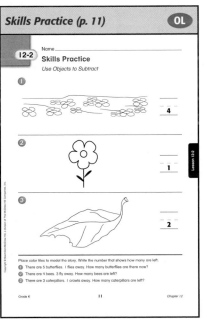	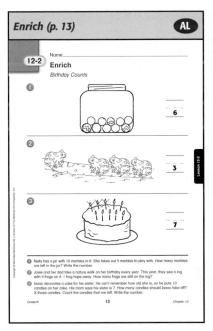	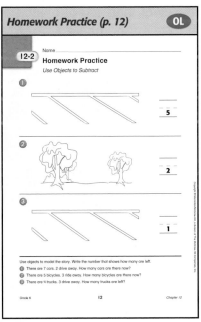

1 Introduce

Circle Time

Activity Choice 1 · Literature

Five Little Monkeys Jumping on the Bed
by Eileen Christelow

Materials: connecting cubes

- Give each student 5 connecting cubes to represent the 5 monkeys.
- As you read the story, students demonstrate their stack of 5 cubes jumping on the bed, then take one off and turn it upside down on the desk (bumping its head).
- After the monkey bumps its head, ask students how many monkeys are left to jump on the bed? How many are injured?
- Repeat the process until there are no monkeys jumping on the bed.

Activity Choice 2 · Hands-On

Materials: buttons, paper, crayons

- Count nine concrete objects such as buttons. Have students write the number nine.
- Take away some buttons counting: one, two, three, and so on. Have students record the number you **take away**.
- Ask volunteers how many buttons are left and to explain their subtraction story.
- Repeat, always starting with the larger amount (fewer than 10) of objects and taking away different numbers.

2 Teach

- Direct students to p. 321.
- Distribute color tiles for subtracting.
- Tell this story:
  Four penguins stood on an iceberg waiting for a friend. Two penguins got tired and went away. How many penguins are left? two
- Observe students' use of color tiles and subtraction. Guide them in writing the number two.
- Repeat the activity using different numbers.

BL Alternate Teaching Strategy

If students have trouble modeling subtraction . . .

Then use one of these reteach options.

1. CRM **Daily Reteach Worksheet** (p. 10)

2. **Use Manipulatives** Model subtraction stories with overhead manipulatives.
   - Have students follow along with manipulatives on a workmat.
   - Have students record the numbers that are modeled on a sheet of paper.
   - Begin with lower number subtraction and increase numbers as students are ready.

> **! COMMON ERROR!**
> Students may confuse subtraction with addition. Have them listen for the key vocabulary of "take away" or "how many are left" to remember to subtract.

Name _____

Use Objects to Subtract

-2

① -1

② -2

Directions:
1–2. Listen to the story. Use color tiles to subtract. Write the number that shows how many are left.

③ -3

④ -4

⑤ -5

Directions:
3–5. Listen to the story. Use color tiles to subtract. Write the number that shows how many are left.

Math at Home Activity: Have your child tell you a short subtraction story and use buttons or dry cereal to model the story.

 **Practice**

Guided Practice

- Direct students to p. 321. Continue using color tiles as you tell these stories for Exercises 1 and 2:
1. **Six snowflakes fell from the sky. Five melted away. How many snowflakes are left?** one
2. **Three snowballs are stacked to make a snowman. One snowball fell off. How many are left?** two

Independent Practice

Have students turn to p. 322. Check as students use color tiles to model these subtraction stories for Exercises 3, 4, and 5.

3. **Five penguins are at the pond. Two walk away. How many penguins are left at the pond?** three
4. **Seven penguins are in an igloo. Three penguins went out to play. How many penguins are left?** four
5. **A penguin had six mittens. She lost one. How many mittens does she have left?** five

④ Assess

Formative Assessment

- Have students use color counters to model subtraction.
- Have students listen to the subtraction story and write the number of animals that are left.
- **Six swans were in the pond. Two swans flew away. How many are left?** four

Quick Check	Are students still struggling to solve subtraction problems using objects?

If Yes → Small Group Options (p. 321B)

If No → Independent Work Options (p. 321B)

　　　CRM Skills Practice Worksheet (p. 11)

　　　CRM Enrich Worksheet (p. 13)

Lesson 12-2 Use Objects to Subtract   **322**

Lesson Planner _____

Objective
Use the minus sign (–) to show subtraction.

Vocabulary
minus sign (–)

Resources
Materials: paper, crayons
Manipulatives: connecting cubes
Literature Connection: *Ten Tiny Monsters* by Sheila White Shannon
Alternate Lesson: Use *Subtraction Cards* on page 238 of *Math Their Way* to provide practice using the minus sign to show subtraction.
Teacher Technology
🔘 TeacherWorks

Focus on Math Background

This lesson introduces kindergarteners to the minus sign (–) as a symbol used to represent the separation of objects from a larger set. The act of taking away parts from a whole is the most familiar situation that students associate with the formal operation of subtraction. In first grade, however, students will begin to expand their understanding of subtraction as a process useful for finding differences as well as a way to undo addition.

Daily Routine _____

Use these suggestions before beginning the lesson on p. 323

5-Minute Check
Have students use connecting cubes to model and solve the subtraction sentences below.

   1. $4 - 3 = 1$ **3.** $6 - 4 = 2$
   2. $7 - 2 = 5$ **4.** $5 - 1 = 4$
                              5. $6 - 3 = 3$

Problem of the Day
Draw a picture to show this subtraction story: Molly had six carrots. She ate four carrots. How many carrots does Molly have left? two

LINE UP Have students tell a subtraction number story and line up. Have students tell which symbol would be used to show the subtraction.

Building Math Vocabulary

- Draw on the chalkboard three rabbits hopping away from four other rabbits in a yard.

- Write the numbers 7 and 4 on the chalkboard with a space between. **How can we find the number of rabbits that are still in the yard?** Count all the rabbits, take away the number of rabbits that are hopping away, and count the rabbits that are still in the yard.

- Write the minus sign between the numbers 7 and 4. Tell students that a **minus sign (–)** tells us to subtract, or separate, some of the rabbits from the group. Repeat with other examples.

Differentiated Instruction

Small Group Options

Option 1 — Below/Approaching Level (BL)
KINESTHETIC

Materials: modeling clay, spinner, connecting cubes, toothpicks

- Have students work at a table to make a large minus sign with modeling clay.
- Have the student spin a spinner twice. Ask students to make a train of cubes to show the larger number and lay it down in front of the minus symbol. Ask students to make a train to show the smaller number and lay it down after the minus sign.
- Students subtract and make a train to show the answer.

Option 2 — English Language Learners (ELL)
VISUAL/SPATIAL, LOGICAL

Core Vocabulary: how many, minus, star
Common Use Verb: take

See Math This strategy helps teach the minus symbol.

- Show 3 overhead counters with star stickers applied. Write: "3." Pull off a star, leaving a counter, and write "-1."
- Give a student a star.
- Write "2" and take off the empty counter.
- Repeat the -1 process until all the stars are removed.

Independent Work Options

Option 1 — Early Finishers (OL) (AL)
LINGUISTIC

Materials: construction paper, crayons

- Have students draw pictures on a sheet of construction paper to model a subtraction problem.
- Ask students to write the numbers they are subtracting below their picture.
- Have students share their number story with the class.

5 – 2

Option 2 — Student Technology

Math Online macmillanmh.com

Math Adventures

Option 3 — Learning Station: Health (p. 313G)

Direct students to the Health Learning Station for opportunities to explore and extend the lesson concept.

Leveled Lesson Resources
Additional support for English Language Learners can be found in the ELL Guide (p. 97). (ELL)

Reteach (p. 14) (BL)	Skills Practice (p. 15) (OL)	Enrich (p. 17) (AL)	Homework Practice (p. 16) (OL)
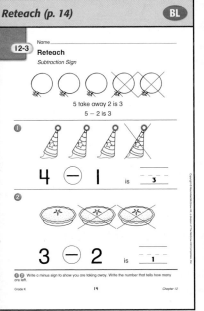	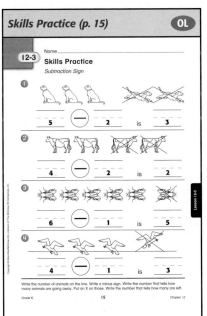	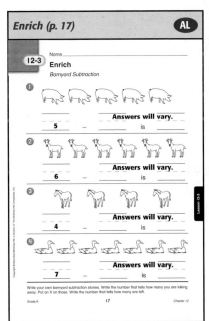	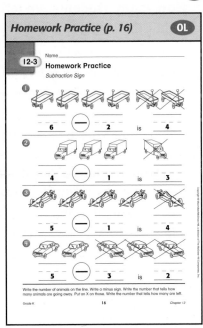

① Introduce

 **Circle Time**

Activity Choice 1 • Literature

Ten Tiny Monsters
by Sheila White Shannon

- Draw 5 peaches on the board. Ask students how many would be left if two were eaten. Explore various ways to denote their removal.

- Tell students that the minus sign is a math symbol meaning take away. Explain that 5−2=3 is the subtraction sentence describing the problem with numbers and symbols.

- Read the story, prompting students to use vocabulary while stating subtraction sentences.

- Students draw pictures that denote subtraction, and write the number sentence on the back. They hold up their cards, and classmates guess what the number sentence is.

Activity Choice 2 • Hands-On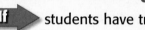

- Invite five students to stand in front of the class, and have the seated students count them as you point to each student.

- **How many students are in the front of the class?** five

- Write the number 5 on the chalkboard.

- Tap two students and have them return to their seats.

- **How many students are left?** three

- Count the students.

- Model the subtraction example again using five students, taking away two students.

- Have students repeat, "Five minus two is three."

- Write on the chalkboard and say, "Five take away two." Erase the words "take away" and write a **minus sign (−)**. Identify the (−) sign by calling it minus sign.

- Tell students that the minus sign shows us to take away from a set.

② Teach

- Call students' attention to the top of p. 323.
- Have them identify the five birds on the page.
- Help students see that two birds are flying away. Guide them to suggest that they can subtract the birds that are flying away from the set to find the birds that are still in the nest.
- **What does the minus sign show?** It shows that something is being taken away.
- Have students trace the minus sign and write the numbers.

ⓑⓛ Alternate Teaching Strategy

If students have trouble understanding how to use the minus sign . . .

Then use one of these reteach options.

1 [CRM] **Daily Reteach Worksheet** (p. 14)

2 **Use the Minus Sign** Provide each student with a handful of connecting cubes. Ask students to make a train of six cubes.

- Have students **model subtraction by taking two cubes away from the train.**

- **What is the subtraction story you just showed with two cubes?** six minus two

- **How many cubes are left?** four

- Have students write the numbers they subtracted with the minus sign between the numbers on a sheet of paper.

- Continue subtracting with other groups of cubes.

 COMMON ERROR!

Some students may have difficulty associating the minus sign with separating sets. Help them understand the minus sign by saying a subtraction number sentence and separating a set to show how many are left.

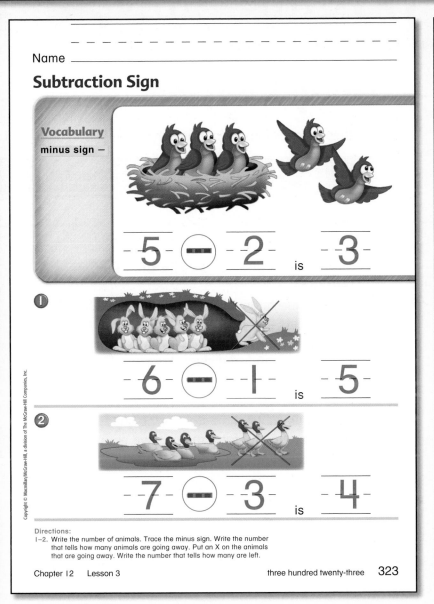

Name _____

Subtraction Sign

Vocabulary
minus sign —

5 ⊖ 2 is 3

① 6 ⊖ 1 is 5

② 7 ⊖ 3 is 4

Directions:
1–2. Write the number of animals. Trace the minus sign. Write the number that tells how many animals are going away. Put an X on the animals that are going away. Write the number that tells how many are left.

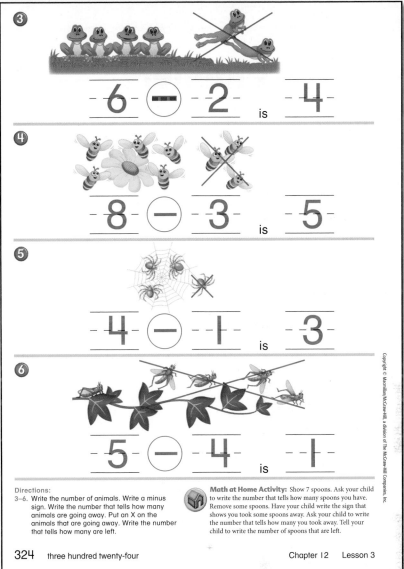

③ 6 ⊖ 2 is 4

④ 8 ⊖ 3 is 5

⑤ 4 ⊖ 1 is 3

⑥ 5 ⊖ 4 is 1

Directions:
3–6. Write the number of animals. Write a minus sign. Write the number that tells how many animals are going away. Put an X on the animals that are going away. Write the number that tells how many are left.

 Math at Home Activity: Show 7 spoons. Ask your child to write the number that tells how many spoons you have. Remove some spoons. Have your child write the sign that shows you took some spoons away. Ask your child to write the number that tells how many you took away. Tell your child to write the number of spoons that are left.

❸ Practice

Guided Practice

• Direct students to the bottom of p. 323.
• Work through Exercises 1 and 2. Make sure students understand that they use the minus sign to show taking away.

Independent Practice

Have students turn to p. 324. Explain the directions. Have students work independently on the exercises.

❹ Assess

✓ Formative Assessment

• **What does the minus sign tell you?** to subtract numbers or to take away from a set
• Tell a subtraction story and use cubes to model it. Have students write how many were taken away and how many are left.
• Have students use a minus sign to show the subtraction.

Quick Check Are students still struggling to show a minus sign in a number sentence?

If Yes → Small Group Options (p. 323B)
If No → Independent Work Options (p. 323B)
    CRM Skills Practice Worksheet (p. 15)
    CRM Enrich Worksheet (p. 17)

Lesson 12-3 Subtraction Sign   **324**

Lesson Planner

Objective

Use concrete objects and pictures to show ways to subtract from 4 and 5.

Review Vocabulary

four, five

Resources

Materials: 0–5 number line made from plastic placemats
Manipulatives: color tiles, connecting cubes
Alternate Lesson: Adapt *Subtraction Race* on page 227 of *Math Their Way* for practice in showing ways to solve for 5 in subtraction.
Literature Connection: *Five Little Monkeys Sitting in a Tree* by Eileen Christelow
Teacher Technology
  💿 TeacherWorks • Concepts in Motion

Daily Routine

Use these suggestions before beginning the lesson on p. 325.

5-Minute Check

(Reviews Lesson 12-3)
Model with cubes and write the number sentence.
1. five blue birds and three fly away $5 - 3 = 2$
2. four cats and one runs away $4 - 1 = 3$
3. three girls and two walk away $3 - 2 = 1$
4. two boys and one skates away $2 - 1 = 1$

Problem of the Day

Model this subtraction story using cubes. Nine people are in line for a movie. Five go in. How many people are still in line? four

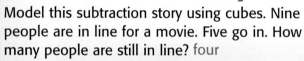 Have five students line up. Create a new line by subtracting students from the first line by two, three, or four. Repeat until all students are in line.

Review Math Vocabulary

- Have students make a connecting cube train with **four** cubes.
- Ask students to take away two cubes from the train.
- **How many cubes are left?** two
- Have students count each cube aloud to verify.
- Repeat, asking students to take away a different number of cubes.
- Repeat with a train of **five** cubes.

Differentiated Instruction

Small Group Options

Option 1   LOGICAL

Below/Approaching Level (BL)

Materials: play money, pencils, paper

- Give five pennies to each pair of students.
- Have one student model subtraction by showing four or five pennies and telling the other students how many pennies to take away. Have students take away the pennies and say how many are left.
- Have students draw circles on paper to represent pennies, and cross out circles to solve subtraction problems.

Option 2   VISUAL

English Language Learners (ELL)

Materials: overhead color counters, overhead marker
Core Vocabulary: purple, counters altogether, leaves
Common Use Verb: must go

See Math This strategy teaches subtraction vocabulary.

- Put 2 green and 2 purple counters on the overhead. Write and count: "4 **counters altogether.**"
- Say: "The **purple ones must go**!" Write "minus 2 purple."
- Count the number left over and write "leaves 2."
- Underneath the words, write "4 − 2 = 2."

Independent Work Options

Option 1   INTERPERSONAL

Early Finishers (OL) (AL)

- Have student pairs model subtraction by counting to four and then showing any number (0–5) of fingers on one hand.
- Have the partners make a subtraction story about the fingers and figure out how many are left.
- Repeat the activity, counting to five.

Option 2

Student Technology

Math Online  macmillanmh.com

Math Adventures

Option 3

Learning Station: Language Arts (p. 313H)

Direct students to the Language Arts Learning Station for opportunities to explore and extend the lesson concept.

Leveled Lesson Resources

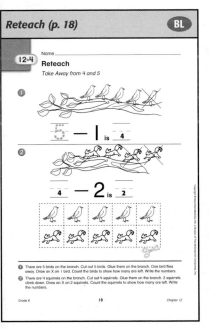

Reteach (p. 18) (BL)

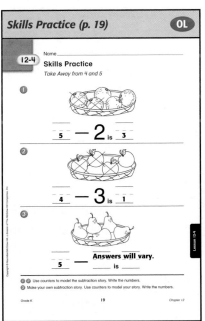

Skills Practice (p. 19) (OL)

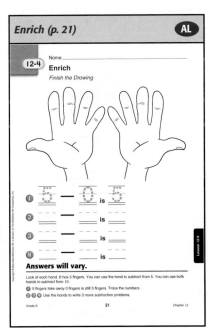

Enrich (p. 21) (AL)

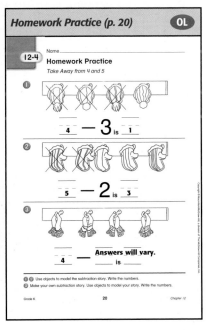

Homework Practice (p. 20) (OL)

1 Introduce

Circle Time

Activity Choice 1 • Literature

Five Little Monkeys Sitting in a Tree by Eileen Christelow

- Get out **five** tiles for each student.
- Read the story. Each time a monkey falls out of the tree, have students hide one tile. At the end of the story bring all five tiles back out.
- After the story, ask the question, "What would happen if two monkeys fell out of the tree? How many would be left?" Have students show the answer with their tiles.
- Show students how to write the subtraction problem 5 – 2 is 3. Repeat with **four**, using the subtraction problem 4 – 2 is 2.
- Ask students to show each subtraction sentence using tiles.

Activity Choice 2 • Hands-On

Materials: rulers

- Distribute rulers to students.
- Have students put a finger on 5.
- Tell them to take away two by counting back. Have them move their finger down the large numbers on the ruler two times.
- **How many are left?** 3
- Repeat the activity, starting at 4 or 5 and subtracting different numbers.

2 Teach

- Direct students to the top of p. 325.
- Discuss how dolphins can hold rings on their nose.
- Act out the number story using color tiles.
- Tell students to trace the start number on the line. Explain that this is the beginning of a number sentence.
- Have them put an X on each ring that is taken away.
- Then have them trace the answer on the line where 2 is taken away from 4.
- Repeat the activity using 5 as the start number.

> **! COMMON ERROR!**
>
> Students may have trouble differentiating between counting backwards and counting back. Explain that counting backward is 5, 4, 3, 2, 1, and counting back is tracking the number of spaces you are taking away from the starting number.

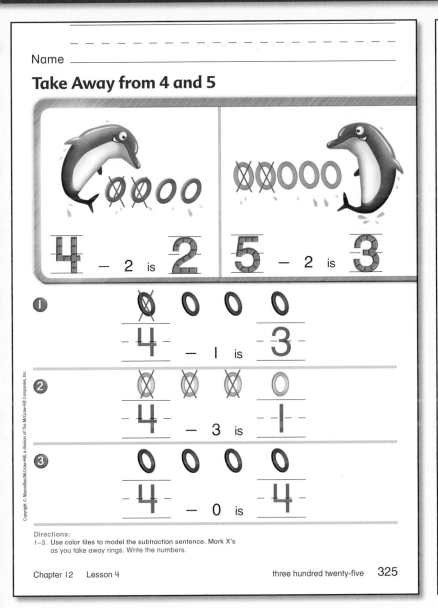

Name _____

Take Away from 4 and 5

$4 - 2$ is 2

$5 - 2$ is 3

① $4 - 1$ is 3

② $4 - 3$ is 1

③ $4 - 0$ is 4

Directions:
1–3. Use color tiles to model the subtraction sentence. Mark X's
as you take away rings. Write the numbers.

Chapter 12   Lesson 4   three hundred twenty-five   325

④ $4 - 4$ is 0

⑤ Check students' work.

$4 -$ _____ is _____

⑥ Check students' work.

$4 -$ _____ is _____

⑦ Check students' work.

$4 -$ _____ is _____

Directions:
4. Use color tiles to model the subtraction sentence. Mark X's
as you take away rings. Write the numbers.
5–7. Create your own subtraction sentence. Use color tiles
to model your sentence and write the numbers.

GO on

326   three hundred twenty-six   Chapter 12   Lesson 4

Alternate Teaching Strategy

If students have trouble with subtracting from 4 or 5 . . .

Then use one of these reteach options.

1 **CRM** **Daily Reteach Worksheet** (p. 18)

2 **Use Number Lines** Make a 0–5 number line of plastic placemats taped together end-to-end.

- **How much is left if a frog starts at 5 and takes away 4 by hopping back 4 times?** 1

  - Have students start at 5 and take away 4 by hopping back 4 times on the number line.

  - Repeat with the start number of 4 and have students hop back 3 or 2 times on the number line.

③ Practice

Guided Practice

- Direct students to p. 325.
- Have students act out the number story in Exercise 1 using color tiles.
- Have students write the number of total rings in the first box.
- Have them put an X on each ring that is taken away and and write the number of rings that are left in the last box.
- Repeat the activity for Exercises 2 and 3.

Independent Practice

Have students turn to pp. 326–328 and work independently on the exercises.

Name _____

8

$$\underline{5} - 0 \text{ is } \underline{5}$$

9

$$\underline{5} - 1 \text{ is } \underline{4}$$

10

$$\underline{5} - 5 \text{ is } \underline{0}$$

11

$$\underline{5} - 3 \text{ is } \underline{2}$$

Directions:
8-11. Use color tiles to model the subtraction sentence. Mark X's as you take away rings. Write the numbers.

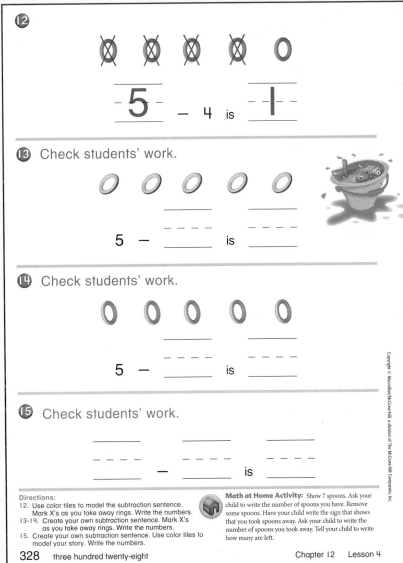

12

$$\underline{5} - 4 \text{ is } \underline{1}$$

13 Check students' work.

$$5 - \underline{} \text{ is } \underline{}$$

14 Check students' work.

$$5 - \underline{} \text{ is } \underline{}$$

15 Check students' work.

$$\underline{} - \underline{} \text{ is } \underline{}$$

Directions:
12. Use color tiles to model the subtraction sentence. Mark X's as you take away rings. Write the numbers.
13-14. Create your own subtraction sentence. Mark X's as you take away rings. Write the numbers.
15. Create your own subtraction sentence. Use color tiles to model your story. Write the numbers.

Math at Home Activity: Show 7 spoons. Ask your child to write the number of spoons you have. Remove some spoons. Have your child write the sign that shows that you took spoons away. Ask your child to write the number of spoons you took away. Tell your child to write how many are left.

4 Assess

✓ Formative Assessment

- **Five fish are in a pond. Two fish swim away. How many fish are left?** 3
- Have students solve the number story by modeling with connecting cubes.

Quick Check	Are students still struggling to subtract from 4 and 5?

If Yes → Small Group Options (p. 325B)

If No → Independent Work Options (p. 325B)
- CRM Skills Practice Worksheet (p. 19)
- CRM Enrich Worksheet (p. 21)

Lessons 12-1 to 12-4

Formative Assessment

Use the Mid-Chapter Check to assess students' progress in the first half of the chapter. Read this story to students.

1. There are 4 frogs on a log. 2 frogs hop off. How many frogs are left? two

Assessment Suite

Customize and create multiple versions of your Mid-Chapter Check and the test answer keys.

FOLDABLES Dinah Zike's Foldables

Use these lesson suggestions for incorporating the Foldables during the chapter.

Lesson 12-1 On the first page of the subtraction journal, use pictures to model subtraction and taking away or separating sets.

Lesson 12-2 Use large paper clips to form and solve subtraction problems and then tape them onto the second page of the journal.

Name _____

①

$$-2$$

②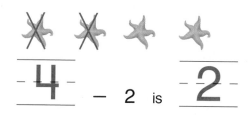

$$\underline{4} - 2 \text{ is } \underline{2}$$

③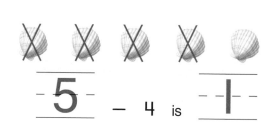

$$\underline{5} - 4 \text{ is } \underline{1}$$

Directions:
1. Listen to the story. Use color tiles to model the subtraction story. Write the number that shows how many are left.
2-3. Use cubes to model the subtraction sentence. Mark X's as you take away objects. Write the numbers.

Chapter 12   three hundred twenty-nine   329

Data-Driven Decision Making

Based on the results of the Mid-Chapter Check, use the following resources to review concepts that continue to give students problems.

Exercises	State/Local Standards	What's the Math?	Error Analysis	Resources for Review
1 Lesson 12-2		Understand simple subtraction problems. Use concrete objects to model subtraction stories.	Does not listen accurately. Chooses incorrect number of tiles for story. Writes the wrong number.	CRM Chapter 12 Resource Masters (Reteach Worksheets)
2–3 Lesson 12-4		Use concrete objects to model subtraction problems and subtract from 4 and 5.	Does not listen well and writes incorrect numbers. Does not use correct number of tiles for subtraction problems. Puts wrong number of "X's."	**Math Online** Concepts in Motion Math Adventures

How Many Are Left?
Subtracting

You Will Need

30 ●

Play with a partner. Take turns.
- Roll the [5].
- Move your cube that number of squares.
- Use the animals shown to create a subtraction story.
- Use ● to model the subtraction story.
- Keep the ● that are left.
- When both players reach **finish**, count to see who has more ●.

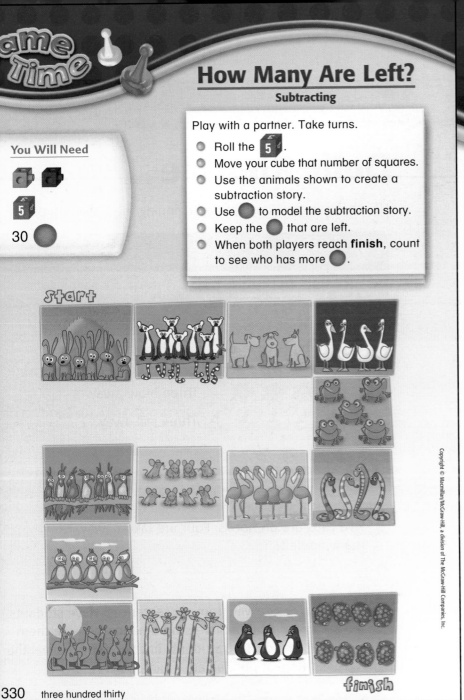

How Many Are Left?

Math Concept:
Subtracting

Manipulatives: 0–5 number cube, connecting cubes, thirty two-colored counters

Introduce the game on page 330 to your students to play as a class, in small groups, or at a learning workstation to review concepts introduced in this chapter.

Instructions

- Assign each student a connecting cube as a game piece.
- Have players take turns rolling a number cube.
- Players move their game piece the number of spaces they roll.
- Use the animal picture that you land on to create a subtraction story.
- Have players use counters to model the subtraction story and then keep the counters that are left.
- Have students use a different number each time they make a subtraction story.
- The first player to reach Finish, wins.

Extend the Game

After modeling the subtraction story shown, have students create another story with the same difference.

Differentiated Practice

Use these leveling suggestions to differentiate the game for all learners.

Level	Assignment
BL Below/Approaching Level	Pair students with an older student or parent volunteer to guide in subtraction stories.
OL On Level	Have students play the game with the rules as written.
AL Above/Beyond Level	Have students write numbers for each square.

Lesson Planner

Objective
Use concrete objects and pictures to show ways to subtract from 6.

Review Vocabulary
take away

Resources
Materials: bunches of six bananas, pencils, drawing paper, crayons, blocks, 5" x 8" cards

Manipulatives: yellow connecting cubes, 0–5 number cube, two-colored counters

Literature Connection: *Roll over! A Counting Song* by Merle Peek (Illustrator)

Teacher Technology
TeacherWorks

Daily Routine

Use these suggestions before beginning the lesson on p. 331.

5-Minute Check
(Reviews Lesson 12-4)

Tell students to mark X's as they take away to find the answer.

1. Three blow away. 1
2. Three sail away. 2
3. One is eaten. 3

Problem of the Day
Five caps are on hooks. Four are taken away. How many are left? 1

LINE UP Say take away from six sentences. Have students hold up some fingers on a hand and hide them with the other hand. Have students line up if they reveal the right answer. Repeat until all are in line.

▷ Review Math Vocabulary
Materials: rocks, drawing paper, crayons

- **There are six rocks. Take away three. How many are left?** three

- Give each student six rocks. Draw six rocks on the chalkboard. Have students draw the rocks.

- Tell them to take away three rocks and hide them behind their backs. Erase three rocks on the chalkboard to take them away. Discuss how erasing is like taking the rocks away.

- Tell students they cannot erase the rocks. Ask them to instead put an X on three rocks to show how many they take away.

Differentiated Instruction

Small Group Options

Option 1 — Gifted and Talented (AL)
LOGICAL

Materials: pattern blocks

- Have students form pairs. Have the first partner make a design with six pattern blocks on a table, then close his or her eyes.
- Have the second partner remove some pieces of the design.
- Tell the first partner to open his or her eyes and tell what is missing.
- Ask pairs to write the subtraction story for the design.

Option 2 — English Language Learners (ELL)
AUDITORY

Materials: overhead line drawing of a house, overhead counters with faces on them, overhead markers
Core Vocabulary: inside, people/person, still/now
Common Use Verb: leave/left
Hear Math Put six faces on the overhead in the house.

- Say: "There are six **people** in the house." Write: "6 **people**."
- Remove one person. Say: "How many **people** are still **inside** the house?"
- Write: "6 – 1 is 5. Say: "There are 5 people left **inside**. There are 5 **people inside now**."
- Repeat as time permits.

Independent Work Options

Option 1 — Early Finishers (AL) (OL)
INTERPERSONAL

Materials: toothpicks

- Have students form pairs. Have the first partner create a design using six toothpicks.
- Tell the second partner to take away some toothpicks to create another design.
- Ask partners to write the subtraction story they created, showing 6 take away ___ is ___.
- Tell partners to trade roles and repeat the activity.

Option 2 — Student Technology

Math Online > macmillanmh.com

Math Adventures

Option 3 — Learning Station: Social Studies (p. 313G)

Direct students to the Social Studies Learning Station for opportunities to explore and extend the lesson concept.

Leveled Lesson Resources

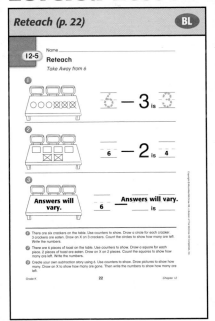

Reteach (p. 22) (BL)

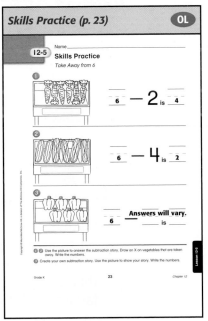

Skills Practice (p. 23) (OL)

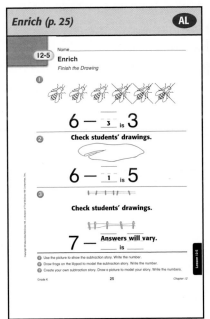

Enrich (p. 25) (AL)

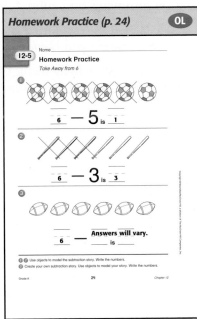

Homework Practice (p. 24) (OL)

① Introduce

Circle Time

Activity Choice 1 • Literature

Roll Over! A Counting Song
by Merle Peek (Illustrator)
Materials: 5" × 8" card, counters

- Read or sing the song aloud. Revisit pages for six.
- Give students six counters and a card for a bed. Have them model: "Six in bed and one falls out."
- **How many are left if two fall out?** four
- Have students create six **take-away** stories.
- As a class, rewrite the story for six in bed and different numbers falling out.

Activity Choice 2 • Hands-On

Materials: bunches of six bananas, yellow connecting cubes

- Give each student six yellow connecting cubes.
- Hold up six bananas. Ask students to create a bunch of six bananas using six connecting cubes.
- Have a volunteer be a monkey and take away one banana. Tell the volunteer to take off one banana. Put the banana behind you.
- Have students model the banana being taken away by removing one cube.
- Discuss how you know that six take away one is five because you have five bananas left.
- Repeat the activity using different number of bananas being taken away.

② Teach

- Direct students to the top of p. 331.
- Discuss how a seal can balance balls on its nose. Act out the number story using counters.
- Tell students to write the number of beach balls on the line to begin a number sentence.
- Have students mark Xs as they take away three balls.
- Tell them to write the number of balls that are left on the line when three is taken away from six.

Ⓑ Alternate Teaching Strategy

If students have trouble with subtracting from six . . .

Then use one of these reteach options.

1. **CRM Daily Reteach Worksheet** (p. 22)

2. **Use Number Cubes** Give each student six counters.
   - Roll a 0–5 number cube. Have students take away that many counters.
   - Have students draw six counters and put an X on how many they are taking away.
   - Have students count and record the answer.
   - Repeat the activity.

⚠ COMMON ERROR!

Students may not understand that putting an X on a picture represents taking away. Have students model taking away with manipulatives, then putting an X on pictures until they are familiar with the process.

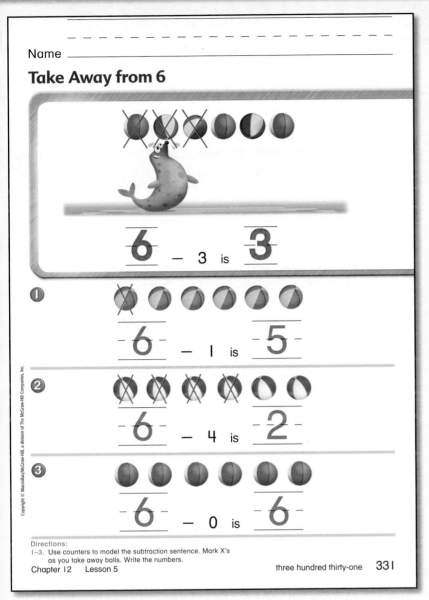

Name _____

Take Away from 6

6 − 3 is 3

① 6 − 1 is 5

② 6 − 4 is 2

③ 6 − 0 is 6

Copyright © Macmillan/McGraw-Hill, a division of The McGraw-Hill Companies, Inc.

Directions:
1–3. Use counters to model the subtraction sentence. Mark X's
      as you take away balls. Write the numbers.
Chapter 12   Lesson 5

three hundred thirty-one   331

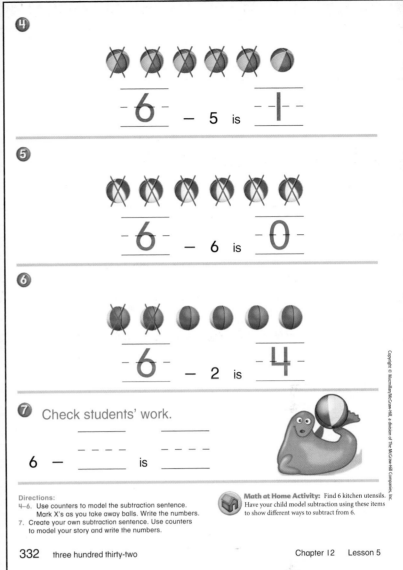

④ 6 − 5 is 1

⑤ 6 − 6 is 0

⑥ 6 − 2 is 4

⑦ Check students' work.

6 − _____ is _____

Copyright © Macmillan/McGraw-Hill, a division of The McGraw-Hill Companies, Inc.

Directions:
4–6. Use counters to model the subtraction sentence.
      Mark X's as you take away balls. Write the numbers.
7. Create your own subtraction sentence. Use counters
   to model your story and write the numbers.

Math at Home Activity: Find 6 kitchen utensils.
Have your child model subtraction using these items
to show different ways to subtract from 6.

332   three hundred thirty-two   Chapter 12   Lesson 5

---

③ Practice

Guided Practice

- Direct students to p. 331.
- Have students use two-colored counters to model the subtraction story in Exercise 1.
- Have students write the total number of balls in the first box.
- Tell them to mark Xs as they take away balls. Have them write the number of balls that are left.
- Repeat the activity for Exercises 2 and 3.

Independent Practice

Have students turn to p. 332 and work independently on the exercises.

④ Assess

✓ Formative Assessment

- **There are six blocks in a tower. Four are removed. How many are left?** 2
- Have students model with blocks and solve the problem using subtraction.

Quick Check	Are students still struggling to subtract from six?

If Yes → Small Group Options (p. 331B)
If No → Independent Work Options (p. 331B)
         CRM Skills Practice Worksheet (p. 23)
         CRM Enrich Worksheet (p. 25)

Lesson 12-5 Take Away from 6   **332**

Take Away from 7

Lesson Planner

Objective
Use concrete objects and pictures to show ways to subtract from 7.

Review Vocabulary
more, less

Resources
Materials: cups, dried beans, pencils, string
Manipulatives: color tiles, attribute buttons
Literature Connection: *Roll Over! A Counting Song* by Merle Peek (Illustrator)
Teacher Technology
● TeacherWorks

Daily Routine

Use these suggestions before beginning the lesson on p. 333

5-Minute Check
(Reviews Lesson 12-5)
How many are left?
1 6 planes are on the ground. 5 fly away. 1
2 6 cats are sleeping. 1 walks away. 5
3 6 kangaroos are standing. 4 hop away. 2
4 6 pumpkins are lined up. 3 roll away. 3

Problem of the Day
Six apples are in a bowl. Four are eaten. How many apples are left? 2

 Have students form sets of seven. Tell three from each set to line up. Ask how many are left in each set. Repeat with different numbers.

Review Math Vocabulary
Materials: clear bowl, goldfish crackers
• Put seven crackers in a bowl.
• Take away two crackers.
• **How many are left?** 5
• Have a volunteer count how many are left.
• Write the subtraction story on the board: 7 minus sign 2 is 5.
• Explain that another way to find how many are left is to start with the set with **more** crackers and subtract the set with **less** crackers.
• Repeat the activity, starting with 7 crackers and taking away 6, 5, 4, 3, 1, or 0 crackers.

Visual Vocabulary Cards
Use Visual Vocabulary Card 20 to reinforce the vocabulary reviewed in this lesson. (The Define/Example/Ask routine is printed on the back of each card.)

Differentiated Instruction

Small Group Options

Option 1 — LOGICAL

Below/Approaching Level (BL)

Materials: pencil, number cubes

- Have students work in pairs. Each partner will take turns drawing seven circles on their paper, while the other partner rolls the number cube.
- The number rolled is the number of circles the student will cross out on the paper.
- The students will write the subtraction problem that goes with the drawn circles and the crossed out circles.
- Each student should take three turns, not duplicating any subtraction problems.

Option 2 — LOGICAL

English Language Learners (ELL)

Core Vocabulary: 7 days in a week, today, let's
Common Use Verb: take off

Hear Math This strategy helps students subtract 7.

- Chant the days of the week. Put a counter on the calendar for each day. Write: "7 days in a week."
- Say: "Today is Monday. Let's take today off." Take 1 day off and write $7 - 1 = 6$. Repeat daily, leaving the written problems. Discuss what to do on the next Monday.

Independent Work Options

Option 1 — SPATIAL

Early Finishers (AL) (OL)

Materials: drawing paper, crayons

- Have each student draw a flower with seven petals.
- Tell them to cross out some of the petals, saying that these petals have blown away.
- Have them trade papers with a partner. Have partners write the subtraction story.

Option 2

Student Technology

Math Online > macmillanmh.com

Math Adventures

Option 3

Learning Station: Health (p. 313G)

Direct students to the Health Learning Station for opportunities to explore and extend the lesson concept.

Leveled Lesson Resources

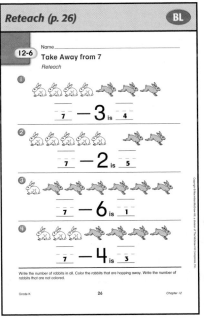

Reteach (p. 26) (BL)

Skills Practice (p. 27) (OL)

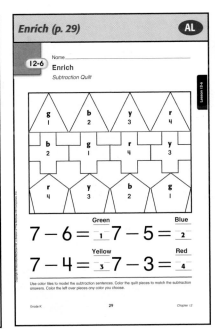

Enrich (p. 29) (AL)

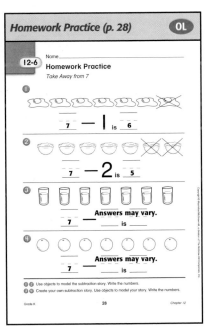

Homework Practice (p. 28) (OL)

① Introduce

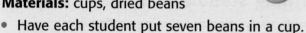

Ⓒircle Time

Activity Choice 1 • Literature

Roll Over! A Counting Song
by Merle Peek (Illustrator)

- Flip to the page of the book which shows the illustration for seven.
- Ask students to count along with you as you identify seven objects in the illustration.
- Lead them through reducing each animal in the illustration, one-by-one. Each time, stop to ask what the new total number of animals in the illustration would be.
- If it would be helpful, provide counters or tiles to students to take away one from their grouping as you take away one from the illustration each time.
- Read the rest of the book to confirm the class's answers.

Activity Choice 2 • Hands-On

Materials: cups, dried beans

- Have each student put seven beans in a cup.
- Call out a number between zero and seven.
- Have students remove that many beans from their cup.
- Have them count how many are left.
- **Is the number of beans left in the cup more or less than the number you removed?** Sample answer: less
- Write the subtraction story.
- Repeat the activity two or three times calling out different numbers.

② Teach

- Direct students to the top of p. 333.
- Discuss how a dog can wear a clown hat. Act out the number story using counters.
- Have students trace 7, the total number of clown hats.
- Have students trace 4, the number of clowns that are left.
- Explain that the subtraction story is 7 take away 3 is 4.

ⒷⓁ Alternate Teaching Strategy

If students have trouble with subtracting from 7 . . .

Then use one of these reteach options.

1 Ⓒⓡⓜ **Daily Reteach Worksheet** (p. 26)
2 **Use Attribute Buttons** Have students string seven attribute buttons together.
   - Tell students how many to buttons take off the string.
   - **What is the math story? How many are left?** Sample answers: 7 − 3; 4
   - Repeat the activity two or three times.

⚠ **COMMON ERROR!**

Students may struggle to keep track of which is their answer when separating objects into two sets. Have them move the objects being taken away out of sight before they count to get the answer.

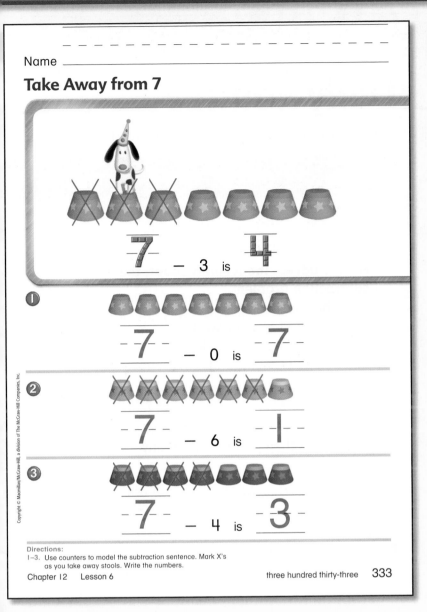

Name _____

Take Away from 7

$7 - 3$ is 4

① $7 - 0$ is 7

② $7 - 6$ is 1

③ $7 - 4$ is 3

Directions:
1–3. Use counters to model the subtraction sentence. Mark X's as you take away stools. Write the numbers.

Chapter 12   Lesson 6

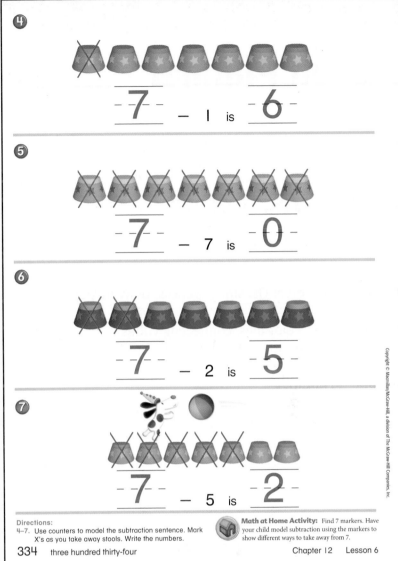

④ $7 - 1$ is 6

⑤ $7 - 7$ is 0

⑥ $7 - 2$ is 5

⑦ $7 - 5$ is 2

Directions:
4–7. Use counters to model the subtraction sentence. Mark X's as you take away stools. Write the numbers.

Math at Home Activity: Find 7 markers. Have your child model subtraction using the markers to show different ways to take away from 7.

Chapter 12   Lesson 6

3 Practice

Guided Practice

Direct students to p. 333.

Have students use counters to make up a subtraction story for Exercise 1. Remind them that 0 is a number.

What is the total number of stools? 7 **What is the number of stools that are left?** 7 Have students write the numbers.

Repeat the activity for Exercises 2 and 3.

Independent Practice

Have students turn to p. 334 and work independently on the exercises.

4 Assess

✓ Formative Assessment

- **Seven flowers are in a vase. Four flowers are taken away. How many are left?** 3

- Have students solve the problem using subtraction, modeling the problem using color tiles.

Quick Check **Are students still struggling to subtract from 7?**

If Yes → Small Group Options (p. 333B)

If No → Independent Work Options (p. 333B)

CRM Skills Practice Worksheet (p. 27)

CRM Enrich Worksheet (p. 29)

Lesson 12-6 Take Away from 7   **334**

Lesson Planner

Objective
Use concrete objects and pictures to show ways to subtract from 8.

Review Vocabulary
take away

Resources
Materials: dry cereal Os, string, pencils, drawing paper, crayons

Manipulatives: color tiles, connecting cubes

Literature Connection: *Monster Musical Chairs* by Stuart J. Murphy

Teacher Technology
- TeacherWorks

Daily Routine

Use these suggestions before beginning the lesson on p. 335.

5-Minute Check
(Reviews Lesson 12-6)

Have students model with cubes, then write the subtraction problem.

1. 7 balloons and 5 pop $7 - 5 = 2$
2. 7 fish and 4 swim away $7 - 4 = 3$
3. 7 dandelions and 2 blow away $7 - 2 = 5$
4. 7 butterflies and 7 fly away $7 - 7 = 0$

Problem of the Day

Seven horses are running together. The owner takes six of them home. How many are left? 1

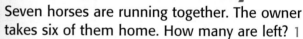 Have students take away their age from eight. Then call out possible answers. If it matches their answer, have them line up. Continue until all are in line.

▷ Review Math Vocabulary

- Tell a subtraction story about eight fish and two that swim away.
- Have students model the problems by taking away two counters.
- Write on the chalkboard: 8 **take away** 2 is 6.
- Discuss how take away is represented by a symbol, the minus sign.
- Erase the words and write: 8 − 2 is 6.
- Repeat the activity with similar problems.

Differentiated Instruction

Small Group Options

Option 1 — Gifted and Talented (AL)
LOGICAL

Materials: spinners, counters, paper, pencils

- Have students form small groups. Give each group a spinner, eight counters, paper, and pencils.
- Have students take turns laying out eight counters, then drawing circles to represent the counters.
- Have others spin the spinner, take away that many counters, and cross out that many circles.
- Have students trade roles and repeat the activity so all students get a turn.

Option 2 — English Language Learners (ELL)
LOGICAL, SOCIAL

Core Vocabulary: the fence, our zoo, How many are left?
Common Use Verb: jumped over
Do Math This strategy helps students internalize subtracting from 8.

- Write scaffolding: "We have ____ animals in our zoo. ____ jumped over the fence! How many are left?"
- Have eight students act like lions, monkeys, or bears. Have them act out the subtraction story as you read it.

Independent Work Options

Option 1 — Early Finishers (AL) (OL)
KINESTHETIC

Materials: scissors, paper, hole punch, string

- Cut out circles. Punch eight holes in each circle for legs. Cut string into 8-inch lengths.
- Give each student a prepared circle and eight strings. Say that the circle is a spider and to loop a string through each hole to make eight legs.
- Tell students a take away from eight problem, such as 8 − 4. Have students take four legs off the spider, then count to see that four legs are left.
- Have them put all legs on the spider. Repeat the activity with different take away from eight problems.

Option 2 — Student Technology

Math Online 〉 macmillanmh.com

Math Adventures

Option 3 — Learning Station: Language Arts (p. 313H)

Direct students to the Language Arts Learning Station for opportunities to explore and extend the lesson concept.

Leveled Lesson Resources

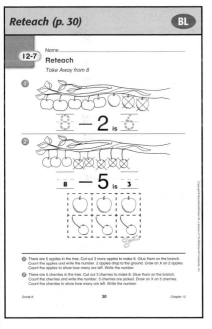

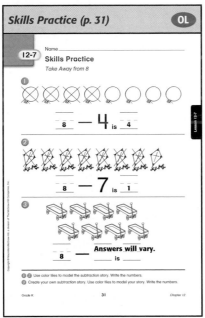

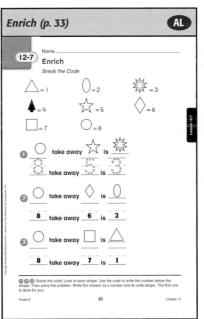

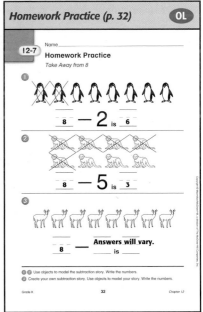

1 Introduce

Circle Time

Activity Choice 1 • Literature

Monster Musical Chairs
by Stuart J. Murphy

- After reading the story, play musical chairs with the class. Play two games with only eight students in a game. Show how every round someone is out and that we take away one person.

- Say a new sentence when each student is out. For example, "Eight take away one is seven students left in the game."

- If desired, take out more than one chair every time. This will show different subtraction numbers.

Activity Choice 2 • Hands-On

Materials: dry cereal Os, string

- Have students make a bracelet by stringing eight pieces of cereal on a string.

- Tell students to take away three. Have students take away three by eating them.

- **How many are left?** 5

- Have students refill their necklaces to eight.

- Repeat the activity with other numbers.

2 Teach

- Direct students to the top of p. 335.

- Discuss snorkeling and how the goggles allow you to see fish underwater.

- Have students count the number of goggles.

- Have students mark Xs as they take away goggles.

- Direct students to write the number of goggles that are left on the next line.

- Repeat with the snorkels.

BL Alternate Teaching Strategy

If students have trouble with taking away from eight . . .

Then use one of these reteach options.

1 CRM **Daily Reteach Worksheet** (p. 30)

2 **Use Color Tiles** Have students make up their own "take away from eight" story. Then have them draw their story on the front of a piece of drawing paper.

- On the back, have them show how to model their problem with color tiles. Then have them draw what they did.

- On both sides of the paper, tell them to write their subtraction story.

! COMMON ERROR!

Students may struggle with problems that do not say "take away." Review ways that things can be taken away, such as a fish can swim away or a grape can be eaten.

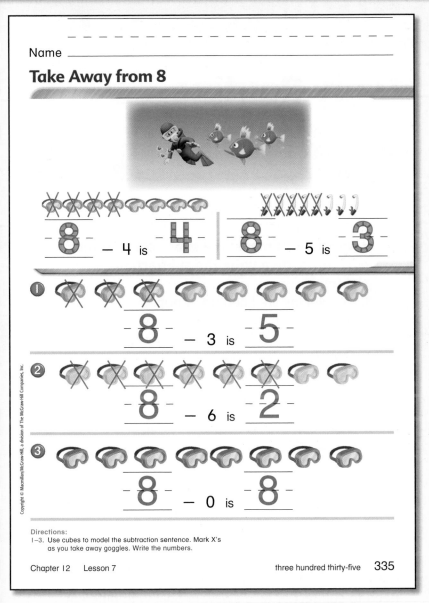

Name _____

Take Away from 8

$8 - 4$ is 4 | $8 - 5$ is 3

① $8 - 3$ is 5

② $8 - 6$ is 2

③ $8 - 0$ is 8

Directions:
1–3. Use cubes to model the subtraction sentence. Mark X's as you take away goggles. Write the numbers.

Chapter 12   Lesson 7   three hundred thirty-five   335

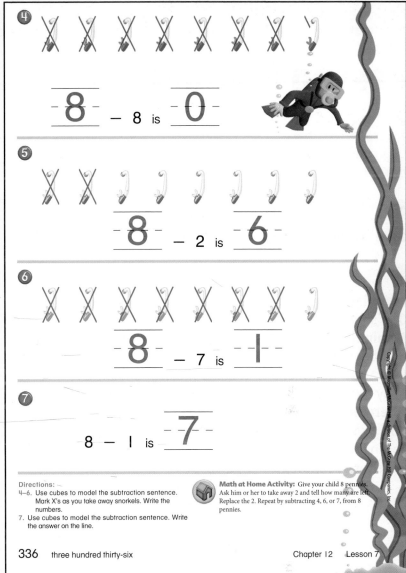

④ $8 - 8$ is 0

⑤ $8 - 2$ is 6

⑥ $8 - 7$ is 1

⑦ $8 - 1$ is 7

Directions:
4–6. Use cubes to model the subtraction sentence. Mark X's as you take away snorkels. Write the numbers.
7. Use cubes to model the subtraction sentence. Write the answer on the line.

Math at Home Activity: Give your child 8 pennies. Ask him or her to take away 2 and tell how many are left. Replace the 2. Repeat by subtracting 4, 6, or 7, from 8 pennies.

336   three hundred thirty-six   Chapter 12   Lesson 7

③ Practice

Guided Practice

- Direct students to p. 335.
- Have them use cubes to model the subtraction story in Exercise 1.
- Tell them to mark Xs as they take away goggles. Have them write the number of goggles that are left.
- Repeat the activity for Exercises 2 and 3.

Independent Practice

Have students turn to p. 336. Explain the directions and have students work independently on the exercises.

④ Assess

Formative Assessment

- There are eight fish in a bowl. Six of them are removed. How many are left? 2
- Have students model with cubes and solve the problem using subtraction.

Quick Check	**Are students still struggling to subtract from eight?**

If Yes → Small Group Options (p. 335B)

If No → Independent Work Options (p. 335B)

CRM Skills Practice Worksheet (p. 31)

CRM Enrich Worksheet (p. 33)

Lesson 12-7 Take Away from 8   **336**

Lesson Planner

Objective

Use concrete objects and pictures to show ways to subtract from 9.

Review Vocabulary

take away

Resources

Materials: egg cartons, pencils, plastic bag, crayons, 0–9 spinner

Manipulatives: connecting cubes, two-color counters, number cubes, connectiong cubes

Literature Connection: *Monster Musical Chairs* by Stuart J. Murphy

Alternate Lesson: Adopt *Lift the Bowl* on pages 181 and 182 of *Math Their Way* to provide practice with subtraction solving for 9.

Teacher Technology

💿 TeacherWorks

Daily Routine

Use these suggestions before beginning the lesson on p. 337.

5-Minute Check

(Reviews Lesson 12-7)

Have students model the subtraction stories with cubes, then write the subtraction problems.

1. 8 balloons are lined up. 5 pop. $8 - 5 = 3$
2. 8 fish are in a group. 4 swim away. $8 - 4 = 4$
3. 8 leaves are on a branch. 2 blow away. $8 - 2 = 6$
4. 8 rocks are in a pile. 8 tumble away. $8 - 8 = 0$

Problem of the Day

8 dogs are playing together. 6 go home. How many are left? 2

LINE UP Have nine students line up. Say that you want seven students in line. Ask how many do you need to subtract or take away. Repeat with different numbers until all students are in line.

▶ Review Math Vocabulary

- Have nine volunteers sit in front of the class. Play the game called *Hot Potato*. Take away one student each round.

- Write the subtraction problem on the chalkboard.

- Ask students the answer for each round of hot potato. **How many students are sitting down now?** Sample answer: 8

Differentiated Instruction

Small Group Options

Option 1 · Gifted and Talented (AL)
LOGICAL

Materials: connecting cubes, number cubes, paper, pencil

- Each pair of students should make six rows of connecting cubes with nine cubes in each row.
- The partners will take turns rolling a number cube and breaking that number of connecting cubes off of one of the rows. The students will write the subtraction problem describing how many cubes they started with and taking away the number of cubes shown on the number cube they rolled.
- Have students take turns until they have made six different subtraction problems.

Option 2 · English Language Learners (ELL)
AUDITORY, KINESTHETIC

Core Vocabulary: silly, jumps down, swinging
Common Use Verb: sit
Talk Math This strategy teaches taking away from 9.

- Chant the following as students act it out:

  9 little monkeys swinging in the tree.
  They're as silly as can be.
  One jumps down to sit with me.
  Now there are 8 little monkeys still to see.

- Repeat as time permits.

Independent Work Options

Option 1 · Early Finishers (AL) (OL)
LOGICAL

Materials: drawing paper, counters of two different colors, pencils, paper

- Draw a tic-tac-toe board on paper. Distribute to each student. Have them put a counter in each of the nine spaces.
- Tell them to take away all the counters of one color.
- Have them record the subtraction story on a separate sheet of paper, then write the answer.
- Have students repeat the activity with different combinations of counters.

Option 2 · Student Technology

Math Online ▷ macmillanmh.com

Math Adventures

Option 3 · Learning Station: Art (p. 313G)

Direct students to the Art Learning Station for opportunities to explore and extend the lesson concept.

Leveled Lesson Resources

Reteach (p. 34) BL	Skills Practice (p. 35) OL	Enrich (p. 37) AL	Homework Practice (p. 36) OL
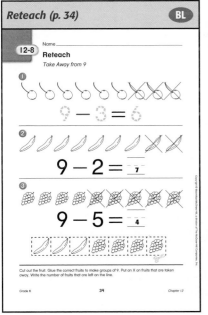	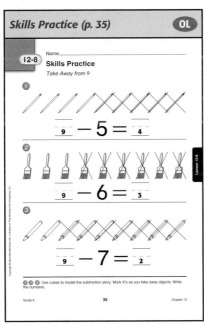	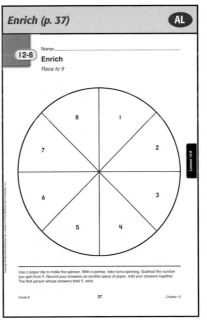	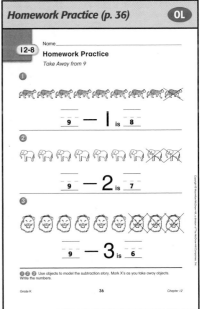

1 Introduce

Circle Time

Activity Choice 1 • Literature

Monster Musical Chairs
by Stuart J. Murphy

- Read the story.
- Have volunteers draw nine monsters on the board.
- Have a volunteer roll a number cube. The number that they roll will determine how many monsters to cross out.
- Ask the class how many monsters are left.
- Play until there are exactly 0 monsters on the board.
- Repeat the activity if time permits.

Activity Choice 2 • Hands-On

Materials: 18-count egg cartons, connecting cubes

- Cut 18-count egg cartons in half so that each half has nine spaces.
- Distribute a prepared egg carton and nine cubes to each student.
- Tell them to put a cube in each space.
- Instruct students to take away 0–9 cubes.
- **How many are left?** Sample answers: six
- Ask a volunteer to say the subtraction problem.
- Repeat the activity using other numbers of cubes to take away.

2 Teach

- Direct students to the top of p. 337.
- Discuss how some ships carry treasure. Act out the number story using connecting cubes for the treasure chests.
- Tell students to trace 9, and begin a number sentence.
- Tell them to trace 5, the number of chests that are left. Explain that the subtraction story is 9 take away 4 is 5.
- Repeat the activity with the coins, having students trace the total number of coins and the number of coins that are left. Explain that the subtraction story is 9 take away 2 is 7.

BL Alternate Teaching Strategy

If students have trouble with subtracting from 9. . .

Then use one of these reteach options.

1. **CRM** **Daily Reteach Worksheet** (p. 34)
2. **Use Crayons** Have each student put nine crayons in a plastic bag.
   - Spin a 0–9 spinner. Tell students that they are to take away that number of crayons from their bag.
   - Have students count how many are left.
   - Record the subtraction problem on the chalkboard.
   - Repeat the activity two or more times.

! COMMON ERROR!

Students may add rather than subtract when using manipulatives. Limit the number of manipulatives they start with to the original number. Gradually add more.

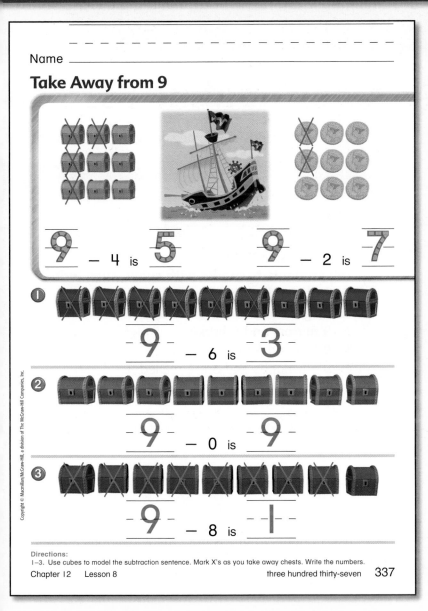

Name _____

Take Away from 9

9 − 4 is 5   9 − 2 is 7

① 9 − 6 is 3

② 9 − 0 is 9

③ 9 − 8 is 1

Directions:
1–3. Use cubes to model the subtraction sentence. Mark X's as you take away chests. Write the numbers.

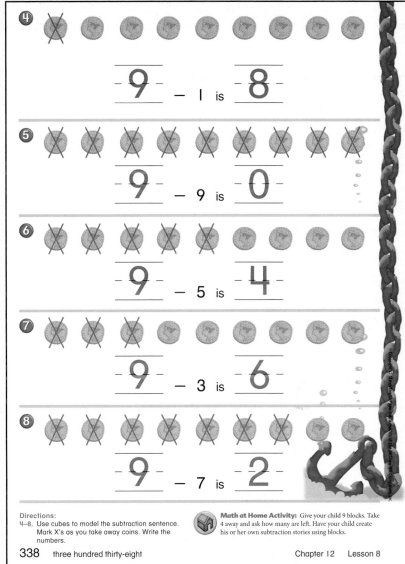

④ 9 − 1 is 8

⑤ 9 − 9 is 0

⑥ 9 − 5 is 4

⑦ 9 − 3 is 6

⑧ 9 − 7 is 2

Directions:
4–8. Use cubes to model the subtraction sentence. Mark X's as you take away coins. Write the numbers.

Math at Home Activity: Give your child 9 blocks. Take 4 away and ask how many are left. Have your child create his or her own subtraction stories using blocks.

③ Practice

Guided Practice

- Direct students to p. 337.
- Have students use cubes to make a subtraction story for Exercise 1.
- **What are the total number of coins and the number of coins that are left?** 9, 3 Have students write the numbers.
- Repeat the activity for Exercises 2 and 3.

Independent Practice

Have students turn to p. 338 and work independently on the exercises.

④ Assess

✓ Formative Assessment

- **There are nine coins in a bowl. Three are given away. How many are left?** 6
- Have students solve the problem using subtraction, modeling the problem using counters.

Quick Check	Are students still struggling to subtract from 9?

If Yes → Small Group Options (p. 337B)

If No → Independent Work Options (p. 337B)

　　CRM Skills Practice Worksheet (p. 35)

　　CRM Enrich Worksheet (p. 37)

Lesson 12-8 Take Away from 9   **338**

Lesson Planner

Objective

Students will use the strategy of *guess and check* to subtract from 7, 8, and 9.

Resources

Materials: pencils, poster paper, markers, sticky notes

Manipulatives: connecting cubes, two-color counters

Literature Connection: *Ten Black Dots* by Donald Crews

Teacher Technology

💿 TeacherWorks

📖 **Real-World Problem Solving Library**

Math and Social Studies: *Pets Find a Home*

Use these leveled readers to reinforce and extend problem-solving skills and strategies.

Leveled for:

OL On Level

ELL Sheltered English

SP Spanish

For additional support, see Real-World Problem Solving Teacher Guide.

On-level title is available in classroom Big Book.

Daily Routine

Use these suggestions before beginning the lesson on p. 339.

5-Minute Check

(Reviews Lesson 12-8)

Tell students to model with cubes, then write the subtraction problem.

1. 9 light bulbs and 2 burned out $9 - 2 = 7$
2. 9 mirrors and 5 broke $9 - 5 = 4$
3. 9 fish and 8 were caught $9 - 8 = 1$
4. 9 envelopes and 3 are mailed $9 - 3 = 6$

Problem of the Day

Ask students to guess how many balloons are left. Have them check their work by counting. GUESS: 3 CHECK: 3

LINE UP **Five apples are lined up and two are eaten. How many are left?** 3 Have a volunteer guess the answer and if it is correct have that many students line up. Have another volunteer check the answer. Have that many students line up. Repeat until all students are in line.

Differentiated Instruction

Small Group Options

Option 1
KINESTHETIC/LOGICAL

Below/Approaching Level BL

Materials: paper, pencil

- Each student should trace each of their hands on their paper so that you can see each of their 10 fingers.
- Have the student use their finger drawings for a clue to write subtraction problems using 10.
- The students should have 10 different subtraction problems.

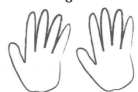

Option 2
VISUAL

English Language Learners ELL

Core Vocabulary: open, by, cover up
Common Use Verb: can prove
Materials: marker, transparency
See Math This strategy teaches algebraic thinking through the guess and check process.

- Pair students. Give each pair 7 to 9 counters.
- Say: "Count your counters."
- Have one student hold some counters behind their back. The other student should guess how many are hidden. Then they should check.
- Have pairs repeat, switching roles.
- Repeat as time permits.

Independent Work Options

Option 1
LOGICAL

Early Finishers AL OL

Materials: five jars, classroom objects, pencils, paper

- Fill each jar with 1–10 objects such as cotton balls, erasers, or pencils.
- Have students guess and record how many objects are in each jar.
- Tell them to check to see if their guesses were correct. Tell them to record their checks on their paper.
- Have students put a check next to each answer that they guessed correctly.

Option 2

Student Technology

Math Online ▶ macmillanmh.com

Option 3

Learning Station: Art (p. 313G)

Direct students to the Art Learning Station for opportunities to explore and extend the lesson concept.

Leveled Lesson Resources

| Reteach (pp. 38–39) BL | Skills Practice (p. 40) OL | Enrich (p. 42) AL | Homework Practice (p. 41) OL |

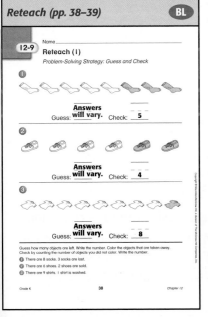

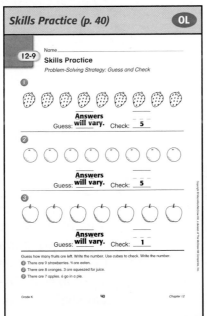

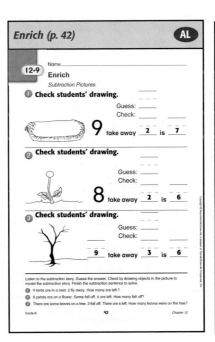

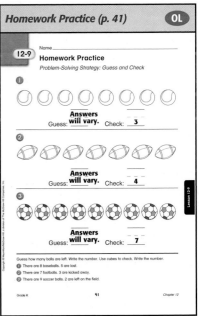

1 Introduce

Circle Time

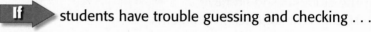

Activity Choice 1 • Literature

Ten Black Dots
by Donald Crews

- Hold up the chart on the last two pages of the book. Discuss how the numbers are represented, and the visual relationships between numbers of different sizes.
- Place seven red counters in a row.
- Model subtraction of one by flipping one chip. Proceed to subtract one from seven and eight in a similar manner.
- Distribute two-colored counters. Have students use the counters to model subtracting one from seven, eight, and nine.

Activity Choice 2 • Hands-On

- Have students stand in sets of five.
- Ask volunteers to guess how many students would remain if three sat down.
- Have three students in each set sit down.
- Check the guesses by counting how many are left aloud with the class.
- Repeat the activity with sets of different numbers and different numbers of students sitting down.

2 Teach

- Direct students to the top of p. 339.

Understand Review what students know and what they need to find for each problem.

Plan Have students discuss their strategy for solving the problems.

Solve Guide students to guess and check in order to solve the problems. Discuss with students what it means to guess. Review how students should check their guesses.

Check Have students look back at the problem to be sure that the answers fit what they already know about the problem.

BL Alternate Teaching Strategy

If students have trouble guessing and checking . . .

Then use one of these reteach options.

1. CRM **Daily Reteach Worksheet** (p. 38-39)

2. **Poster Guesses** Create mini-posters of different subtraction problems, such as: 6 candles, 2 burned, how many are left?
   - Have students write their guesses on sticky notes and put them on the posters.
   - Tell students to use cubes to check their answers.
   - Have students take their sticky notes and write their check number on the backs.

> **! COMMON ERROR!**
> Students may struggle with the idea that their original guess may be incorrect. Emphasize that a good guess may not be correct, but their check fixes it. Explain that guess and check is a two-step process.

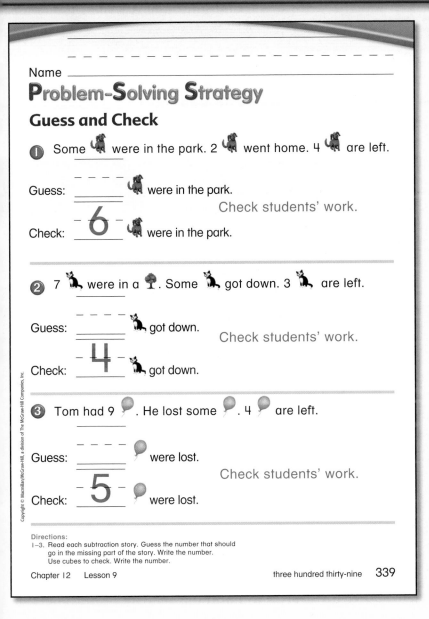
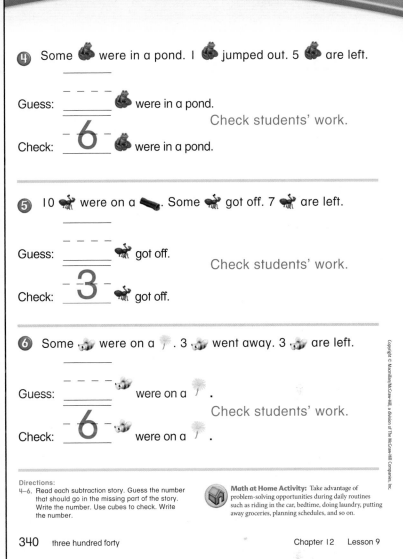

Problem-Solving Strategy

Guess and Check

1 Some 🐕 were in the park. 2 🐕 went home. 4 🐕 are left.

Guess: _____ 🐕 were in the park.

                             Check students' work.

Check: __6__ 🐕 were in the park.

2 7 🐈 were in a 🌳. Some 🐈 got down. 3 🐈 are left.

Guess: _____ 🐈 got down.

                      Check students' work.

Check: __4__ 🐈 got down.

3 Tom had 9 🎈. He lost some 🎈. 4 🎈 are left.

Guess: _____ 🎈 were lost.

                      Check students' work.

Check: __5__ 🎈 were lost.

Directions:
1–3. Read each subtraction story. Guess the number that should go in the missing part of the story. Write the number. Use cubes to check. Write the number.

4 Some 🐸 were in a pond. 1 🐸 jumped out. 5 🐸 are left.

Guess: _____ 🐸 were in a pond.

                      Check students' work.

Check: __6__ 🐸 were in a pond.

5 10 🐜 were on a 🪵. Some 🐜 got off. 7 🐜 are left.

Guess: _____ 🐜 got off.

                      Check students' work.

Check: __3__ 🐜 got off.

6 Some 🐝 were on a 🌼. 3 🐝 went away. 3 🐝 are left.

Guess: _____ 🐝 were on a 🌼.

                      Check students' work.

Check: __6__ 🐝 were on a 🌼.

Directions:
4–6. Read each subtraction story. Guess the number that should go in the missing part of the story. Write the number. Use cubes to check. Write the number.

Math at Home Activity: Take advantage of problem-solving opportunities during daily routines such as riding in the car, bedtime, doing laundry, putting away groceries, planning schedules, and so on.

3 Practice

Guided Practice

- Direct students to p. 339.
- Ask what the dogs are doing in the Exercise 1.
- Ask students to describe the subtraction story that it models.
- Have students write down their guess.
- Have students use cubes to model the problem and write down the check number.
- Repeat this activity with Exercises 2 and 3.

Independent Practice

Have students turn to p. 340 and work independently on the exercises.

4 Assess

✓ Formative Assessment

- **There are some cups of water and students drink three of them. There are five left. How many cups were there to start?** 8
- Have students guess, then check their guess by using manipulatives.

Quick Check	Are students still struggling to use the problem-solving strategy *guess and check*?

If Yes → Small Group Options (p. 339B)

If No → Independent Work Options (p. 339B)

      CRM Skills Practice Worksheet (p. 40)

      CRM Enrich Worksheet (p. 42)

Lesson 12-9 Problem-Solving Strategy **340**

Lesson Planner

Objective

Use the equal sign (=) in addition and subtraction sentences.

Vocabulary

equal sign (=)

Resources

Manipulatives: connecting cubes, two-colored counters

Alternate Lesson: Use *The Hand Game* on page 237 to provide additional practice using the minus, plus, and equal signs.

Use *IMPACT Mathematics*: Unit D to provide practice with comprehending the equal sign.

Literature Connection: *Rooster's Off to See the World* by Eric Carle

Teacher Technology

TeacherWorks

Focus on Math Background

This lesson is the last in a series of lessons in this chapter designed to introduce kindergarteners to symbols related to formal number operations. In this lesson, students practice using and writing (=) to represent equivalent sets. Be aware, however, that instead of thinking about the equal sign in terms of its correct algebraic representation for equivalency, children are often tempted to use this sign to indicate the result of a combining or separating action.

Daily Routine

Use these suggestions before beginning the lesson on p. 341.

5-Minute Check

(Reviews Lesson 12-9)

Have students use color counters to model the ways to subtract from nine by solving the subtraction sentences below.

1. $9 - 3 = 6$ 4. $9 - 6 = 3$
2. $9 - 7 = 2$ 5. $9 - 4 = 5$
3. $9 - 2 = 7$

Problem of the Day

If you have 7 balloons and 2 of them pop, how many balloons do you have left? 5

LINE UP Show students a number card, such as four. Have students say a number sentence using *equals*, such as "three plus one equals four."

Building Math Vocabulary

- Display five red tiles and two blue tiles. Write "5 + 2" on the chalkboard. Ask students to count.
- **How many tiles are there in all?** seven
- Write a 7 to the right of the addition sentence, leaving a space between the 2 and the 7.
- Have students say "five plus two equals seven," and draw an **equal sign (=)** on the chalkboard between the 2 and the 7.
- Help students understand that the equal sign shows that total amounts on each side of the equal sign are the same, or equal.

Differentiated Instruction

Small Group Options

Option 1 **Below/Approaching Level** BL

KINESTHETIC

Materials: connecting cubes, crayons

- Have students use toothpicks and model an equal sign. On one side of the equal sign, have them place three connecting cubes. On the other side two connecting cubes.
- Dictate subtraction stories. Have students model the stories using cubes and toothpicks.
- **How many connecting cubes are left?** one

Option 2 **English Language Learners** ELL

AUDITORY, LINGUISTIC

Core Vocabulary: plus, equals, minus
Common Use Verb: fix
Do Math This strategy teaches equal groups.

- Ask 2 boys to stand to your left and 2 girls to stand to your right.
- Model thumbs up for equal and thumbs down for not equal. Show an equal sign above you.
- Repeat with unequal groups.
- Have a student "fix" unequal groups. Repeat as times permits.

Independent Work Options

Option 1 **Early Finishers** OL AL

LINGUISTIC

Materials: two number spinners, two colors of connecting cubes

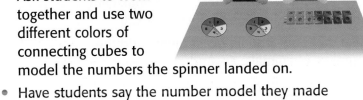

- Have students take turns spinning each spinner.
- Ask students to work together and use two different colors of connecting cubes to model the numbers the spinner landed on.
- Have students say the number model they made including "equals" and the answer. For example: three plus four equals seven.

Option 2 **Student Technology**

Math Online ▷ macmillanmh.com

Option 3 **Learning Station: Social Studies** (p. 313G)

Direct students to the Social Studies Learning Station for opportunities to explore and extend the lesson concept.

Leveled Lesson Resources
Additional support for English Language Learners can be found in the ELL Guide (p. 45). ELL

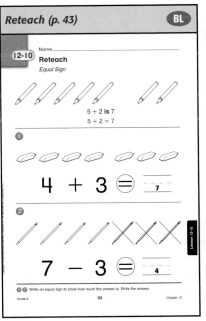

Reteach (p. 43) BL

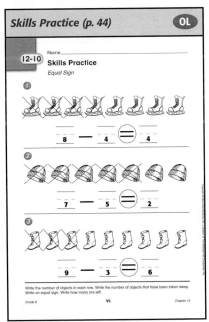

Skills Practice (p. 44) OL

Enrich (p. 46) AL

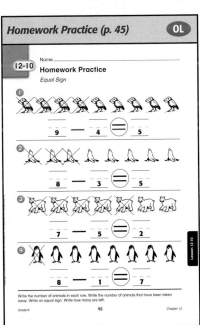

Homework Practice (p. 45) OL

① Introduce

Circle Time

Activity Choice 1 • Literature

Rooster's Off to See the World
by Eric Carle

Materials: connecting cubes

- Distribute 15 connecting cubes to each student.
- As the story is read, have students connect the amount of cubes that corresponds with the number of animals joining Rooster.
- Use the term "equals" as students add the number of animals. Ex. Add one rooster and two cats. How many animals does that equal? Have students count together.
- Continue throughout the story.

After reading, ask students additional questions based on the story. Ex: Add three frogs and four turtles. How many animals does that equal? Write the problems on the board so students see the symbols.

Activity Choice 2 • Hands-On

Materials: connecting cubes

- Have students work in pairs. Give each pair ten connecting cubes. Have one partner model a five-cube train. Have the other partner model taking away a two-cube train.
- Write "5 – 2 is 3" on the chalkboard.
- Have one partner create the three-cube train to show the answer. **What can you say about the two groups of cubes?** They both have three cubes.
- Erase the word "is" from the number story and write the **equal sign (=).**
- Tell the students that the equal sign tells us that the amount on one side of the sign is the same as the amount on the other side.
- Model the subtraction example again using five cubes minus two cubes equals three cubes. Have students repeat "five minus two equals three."
- Repeat the activity with 2 + 2, 1 + 4, and 2 + 1.

② Teach

- Distribute two-colored counters to each student. Call students' attention to the top of p. 341.
- Ask them to describe the illustration.
- Have students model the illustration by placing red counters on top of the four orange slices and yellow counters on top of the two orange slices.
- **How can you find the number of fruit slices in all?** Count them or add four plus two.
- Have students count the counters to find the total, six.
- **What is the total number of fruit slices when the two sets are added together?** six
- Have students say the addition story in unison: "Four plus two equals six." Then have them fill in the numbers 4, 2, and 6. Have them trace the equal sign as they say "equals."

ⒷⓁAlternate Teaching Strategy

If students have trouble understanding how to use the equal sign . . .

Then use one of these reteach options.

1 ⒸⓇⓂ **Daily Reteach Worksheet** (p. 43)

2 **Use the Equal Sign** Provide each student with an index card that has the equal sign on it. Give students a handful of connecting cubes.

- Have students make a train of three cubes, a train of five cubes, and a train of eight cubes. Instruct students to put the two shortest trains on the table, then to put the card to the right of the cubes.
- **How can you show addition using numbers and signs?** $3 + 5 = 8$
- Have students put their eight-cube train on the other side of the equals card.
- **What do both sides of the card equal?** eight

> **! COMMON ERROR!**
>
> Some students may have difficulty understanding the concept of equals. Show them equal groups of items and point out that the number of items on one side of the equal sign is the same as the number of items on the other side.

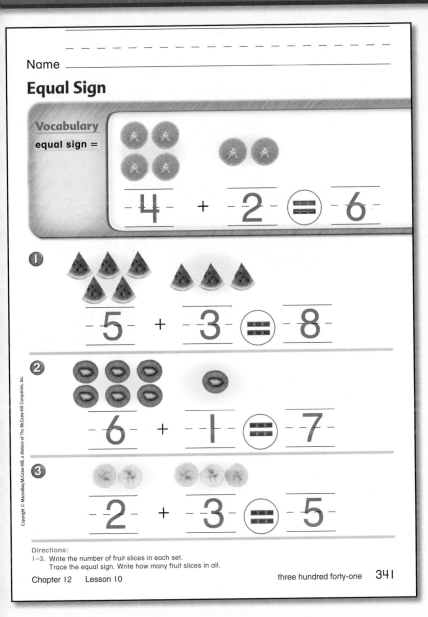

Equal Sign

Vocabulary
equal sign =

$-4- + -2- \bigcirc\!\!= -6-$

① $-5- + -3- \bigcirc\!\!= -8-$

② $-6- + --\!\!|- \bigcirc\!\!= -7-$

③ $-2- + -3- \bigcirc\!\!= -5-$

Directions:
1–3. Write the number of fruit slices in each set.
Trace the equal sign. Write how many fruit slices in all.

Chapter 12   Lesson 10

three hundred forty-one   **341**

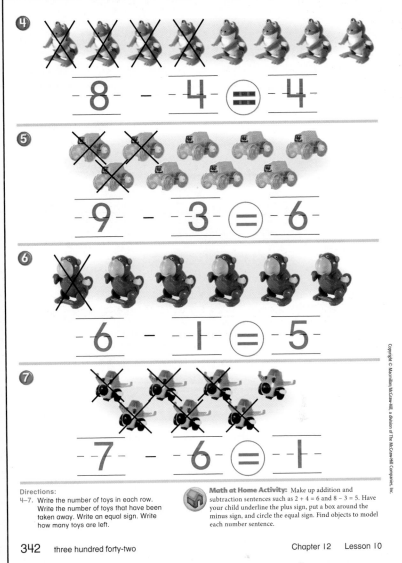

④ $-8- - -4- \bigcirc\!\!= -4-$

⑤ $-9- - -3- = -6-$

⑥ $-6- - --\!\!|- = -5-$

⑦ $-7- - -6- = --\!\!|-$

Directions:
4–7. Write the number of toys in each row.
Write the number of toys that have been
taken away. Write an equal sign. Write
how many toys are left.

Math at Home Activity: Make up addition and
subtraction sentences such as 2 + 4 = 6 and 8 – 3 = 5. Have
your child underline the plus sign, put a box around the
minus sign, and circle the equal sign. Find objects to model
each number sentence.

342   three hundred forty-two

Chapter 12   Lesson 10

---

③ Practice

Guided Practice

• Direct students to p. 341.

• Repeat the procedure for Exercises 1–3. Have students use counters to model the problem and add to solve the problem. Write the numbers and equal sign.

Independent Practice

Have students turn to p. 342. Explain the directions. Have students work independently on the exercises.

④ Assess

✓ Formative Assessment

• Show students an addition or subtraction equation using numbers and the plus sign or minus sign. Show pictures to represent the numbers.

• Have students use color tiles to model the addition or subtraction sentences and to write the minus or plus sign, the equal sign, and the number answer.

Quick Check **Are students still struggling to use the equal sign?**

If Yes → Small Group Options (p. 341B)

If No → Independent Work Options (p. 341B)

[CRM] Skills Practice Worksheet (p. 44)

[CRM] Enrich Worksheet (p. 46)

Lesson 12-10 Equal Sign   **342**

Problem Solving
in Science

Real-World MATH

Earth is not the same in all places.

This book belongs to

_____

A

There is land on Earth.

B

Lesson Planner

Objective Use subtraction to solve problems.

National Standard

Understand organisms and their environments.

Activate Prior Knowledge

Before you turn students' attention to the pages, discuss the Earth.

- **What is Earth?** Sample answers: where we live; a planet
- **Have you ever visited somewhere that is different from where you live?** Sample answer: yes, a desert
- **What are postcards?** Sample answer: small cards with a picture on one side and a short note on the other side
- **Why do people send postcards?** Sample answers: They are on vacation and want someone to see what Earth is like where they are; they want to show what Earth is like where they live.

There is water on Earth.

C

I had 6 pictures of water and land.
I gave 2 away.
How many pictures do I have now?

_____ pictures

D

FOLD DOWN

Create the Book

Guide students to create their book.

- Have them fold the page in half.

- Ask them to write their name on page A.

- Explain that page A is the front cover and page D is the back cover. If necessary, have them practice flipping through the book in order.

- Guide them in reading the information and word problems on each of the pages.

Use the Student Pages

After finishing pages A–C, have students add or count to see how many postcards there are.

Page D Encourage students to use the picture to count the solution. Students also could act out the problem using index cards or real postcards.

WRITING IN ▶ **MATH** Describe a place you would like to visit and the ways it is different from where you live. Draw a picture of this place. Write the number of how many places you remember visiting.

Extend the Lesson

Have students create and solve different postcard subtraction stories.

 FOLDABLES® Dinah Zike's Foldables

Use these lesson suggestions for incorporating the Foldables during the chapter.

Lesson 12-4 On the third page of the journal, use pictures that can be taped or glued into the journal to show different subtraction problems to illustrate taking away from four and five.

Lesson 12-5 On the remaining pages of the journal, use pictures that can be taped or glued into the journal to show different subtraction problems to illustrate taking away from six.

Lesson 12-6 On the remaining pages of the journal, use pictures that can be taped or glued into the journal to show different subtraction problems to illustrate taking away from seven.

Chapter 12 Project

Illustrate Subtraction Number Stories
Lead a discussion on the results of the completed chapter project with the class.

Vocabulary Review

Review chapter vocabulary using one of the following options.

- **Visual Vocabulary Card** (42)
- **eGlossary** at macmillanmh.com

Data-Driven Decision Making

Based on the results of the Chapter Review/Test Check, use the following to review concepts that continue to present students with problems.

Exercises	State/Local Standards	What's the Math?	Error Analysis	Resources for Review
1 Lesson 12-2		Use concrete objects to determine answers to subtraction problems.	Subtracts incorrectly. Writes wrong number.	CRM Chapter 12 Resource Masters (Reteach Worksheets)
2 Lesson 12-7		Use concrete objects to subtract from 8.	Uses incorrect digits in number sentence. Puts wrong number of "X's." Puts "X's" on wrong part of problem.	Math Online ▶ Concepts in Motion Math Adventures
3 Lesson 12-6		Use concrete objects to subtract from 7.	Uses incorrect digits in number sentence. Puts wrong number of "X's." Puts "X's" on wrong part of problem.	
4 Lesson 12-4		Use concrete objects to show ways to subtract from 4 and 5.	Creates an addition story. Write numbers that do not match number used.	

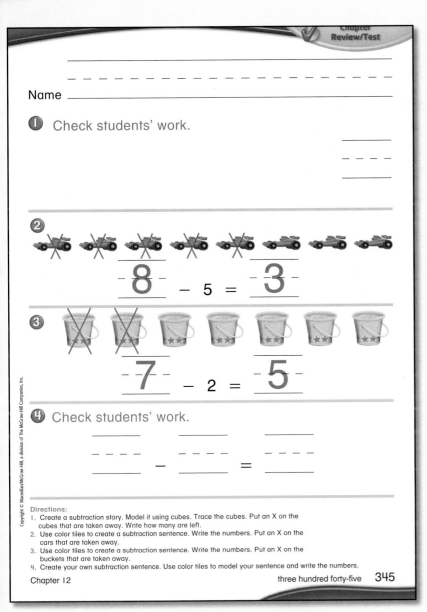

Name _____

① Check students' work.

② 8 – 5 = 3

③ 7 – 2 = 5

④ Check students' work.

___ – ___ = ___

Directions:
1. Create a subtraction story. Model it using cubes. Trace the cubes. Put an X on the cubes that are taken away. Write how many are left.
2. Use color tiles to create a subtraction sentence. Write the numbers. Put an X on the cars that are taken away.
3. Use color tiles to create a subtraction sentence. Write the numbers. Put an X on the buckets that are taken away.
4. Create your own subtraction sentence. Use color tiles to model your sentence and write the numbers.

Chapter 12   three hundred forty-five   345

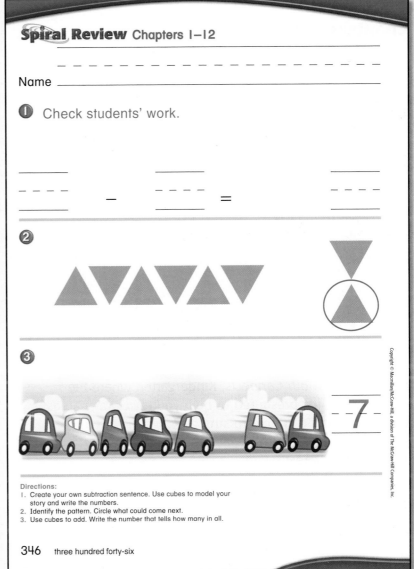

Spiral Review Chapters 1–12

Name _____

① Check students' work.

___ – ___ = ___

②

③ 7

Directions:
1. Create your own subtraction sentence. Use cubes to model your story and write the numbers.
2. Identify the pattern. Circle what could come next.
3. Use cubes to add. Write the number that tells how many in all.

346   three hundred forty-six

Summative Assessment

Use these alternate leveled chapter tests to differentiate assessment for the specific needs of your students.

Leveled Chapter 12 Tests			
Form	Type	Level	CRM Pages
1	Multiple Choice	BL	54–55
2A	Multiple Choice	OL	54–57
2C	Multiple Choice	OL	58–59
2D	Free Response	AL	60–61

BL = below/approaching grade level
OL = on grade level
AL = above/beyond grade level

Spiral Review

Review Chapters 1 to 12

Objective: Review and assess mastery of skills and concepts from previous chapters.

Resources for Review

Based on student results, refer to these lessons for remediation.

- **Exercise 1: Lesson 12-2** (p. 321)
- **Exercise 2: Lesson 3-5** (p. 81)
- **Exercise 3: Lesson 11-6** (p. 299)

Test Practice

 Formative Assessment

You can use Student Edition pp. 347–348 to benchmark student progress.

Additional practice pages can be found in Chapter 12 Resource Masters.

CRM Chapter 12 Resource Masters
Cumulative Test Practice
- Multiple Choice format (pp. 54-59)
- Free Response format (pp. 60-61)

End-of-Year Assessment

Use the **End-of-Year Test** to assess student comprehension of the skills and concepts presented in kindergarten.

Each question in the End-of-Year Test provides the lesson number from *Math Connects*, Kindergarten where the concept was first presented to help you review any areas where students continue to struggle.

CRM Chapter 12 Resource Masters
End-of-Year Test (p. 48)

Create additional practice worksheets or tests.

Test-Taking Tips

For the Teacher
- Make sure each student understands the directions before beginning the test.
- Make sure there are no distractions (audio or visual) in the room.

For the Student
- Instruct students to read all answers before marking one.
- Remind students to listen carefully as you read each question before they choose an answer.

Name _____

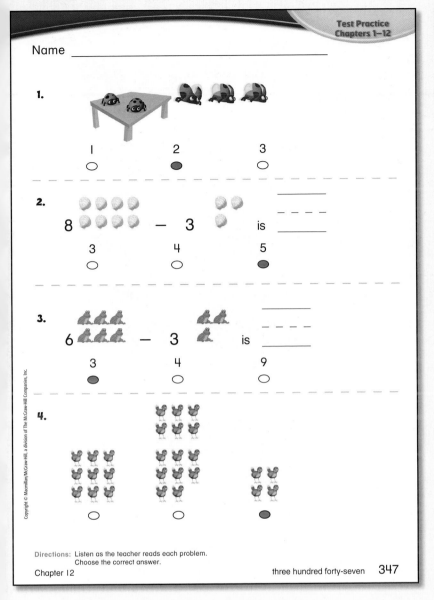

1.

1	2	3
○	●	○

2. 8 − 3 is _____

3	4	5
○	○	●

3. 6 − 3 is _____

3	4	9
●	○	○

4.

○	○	●

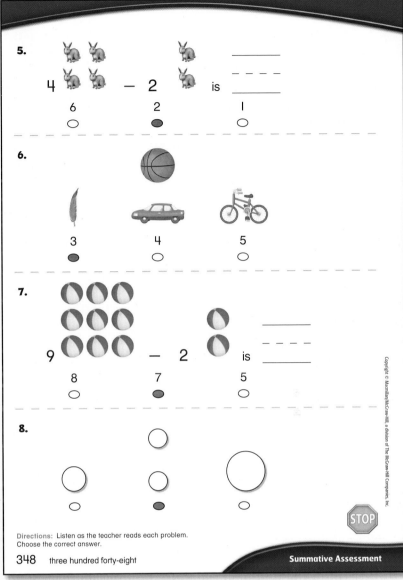

5. 4 − 2 is _____

6	2	1
○	●	○

6.

3	4	5
●	○	○

7. 9 − 2 is _____

8	7	5
○	●	○

8.

○	●	○

STOP

Directions: Listen as the teacher reads each problem. Choose the correct answer.

Test Directions for Teachers

Read the following directions to students before they begin. Then read each question followed by a pause to allow students time to work and choose an answer. The first test item can be worked as a class example.

- **Write your name at the top of the page.**
- **I am going to read each question to you. Listen carefully to the entire question before you choose an answer.**

1. Listen to the story. Ling saw 5 ladybugs on the table. 3 ladybugs flew away. How many ladybugs are left? Mark the number that tells how many are left.

2. Listen to the story. Emma found 8 shells on the beach. She gave 3 shells to Lou. What is 8 take away 3? Mark the number that tells what 8 take away 3 is.

3. Look at the 6 frogs. 3 frogs left. What is 6 take away 3? Mark the number that tells what 6 take away 3 is.

4. Look at the group of birds. Mark the group that shows less.

- **Turn the page over.**

5. Listen to the story. Rita has 4 rabbits. Two rabbits hopped away. How many rabbits does Rita have left? Mark the number that tells how many are left.

6. Look at the objects. Find the object that is lighter than a basketball. Mark the object that is lighter than a basketball.

7. Listen to the story. Kurt took nine beach balls on vacation. Two beach balls popped. Mark the number that tells what 9 take away 2 is.

8. Look at the circles. Find another circle that covers the same area. Mark the other circle that covers the same area.

Chapter 12 Test Practice **348**

Looking Ahead

The lessons in **Looking Ahead** can be used to extend concepts and skills present during the current year. Also, some lessons can be used at the end of the year after your state testing is completed. By presenting these important concepts and skills, you can help students be more successful.

LA1

Let's Look Ahead

Modeling Addition

Lesson Planner

Objective
Add by joining two groups.

Review Vocabulary
add

Resources
Materials: WorkMat 7: Part-Part-Whole
Manipulatives: two-colored counters
Alternate Resources: Adapt *Beans* on p.174 of *Math Their Way* for practice in part-part-whole addition.
Teacher Technology
    ⊙ TeacherWorks • Concepts in Motion

🔍 Focus on Math Background

In this lesson students focus on the meaning of addition by using manipulative materials to represent story structures or to model actions that involve a joining situation. Two types of story structures are introduced:

1. **part-part-whole**—John has two red balls and six blue balls. How many does he have altogether?

2. **joining**—John had two marbles. Sue gave him four marbles. How many marbles does John have now?

Daily Routine

Use these suggestions before beginning the lesson on p. LA3.

5-Minute Check
(Reviews Lesson 12-10)
Write the number of strawberries in each set. Trace the equals sign. Write how many strawberries in all.

Problem of the Day 🗒
Pass out to student volunteers cards with a 2, a 4, a 6, a plus sign, or an equal sign printed on them. Have students stand when they hear their part of the following number story: Two cats plus four cats equal six cats.

LINE UP Assign each student a number beginning with 1 and going up to the number of students. Have them line up in number order.

▷ Review Math Vocabulary

Review with students how to **add**. Show that two parts added together make a whole.

- Show students two sets of connecting cubes. Explain that each set is like a train car. Bring the cars together to make a longer train. Show that each train car is a part by itself. Put them together to show how the new train becomes a whole.

- Have the class help you label *part, part,* and *whole* on the connecting cube "train."

Differentiated Instruction

Small Group Options

Option 1 LOGICAL
Gifted and Talented

Materials: set of number cards from 1 to 5

- Have one of the partners deal out the cards one at a time facedown so that each partner gets 3 cards total.
- Have students count to three and flip over the top card in their facedown pile.
- Have students put the flipped cards next to each other and add the numbers together.
- After both students add the numbers together, have them put the two cards in a discard pile.
- Have students continue until all cards have been added together.

Option 2 KINESTHETIC
English Language Learners **ELL**

Materials: large poster with "whole" written across the back and precut into pieces, tape
Core Vocabulary: part, whole, a puzzle piece
Common Use Verb: will put together

See Math This strategy acts out ways to model addition.

- Say: "This is a **whole**. It is **together**." Display the back of the poster.
- Say: "**Parts** of a **puzzle** are called **pieces**" as you cut, disassemble.
- Have each student choose a puzzle piece, write their name on it and decorate the front.
- Say: "Now we **will put** the **pieces** back **together**."
- Model reassembling the backside with "whole" on it.
- Count and write the number of pieces as an addition sentence. Choose addends in several ways: first, boy pieces plus girl pieces, then names that start with letters A–M and N–Z, etc.

Independent Work Options

Option 1 KINESTHETIC/VERBAL/LOGICAL
Early Finishers **OL**

Materials: number cubes, counters

- Ask a student to say two numbers from 1 to 5.
- Have another student use two-color counters to model each number that was said.
- Have another student create and say an addition number sentence using those two numbers.
- Ask students to work together to find and say the sum of the number sentence.

Option 2
Student Technology

 macmillanmh.com

Math Tool Chest

① Introduce

Circle Time

Activity Choice 1 • Hands-On

Have students fold a piece of paper in half and keep it closed. Have them draw 5 green squares on one side and 1 blue square on the other side.

- How many green squares did you draw? 5
- How many blue squares did you draw? 1
- How many squares did you draw in all? 6
- Which numbers are the parts? 5 and 1
- Which number is the whole? 6

② Teach

Place a part-part-whole workmat on an overhead projector. Place 3 red counters in one part and 4 yellow counters in the other part.

- **How many red counters are there?** 3, Count the red counters together.
- **How many yellow counters are there?** 4, Count the yellow counters together.
- Move all the counters to the whole box. **How many counters are there in all?** 7, Count the counters together and write 7 in the box.
- Explain that when two parts are joined together, you **add** them to make the whole.
- Use the section at the top of p. LA3 to teach the lesson concept.
- Have students use 4 red counters and 1 yellow counter. Have students put the red counters in one part section and the yellow in the other part section. Explain to students that by adding the parts, you can find a whole number. Then have students place all of the counters in the whole section.
- Observe students as you work through the teach box.

BL Alternate Teaching Strategy

If students have trouble understanding what to count to find the whole...

Then use the following reteach option:

1. Show a Model: Using a short book or magazine, explain that the pages of a book are parts. The book is the whole. Have children count the pages and tell how many parts the whole has.

 COMMON ERROR!
Students may try to work in the wrong boxes on their workmats. Make sure that all students place their workmats in the correct position.

Name _____

① Modeling Addition

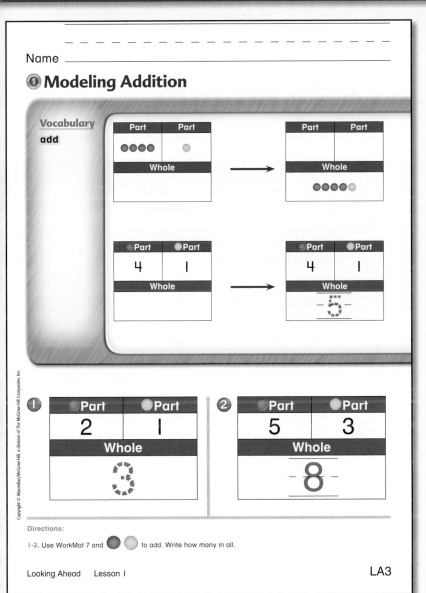

Vocabulary
add

Directions:
1-2. Use WorkMat 7 and ⬤ ◯ to add. Write how many in all.

Looking Ahead   Lesson 1   LA3

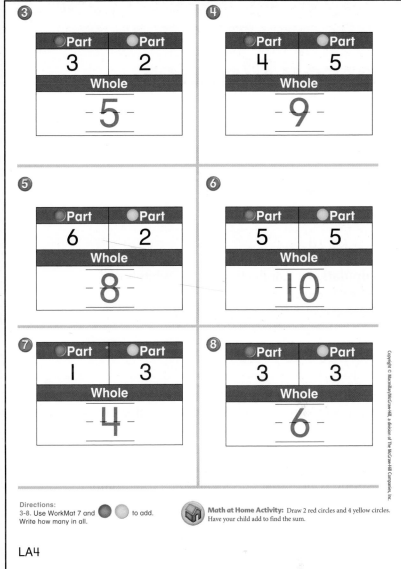

Directions:
3-8. Use WorkMat 7 and ⬤ ◯ to add.
Write how many in all.

Math at Home Activity: Draw 2 red circles and 4 yellow circles. Have your child add to find the sum.

LA4

---

❸ Practice

Guided Practice
Direct students to p. LA3.
Repeat Procedure for Exercises 1 and 2 as a class.

Independent Practice
Have students turn to p. LA4. Explain the directions.
Have students work independently on the exercises.

❹ Assess

✓ Formative Assessment
Give each student a blank workmat. Have them place 3 red counters in one part and 5 yellow counters in the other part.
- **Tell how you can find the whole.** Possible answer: I counted all the counters.
- **What number should be in the whole?** 8

Have students name objects that are in parts, but together make a whole. Example: One shoe is a part, the other shoe is the other part, but together they make a whole pair of shoes.

Looking Ahead Lesson 1   **LA4**

Modeling Subtraction

Lesson Planner

Objective
Use connecting cubes to subtract and find the missing part.

Vocabulary
subtract

Resources
Manipulatives: connecting cubes, whiteboard
Teacher Technology
- TeacherWorks • Concepts in Motion

Focus on Math

In this lesson, students make sense of subtraction by using manipulatives materials, and models to represent situations involving the separation of parts from a whole or the comparison of two sets. First graders need a strong conceptual understanding of all number operations, including subtraction, before moving to more abstract representations of these situations using symbols and procedural operations, such as regrouping.

Daily Routine

Use these suggestions before beginning the lesson on p. LA5.

5-Minute Check
(Reviews Lesson LA1)

1. Vijay saw three lightning bugs in the sky. A few minutes later, Vijay could see two more lightning bugs. How many lightning bugs did Vijay see in all. Model this story with two-colored counters.
5 lightning bugs

2. Four ducks swam in the pond. Four ducks joined them. How many ducks were in the pond? Model this story with two-colored counters. 8 ducks

Problem of the Day
On Monday, Johnny's mother told him to go to the pet store and purchase 1 dog treat. Later that week Johnny's mother had him buy 3 more. How many dog treats did Johnny buy in all that week? 4 dog treats

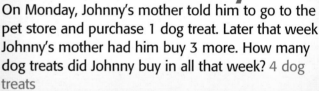 Have students line up and count off. Then have students separate into a boy group and a girl group. Have each group count off again. Explain that each group is a part of the whole group. Write a subtraction sentence that shows the girl group subtracted from the whole group.

Building Math Vocabulary

- On the board draw eight birds. Draw a second picture with only six birds.
- Tell students that 2 birds were **subtracted** from the 8, leaving a difference of 6.
- Start a discussion by asking students about other groups of objects that can be subtracted from to get a difference.

Visual Vocabulary Cards

Use Visual Vocabulary Card 16 to reinforce the vocabulary introduced in this lesson. (The Define/Example/Ask routine is printed on the back of this card.)

circle

Differentiated Instruction

Small Group Options

Option 1
VISUAL, SPATIAL

Below/Approaching Level BL

Materials: 2-foot pieces of string, straws

Give each student a piece of 2-foot string and 10 straws.

Have students form a circle with the string and place their straws inside the circle.

Ask students to create models to solve oral subtraction problems. **You have 10 straws in your circle. Take 5 straws out of the circle. How many straws are left inside the circle?** 5 straws

Repeat oral subtraction problems using the numbers 1 though 10.

Students should put all 10 straws back into the circle after each problem.

Option 2
INTRAPERSONAL, AUDITORY

English Language Learners ELL

Materials: Two oranges, a cup of orange juice (or a picture of it), crayons (including orange), papers with some geometric figures drawn on them

Core Vocabulary: these are, orange color, oranges

Common Use Verb: smell

See Math This strategy models subtraction in a real-world example.

- Explore oranges with students. Say: **"These are oranges"**. Say: "We eat **oranges**".

- Point at the orange section. Say: **"There are orange sections"**. If (call 3 students) each eat one, how many sections are left?

- Repeat for remaining students until everyone has "subtracted" an orange segment.

Independent Work Options

Option 1
KINESTHETIC, LOGICAL

Early Finishers

Materials: subtraction number cards, two-colored counters

- Have students take turns picking a subtraction number card.

- Ask students to use connecting cubes to model the problem to find the difference.

- Have students continue the activity until all cards have been used.

Option 2
Student Technology

Math Online ▶ macmillanmh.com

🍰 Math Tool Chest

1 Introduce

ircle Time

Activity Choice 1 • Hands-On

- Have items available for the whole class to see such as rulers, pencils, staplers, and books.

- Call up two students at a time to model the subtraction process. Give each some rulers and then say: Sally has 5 rulers, and she gives Juan 3 rulers. How many rulers does Sally have left?

- As you write the equation $5 - 3 = 2$ on the board, point out that you are **subtracting** three rulers from the original five.

2 Teach

- Have five students walk to the front of the class. Count the students aloud with the class.

- Ask two of the students to sit.

- **How many students are still standing?** 3 students

- **Is this an addition or a subtraction sentence? How do you know?** Subtraction sentence; sample answer: We ended with less than we began with.

- **We subtracted 2 from 5. The difference is 3. How could you show this subtraction sentence?** Answers will vary. Sample answers: counters, connecting cubes, blocks

- Use the section at the top of p. LA5 to teach the lesson concept.

- Have students use 7 red counters and 2 yellow counters. Have students place all of the markers in the whole section. Explain when you know the whole and a part, you can subtract to find the other part.

- Have students move the yellow counters and then the red counters to model the problem.

BL Alternate Teaching Strategy

If students have trouble using connecting cubes to model subtraction...

Then use this reteach option:

1. Domino Math Work Backwards: Start with the "take away" number in one color of cube and build to the total using a second color. The answer is the number of cubes in the second color.

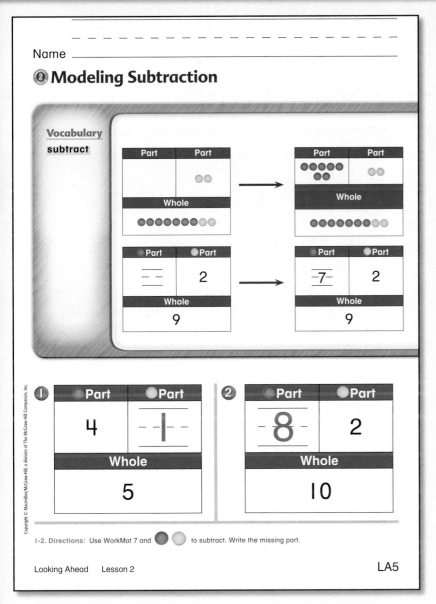

Name _____

② Modeling Subtraction

Vocabulary
subtract

① Part	Part
4	1
Whole	
5	

② Part	Part
8	2
Whole	
10	

1-2. Directions: Use WorkMat 7 and  to subtract. Write the missing part.

Looking Ahead   Lesson 2   LA5

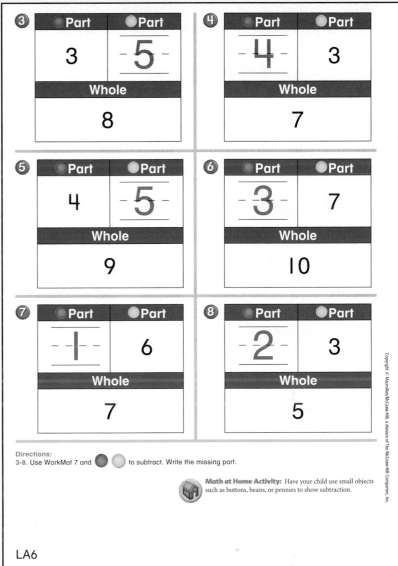

③ Part	Part
3	5
Whole	
8	

④ Part	Part
4	3
Whole	
7	

⑤ Part	Part
4	5
Whole	
9	

⑥ Part	Part
3	7
Whole	
10	

⑦ Part	Part
1	6
Whole	
7	

⑧ Part	Part
2	3
Whole	
5	

Directions:
3-8. Use WorkMat 7 and ⬤ ⚪ to subtract. Write the missing part.

Math at Home Activity: Have your child use small objects such as buttons, beans, or pennies to show subtraction.

LA6

---

③ Practice

Guided Practice
- Direct students to p. LA5.
- Repeat Procedure for Excercises 1 and 2.

Complete Exercises 1 and 2 as a class.

Independent Practice

Have students turn to p. LA6. Explain the directions.
Have students work independently on the excercises.

④ Assess

Formative Assessment
- **Use connecting cubes to model 6 taken away from 10.**
  4
- **Model 3 taken away from 8.** 5

Have students draw a picture that illustrates Exercise 7.

Lesson Planner

Objective

Count and order numbers from 1 to 100 on a hundred chart.

Vocabulary

hundred chart

Resources

Materials: yarn, index cards, clothespins, class-size number line, student number lines (0–20)

Teacher Technology

    TeacherWorks

Focus on Math

Students use a hundred chart in this lesson in order to visualize the resulting patterns that unfold as the numbers are organized and displayed in a 10 by 10 grid. When students look at a hundred chart, they will notice, among many other patterns, how the digits in the ones place repeat in a 1–9 sequence and how the digits in the tens place remain the same going horizontally from left to right.

Daily Routine

Use these suggestions before beginning the lesson on p. LA7.

5-Minute Check
(Reviews Lesson LA2)

Ezra was using seven crayons to color a picture. He gave away three of his crayons. How many crayons does Ezra have left? Model this story using crayons.

Problem of the Day

Kamryn caught 9 fish. Then she let 3 of the fish swim away. How many fish did she have left?

6 fish

 LINE UP Have students count by tens as they line up. The first student should say *ten*, the second student *twenty*, and so on. After 10 students have lined up, have the next student begin again at *ten*.

Building Math Vocabulary

Materials: connecting cubes

- Write the word **hundred chart** on the board. Beside it, display a class-size hundred chart or a hundred chart on an overhead projector. Explain that it is called a hundred chart. Have children call out what they notice about the hundred chart. Answers will vary. Sample answers: The numbers are in order; The numbers at the end of each row have a zero/are tens; There are patterns reading across and reading down.

- Explain that a hundred chart is a table that has ten rows, ten columns, and the numbers 1–100 in order. A hundred chart is read from left to right with return sweeps the same direction that you read a book.

Differentiated Instruction

Small Group Options

Option 1

LINGUSTIC, LOGICAL

Below/Approaching Level BL

Materials: hundred chart

1	2	3	4	5	6	7	8	9	10
11	12	13	14	15	16	17	18	19	20
21	22	23	24	25	26	27	28	29	30
31	32	33	34	35	36	37	38	39	40
41	42	43	44	45	46	47	48	49	50
51	52	53	54	55	56	57	58	59	60
61	62	63	64	65	66	67	68	69	70
71	72	73	74	75	76	77	78	79	80
81	82	83	84	85	86	87	88	89	90
91	92	93	94	95	96	97	98	99	100

- Point to and say a number on the hundred chart, for example, **17**. Then have a student read that whole number and count on the next five numbers in order from memory: 18, 19, 20, 21, 22.

- Have the rest of the group check the numbers by following along on the hundred chart. Repeat with larger and larger numbers to help students build fluency reading a hundred chart and counting on.

Option 2

AUDITORY, SPATIAL

English Language Learners ELL

Materials: overhead 100's chart, counters

Core Vocabulary: numbers 1-100

Common Use Verb: cover

Do Math This strategy introduces the hundred chart and how to verbalize counting to 100.

- Show the hundreds chart. Cover 1 with a counter and say "one." Repeat for "two," encouraging students to uncover the numbers and count with you.

- Once the numbers have been uncovered, have students read the numbers chorally down from 100.

Independent Work Options

Option 1

VISUAL/SPATIAL, LOGICAL

Early Finishers OL

Materials: grid paper, crayons

1	2	3	4	⑤	6	⑦	8	9	10
11	12	13	14	⑮	16	⑰	18	19	20
21	22	23	24	㉕	㉖	㉗	28	29	30
31	32	33	34	35	36	37	38	39	40
41	42	43	44	45	46	47	48	49	50
51	52	53	54	55	56	57	58	59	60
61	62	63	64	65	66	67	68	69	70
71	72	73	74	75	76	77	78	79	80
81	82	83	84	85	86	87	88	89	90
91	92	93	94	95	96	97	98	99	100

- Have partners take turns secretly coloring in a number on a hundred chart.

- Have one student describe a number by telling the number that comes before, after, above, and below it. Then have their partner guess.

Option 2

Student Technology

Math Online > macmillanmh.com

1 Introduce

Circle Time

Activity Choice 1 • Hands-On

- Display a **hundred chart.** Explain that one of the fun things we can do with a hundred chart is start any place and count forward or backward.

- Start at 1. Touch each number and count to 15.

- Ask a volunteer to name or point to a number on the hundred chart. Have students tell the number that comes before and after the number chosen by the volunteer. Repeat with different numbers.

2 Teach

- Display a hundred chart on the overhead. Touch a number. Say the number. Have students say the number aloud. Ask what number comes before and what number comes after that particular number.

- On the overhead, write a set of five or six numbers in order with a number missing. Have students use the hundred chart to tell what number is missing from the set.

Alternate Teaching Strategy

 students have trouble putting numbers in order between 1 and 100...

Then use the following reteach option:

1. Count to 100 Have student pairs practice counting from 1-100, using objects such as pennies, corn kernels, macaroni noodles, or other similar items.

! COMMON ERROR!

Students may not understand that numbers that are not consecutive can be placed in order. Use a hundred chart to reinforce the idea that putting in order means telling which comes before and which comes after, even if other numbers come between.

Name _____

⓪ Counting to 100

Vocabulary
hundred chart

Directions: Touch, count, and color the numbers from 1 to 100 in the number order: touch, count, and color 1 to 25 yellow. Touch, count, and color 26 to 50 blue. Touch, count, and color the numbers 51 to 100 red.

1	2	3	4	5	6	7	8	9	10
11	12	13	14	15	16	17	18	19	20
21	22	23	24	25	26	27	28	29	30
31	32	33	34	35	36	37	38	39	40
41	42	43	44	45	46	47	48	49	50
51	52	53	54	55	56	57	58	59	60
61	62	63	64	65	66	67	68	69	70
71	72	73	74	75	76	77	78	79	80
81	82	83	84	85	86	87	88	89	90
91	92	93	94	95	96	97	98	99	100

❶ 13   35   21 $\overline{13}$ $\overline{21}$ $\overline{35}$

❷ 52   46   65 $\overline{46}$ $\overline{52}$ $\overline{65}$

❸ 26   18   72 $\overline{18}$ $\overline{26}$ $\overline{72}$

❹ 98   100   97 $\overline{97}$ $\overline{98}$ $\overline{100}$

Directions:
1-4. Use the hundred chart. Write the numbers in order.

Math at Home Activity: Have your child choose a number and show you how to count backwards to 1 and forward to 100 from that number.

❸ Practice

Guided Practice

- Have students touch, count, and color the numbers from 1 to 25 yellow.

- Have students touch, count, and color the numbers 26 to 50 blue.

- Have students touch, count, and color the numbers 51 to 100 red.

Independent Practice

Have students turn to p. LA8. Explain the directions. Have students work independently on the exercises.

❹ Assess

✓ Formative Assessment

Have students use a hundred chart to help answer the questions.

- **How can you use a hundred chart to put three numbers in order from least to greatest?** Find them on the chart and see which one comes first, second, and last.

- **Put these numbers in order from least to greatest: 52, 14, 33.** 14, 33, 52

Place Value

Lesson Planner _____

Objectives

Learn to show numbers as tens and ones.

Vocabulary

ones, tens

Resources

Materials: pencils, overhead marker
Manipulatives: connecting cubes
Teacher Technology
- TeacherWorks

Focus on Math Background

This lesson introduces the concept of describing and labeling quantities by sets of tens and ones. Grouping numbers into units of tens and ones is a procedure fundamental to understanding place value.

Daily Routine _____

Use these suggestions before beginning the lesson on p. LA9.

5-Minute Check

(Reviews Lesson LA4)

Fill in the missing numbers.
0, 10, 20, 30, __, 50, 60, 70, __, 90, 100
40, 80

Problem of the Day

Make a number line with the numbers from this month's calendar going from number 1 until the end of the month. Mix up the order of a few of the days on the number line. Have students come to the board and correct the mistakes in the number line.

LINE UP Ask ten students to line up. Have all students count up from 10 as the rest of the students line up one at a time. When there are 20 students in line, ask How many groups of ten are there? 2 groups of ten

Building Math Vocabulary

Materials: connecting cubes, overhead projector

- Show the number 15. Explain that the 5 is in the **ones** place, so this number has 5 ones.
- Write the number 12 on a transparency. Explain that the number 12 represents one group of tens and 1 one. Show this number with 1 rod and 2 units.
- Review eleven, thirteen, fourteen, fifteen, sixteen, seventeen, eighteen, nineteen, and twenty in the same way. Write each number on the overhead and model building it with connecting cubes. Have students use connecting cubes and build each number.

Differentiated Instruction

Small Group Options

Option 1 — Gifted and Talented

Materials: pencils, paper
Manipulatives: connecting cubes

- Prepare ten "trains" with varying numbers of connecting cubes up to 20 in each. Explain that students should make each train 20 cubes long.

- Have students count and record the total number of cubes in each train.

- For each train, have students decide whether they need to add cubes to make it exactly 20 cubes long.

- Ask students to put each train back in its original form so it will be ready for the next group of students to use.

Option 2 — English Language Learners ELL

Core Vocabulary: cube, rod, whole
Common Use Verb: break apart

Talk Math This strategy uses background knowledge to help students understand place value.

- Using rods, model and write: "20 − 10 = 10." All students repeat activity in small groups.

- Write "20 − 5 = 15." Ask groups to model. Discuss why this is not possible, restating student language.

- Model doing the problem with cubes and rods. Allow students to repeat.

- Continue with other problems as time permits.

Independent Work Options

Option 1 — Early Finishers

Materials: thin markers, chart paper

- Have students work together to make a chart that uses tally marks to illustrate the numbers 11–20.

- Ask students to write each number and then make the correct number of tallies next to it.

- In each set of tallies, have students circle the tens (2 groups of 5) in red and circle the ones in green.

11	卌 卌 ⦶
12	卌 卌 ⦶⦶
13	卌 卌 ⦶⦶⦶
14	卌 卌 ⦶⦶⦶⦶
15	卌 卌 卌
16	卌 卌 卌⦶
17	卌 卌 卌 ⦶⦶
18	卌 卌 卌 ⦶⦶⦶
19	卌 卌 卌 ⦶⦶⦶⦶
20	卌 卌 卌 卌

Option 2 — Student Technology

Math Online macmillanmh.com

1 Introduce

Circle Time

Activity Choice 1 • Hands-On

Give each student a handful of connecting cubes up to 20, and have students separate the connecting cubes into groups of ten.

- **How many groups of ten do you have?** Possible answers: 0, 1, or 2 groups of ten

- **How many ones are left over?** Answers will vary depending on the number of cubes they have.

2 Teach

- On the overhead, display vertically a group of ten connecting cubes on the left and five connecting cubes on the right.

- As you write 1 above the group of ten and 5 above the group of 5, explain that there is 1 group of ten and 5 ones. The connecting cubes represent 15.

- Repeat with 1 group of ten and 8 ones.

- **How many groups of ten are there?** 1

- **How many ones are there?** 8

- **What number do the tens and ones represent?** 18

- Have students use place value to compare. **Which number is greater, 15 or 18?** 18 **Why?** They both have 1 ten but 8 ones is more than 5 ones. So 18 is greater than 15.

BL Alternate Teaching Strategy

> **If** students do not understand the place-value concepts of tens and ones in two-digit numbers . . .

> **Then** use this reteach option.

1. Quantity Value Versus Column Value Build understanding of column value (25 is 2 tens and 5 units), by first describing the quantity value (25 is 20 plus 5).

COMMON ERROR!

Students may forget to use 0 as a place holder and write 2 rather then 20 for example. When recording tens and ones, ask students to draw two blanks and to point to the blank where they will record the number in each category.

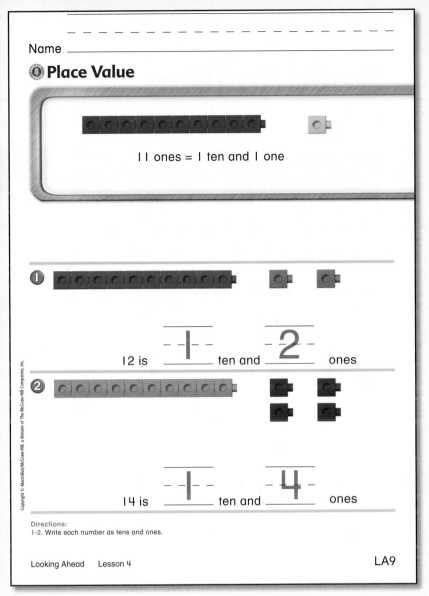

Place Value

11 ones = 1 ten and 1 one

1 12 is _____ **1** ten and _____ **2** ones

2 14 is _____ **1** ten and _____ **4** ones

Directions:
1-2. Write each number as tens and ones.

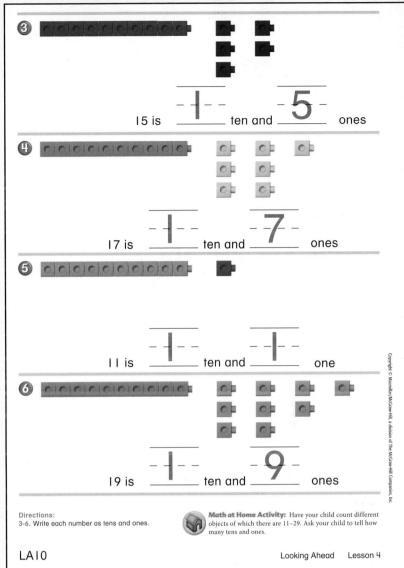

3 15 is _____ **1** ten and _____ **5** ones

4 17 is _____ **1** ten and _____ **7** ones

5 11 is _____ **1** ten and _____ **1** one

6 19 is _____ **1** ten and _____ **9** ones

Directions:
3-6. Write each number as tens and ones.

Math at Home Activity: Have your child count different objects of which there are 11–29. Ask your child to tell how many tens and ones.

3 Practice

Guided Practice

- Direct students to p. LA9.
- Guide students through the process of identifying tens and ones.

Independent Practice

Have students turn to p. LA10. Explain the directions. Have students work independently on the exercises.

4 Assess

✔ Formative Assessment

Give students a handful of counters. Have them put the counters into groups of tens, tell how many tens and ones, and then name the number.

Lesson Planner _____

Objective
Put figures together to form new figures.

Vocabulary
parallelogram, trapezoid

Review Vocabulary
rectangle, square, triangle, hexagon

Resources
Manipulatives: pattern blocks

Focus on Math Background

To build figures from other figures is one of the most important activities in early work with geometry. Whether reconstructing a given figure or creating new figures, this activity supports development of spatial sense. Much of today's children's play takes place in a virtual three-dimensional world that is "on-screen" and therefore, in reality, is only two-dimensional. Building and exploring with real objects helps develop critical spatial sense in a three-dimensional world.

Daily Routine _____

Use these suggestions before beginning the lesson on p. LA11.

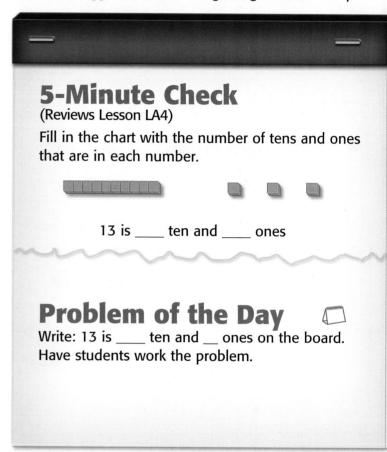

5-Minute Check
(Reviews Lesson LA4)
Fill in the chart with the number of tens and ones that are in each number.

13 is ____ ten and ____ ones

Problem of the Day
Write: 13 is ____ ten and __ ones on the board. Have students work the problem.

LINE UP Name a pattern block (e.g. hexagon) and have students name what figures could be put together to make that figure.

Math Vocabulary

- Introduce **parallelogram** and **trapezoid** by drawing an example of each.
- Have students look around the room and find examples of each figure.
- Have students point to the figure they have found in the room.

Differentiated Instruction

Small Group Options

Option 1 **Below/Approaching Level** BL   VISUAL

Materials:
6 pattern block triangles for each student

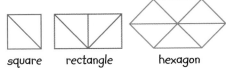

square   rectangle   hexagon

- Have students use the 6 triangles to make as many different figures as they can.
- Have students trace their new figures on paper and label them.

Option 2 **English Language Learners** ELL   VISUAL/SPATIAL, KINESTHETIC

Materials: picture book, paper shapes
Core Vocabulary: everywhere, think about, edge to edge
Common Use Verb: name

Hear Math This strategy helps students integrate the vocabulary of figures by pointing out examples and teaching them to think of the names.

- Read a picture book. Talk about and name figures in the book as you read.
- Close the book. Ask students to close their eyes. Tell them to picture the figures and think of their names as you retell the story.
- Explain that figures are everywhere in the world. Look outside a window and describe a building or other objects in terms of its shape. Name it. Point out figures in the classroom including posters, doors, and windows. Encourage students to hear the names of the figures they see as they go about their day.
- Give students paper shapes and model putting them edge to edge to create new figures.
- Allow students to repeat.
- Extend the activity by allowing students to glue shapes into buildings and combine them into a cityscape.

Independent Work Options

Option 1 **Early Finishers**   LOGICAL

Materials: pattern blocks

- Have students draw a picture that includes at least two figures that are made by combining two other figures. Tell them that they may choose to trace pattern blocks when drawing the new figures.

Option 2 **Student Technology**

Math Online > macmillanmh.com

1 Introduce

Circle Time

Activity Choice 1 • Hands-On

- Distribute pattern blocks to students.
- **How many triangles do I need to form a trapezoid?** 3
- Demonstrate with pattern blocks by arranging three triangles on top of a trapezoid. Have students do the same.
- **How many trapezoids do I need to form a hexagon?** 2
- Demonstrate and have students follow your model.

2 Teach

Display two squares on the overhead.

- Show students that they can use pattern blocks to make new figures. Allow them time to explore the relationships between the different pattern blocks.
- **What did you notice as you explored with the pattern blocks?** Sample answer: If you put the same type of pattern blocks together you can create many different figures.
- Invite students to share relationships they found between the different pattern block shapes. Sample answer: 2 triangles can be arranged in a parallelogram; 6 triangles can make a hexagon.

BL Alternate Teaching Strategy

 If students have difficulty using concrete two-dimensional figures to make new geometric figures . . .

 Then use the following reteach option.

1. Use pattern blocks Draw a geometric figure, such as a hexagon, on a piece of paper. Draw dotted lines to show how smaller geometric figures, such as two trapezoids, can form the larger one. Have students use pattern blocks to follow the model and cover the larger shape.

 COMMON ERROR!

It is very difficult for children to differentiate figures in a picture. Encourage students to use pattern blocks to create different objects and then trace around each figure.

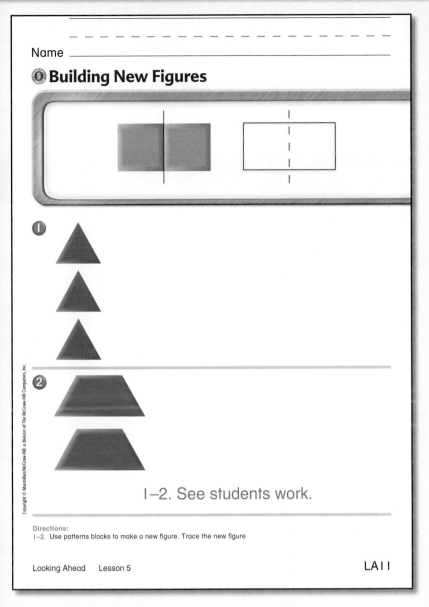

Name _____

Building New Figures

1.

2.

1–2. See students work.

Directions:
1–2. Use patterns blocks to make a new figure. Trace the new figure

Looking Ahead   Lesson 5   LA11

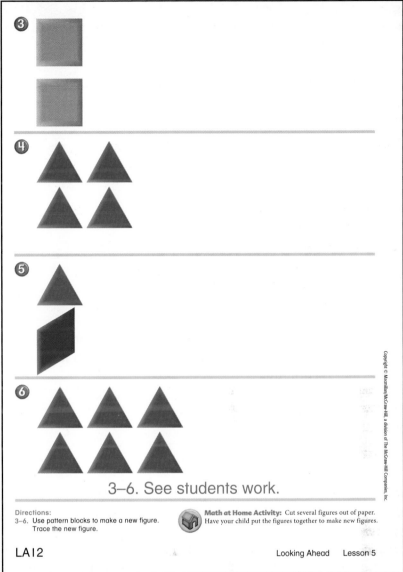

3.

4.

5.

6.

3–6. See students work.

Directions:
3–6. Use pattern blocks to make a new figure.
Trace the new figure.

Math at Home Activity: Cut several figures out of paper.
Have your child put the figures together to make new figures.

LA12   Looking Ahead   Lesson 5

---

3 Practice

Guided Practice

- Direct students to p. LA11.
- Guide students through the process of building new figures using pattern blocks.
- Trace the new figure.

Independent Practice

Have students turn to p. LA12. Explain the directions.
Have students work independently on the exercises.

4 Assess

Formative Assessment

Have students trace a hexagon pattern block on a piece of paper and show how different pattern blocks can be used to make a hexagon. Sample answers: 1 hexagon;

2 trapezoids; 6 triangles

Equal Parts

Lesson Planner

Objective
Identify equal parts of a whole.

Vocabulary
unequal parts

Review Vocabulary
equal parts

Resources
Alternate Lesson: Adapt *Pattern Block Puzzles* on page 349 of *Math Their Way* to provide practice with fractions.
Teacher Technology
  💿 TeacherWorks

Focus on Math Background

In this lesson, students begin to identify equal parts and count how many parts there are in a whole. Students begin to prepare themselves so in the future they can work with fractions and decimals. The objects and geometrical figures (pattern blocks) used in this lesson are designed to show both equal and unequal parts.

Daily Routine

Use these suggestions before beginning the lesson on p. LA13.

5-Minute Check
(Reviews Lesson LA5)

Give students three triangular pattern blocks. What figure do you get when you put the three triangles together? a trapezoid

Problem of the Day

Give students two square pattern blocks. What figure do you get when you put two squares together? a rectangle

LINE UP Have each student point to and explain how a classroom object is split into equal parts. Then have that student line up.

Building Math Vocabulary

- Show students a construction paper rectangle. Fold it in half and show students the two **equal parts**.
- Fold the rectangle in half again to make four equal parts. **How many equal parts are there now?** four
- Fold the rectangle again to make eight equal parts.
- Have them open up the construction paper.
- Have students number each part.
- **Are the parts of this rectangle equal?** yes **How?** We folded the rectangle every time equally.
- Repeat this activity using other figures.

Differentiated Instruction

Small Group Options

Option 1 Below/Approaching Level
SPATIAL

Materials: figure cards

- Have students work in pairs.
- Give each pair a deck of figure cards. On each figure card show half of a shape.
- Have students mix up the cards and place them face up.
- The pairs can take turns matching cards to create a figure.

Extension: If students get proficient have them flip the cards over and play memory by matching the equal parts.

Option 2 English Language Learners ELL
VISUAL/SPATIAL, LOGICAL

Materials: die-cut capital letters (or big letters written very neatly)

Core Vocabulary: equal parts, both sides are the same, into
Common Use Verb: fold

Do Math This strategy lets students see, experiment with, and vocalize the idea of equal parts.

- Hold up a paper square. Fold it symmetrically; unfold it. Say: "Are **both sides the same?** Yes, they are **equal parts.**"
- Hold up the O die-cut. Say: "Can you make **equal parts?**" Fold it horizontally – yes. Fold it vertically – yes. Do the same with other symmetric letters.
- Give students one letter each. Say: "Fold them into equal parts."
- Have students divide letters into equal parts.

Independent Work Options

Option 1 Early Finishers
LINGUISTIC

Materials: construction paper objects

- Have students try to fold a construction paper heart, circle, triangle, and star into as many equal parts as they can.
- Have them write the number of equal parts they folded their shape into.
- Have them order the shapes from the least number of equal parts to the most equal parts.

Option 2 Student Technology

Math Online ▷ macmillanmh.com

1 Introduce

Circle Time

Activity • Hands-On

- Lead students in a discussion about sharing. Guide them to say that when they share, they usually want to have **equal parts.**
- Show students a sandwich in the shape of a square.
- **How might you share this sandwich with a friend?** Split it so each person has the same amount.
- **What are some ways you could divide, or split, the sandwich into equal parts?** Cut an up-and-down line through the middle; cut a sideways line across the middle.
- **How many equal parts could you split the sandwich into?** Sample answer: four parts
- Invite a volunteer to come to the front of the room to show how to split the square in half.
- **What other way could you show the two equal parts?** Cut a diagonal line.
- Draw additional figures on the board so that students can draw all possible ways for each figure to show two equal parts.

2 Teach

- Call students' attention to the top of p. LA13.
- **How are the muffins the same? How are they different?** They are all muffins. One is split into equal parts and the others are not.
- Trace a line around the muffin with equal parts.
- **How can you tell the parts are equal?** The parts on either side of the line are the same size and shape.

BL Alternate Teaching Strategy

 If students have trouble understanding equal parts . . .

Then use this reteach option.

Make Equal Parts Provide construction paper figures (rectangles, diamonds, triangles) for each student to use.

- Have students begin this activity with the triangle.
- **How can we divide this shape into two equal parts?** Fold it in half.
- Model how to fold the triangle in half. Ask students to open the triangle to show two equal parts.
- **Can we divide the triangle into four equal parts?** No, it does not make four equal parts.

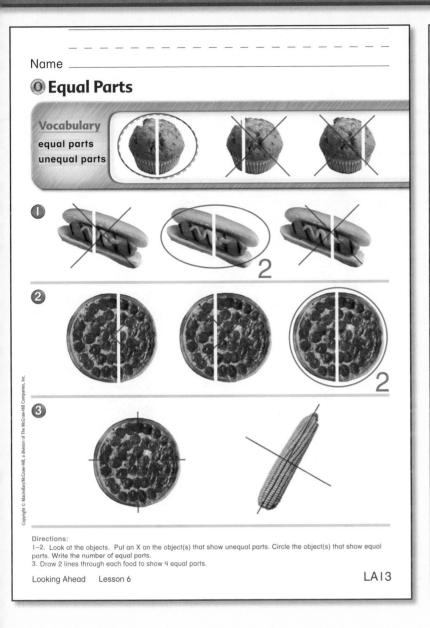

Equal Parts

Vocabulary
equal parts
unequal parts

① ② ③

Directions:
1–2. Look at the objects. Put an X on the object(s) that show unequal parts. Circle the object(s) that show equal parts. Write the number of equal parts.
3. Draw 2 lines through each food to show 4 equal parts.

Looking Ahead   Lesson 6

LA13

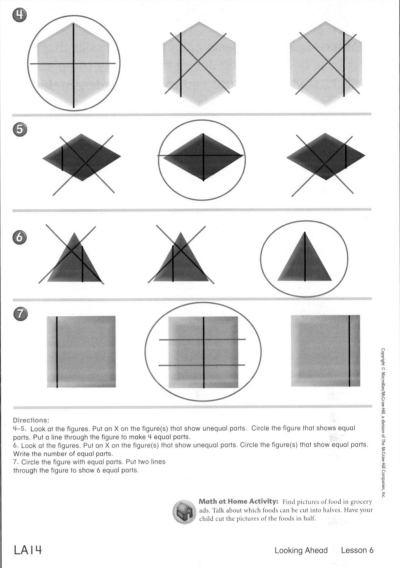

④ ⑤ ⑥ ⑦

Directions:
4–5. Look at the figures. Put an X on the figure(s) that show unequal parts. Circle the figure that shows equal parts. Put a line through the figure to make 4 equal parts.
6. Look at the figures. Put an X on the figure(s) that show unequal parts. Circle the figure(s) that show equal parts. Write the number of equal parts.
7. Circle the figure with equal parts. Put two lines through the figure to show 6 equal parts.

 Math at Home Activity: Find pictures of food in grocery ads. Talk about which foods can be cut into halves. Have your child cut the pictures of the foods in half.

LA14

Looking Ahead   Lesson 6

---

③ Practice

Guided Practice

- Direct students to Exercises 1-3 on p. LA13.
- Have students look at the hotdog showing two parts. **Which picture shows equal parts?** the middle one **How can you tell?** They are the same size and shape; one part is not much larger than the other parts.
- Have students look at the pizzas.
- **Which picture shows equal parts?** the last one **How can you tell?** They are the same size and shape.
- In Exercise 1-2 help students put an X by the objects that show unequal parts.
- Tell students to circle the object(s) that show equal parts. Count the number of equal parts.
- Ask students to write the number of equal parts next to that object.
- Explain and model the directions for Exercise 3.

Independent Practice

Have students turn to p. LA14. Explain the directions and have students work independently on the exercises

④ Assess

✓ Formative Assessment

Show students a rectangle. Ask students to draw a line to show equal parts.

- **What lines can be drawn to show equal parts?** Sample answer: lines through the middle of the rectangle going across or up and down.

Looking Ahead Lesson 6 **LA14**

Problem-Solving Projects

The **Problem-Solving Projects** apply the Math skills that students have been building during the year. By completing the projects, students will use and connect Kindergarten mathematics to everyday situations and activities.

End-of-Year Assessment

Use the **End-of-Year Test** to assess student comprehension of the skills and concepts presented in Kindergarten.

CRM **Chapter 12 Resource Masters**
End-of-Year Test (p.64)

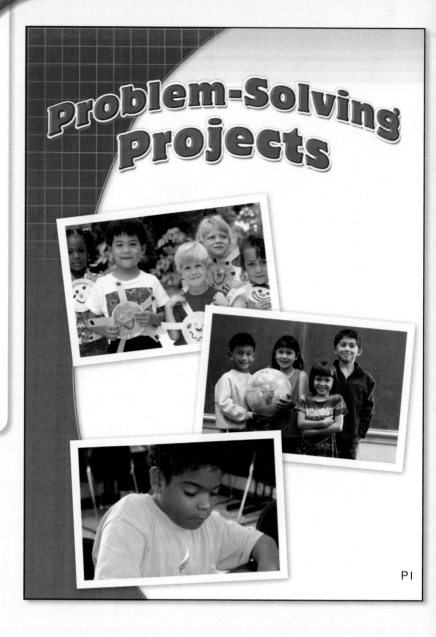

Problem-Solving Projects

P1

Problem-Solving Projects

Lesson Planner

Objective

Students use numbers to describe how many are in a set, compare containers according to capacity, construct graphs to answer questions, count by ones, describe and identify objects based on attributes, sequence events, and identify patterns to prepare for planning a garden that they will plant at the end of the week.

Review Vocabulary

count, holds less, holds more, pattern, sort

Resources

Materials: planters and containers of various sizes, foam cups, picture cards showing three stages of growth of various plants, drawing paper, crayons, various kinds of flower seeds.

Day 1

Share with students that they will be learning about flower gardens and how to design their own garden. Tell students that they will help plan and plant their flower garden at the end of the week.

- Discuss the picture on page P3 with students.
- Ask students to name the objects in the picture. Discuss which types of animals live in a garden.
- Have students name the animal in Exercise 1. **How many ants are in the picture?** 14 Tell students to write that number next to the ant.
- Repeat that process for Exercises 2-4.
- Discuss what types of animals might live in their garden if they were to plant it outside.
- Remind students that they will be creating their own classroom garden. Tell students that their indoor garden will not have the same animals living in it as an outdoor garden would.
- Tell them that they will help choose a container to hold enough plants for the entire class.
- Show students planters and containers of various sizes. Point out that some containers **hold more** and some **hold less**. Review the concepts that students learned about capacity.
- Help them choose the planter that will hold the right number of plants by determining which planter will best hold a certain number of foam cups placed side by side.

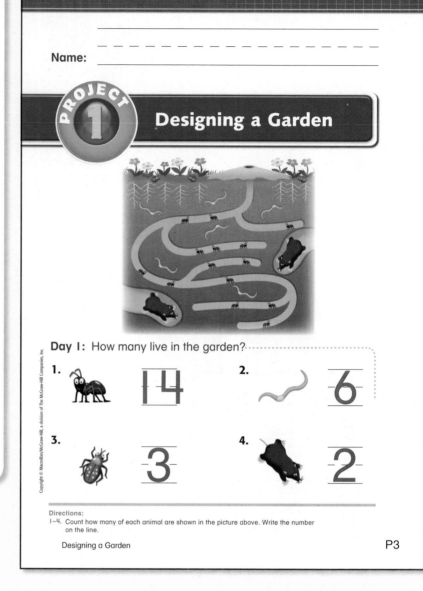

Day 2: Favorite Flowers · · · · · · · · · · · See students' work. · · · · · · · · · · ·

10
9
8
7
6
5
4
3
2
1

Directions: Ask 10 classmates which flower shown on the graph is his or her favorite.
Draw a flower in one box for each person's favorite flower. Write the total number on the line below the flower.

Designing a Garden

Day 2

- Discuss the graph on page P4 with students.
- Have students ask 10 classmates to choose their favorite flower from the choices given.
- Have students record the results on the graph by drawing a flower in one square for each person's favorite flower.
- Use the results to help decide what type of flowers the students should plant in their classroom garden.
- Have students write the total number of each type of flower directly underneath that flower.
- Begin to discuss with students how the flower garden should look.
- Ask students how many rows there should be in the garden and how many flowers should be planted in each row.
- Make sure students keep in mind the type of planter or container they chose to use for their classroom flower garden.

Day 3

- Discuss the growth cycle of plants with students. Explain that plants need food, air, and water to live and grow.
- Have students use picture cards showing the different stages in the life cycle of a plant, and order them according to their growth stage. Ask them to order each group of cards from planting a seed to a grown plant.
- Help students make a list of other living things. Discuss the life cycle of each of these living things.
- Discuss what each living thing listed needs to live and grow.
- Have students discuss the differences between the flowers shown on page P5 and sort them into the correct gardens.
- Ask students to **sort** the flowers by drawing a line from each flower to the garden where it should be planted.

Day 3: Flower Sort

Directions: Draw a line from each flower to the garden where it should be planted.

Designing a Garden   P5

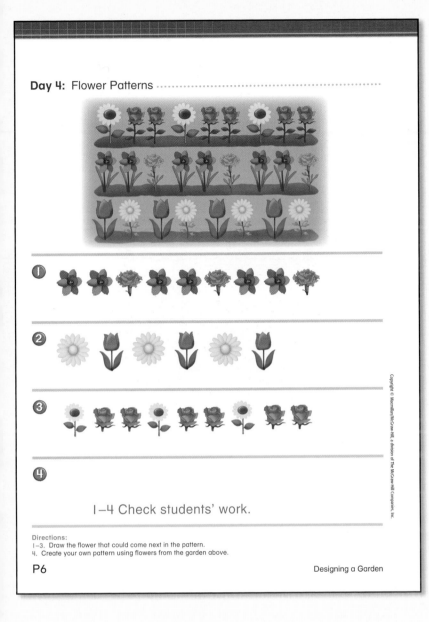

Day 4: Flower Patterns ....

①

②

③

④

1–4 Check students' work.

Directions:
1–3. Draw the flower that could come next in the pattern.
4. Create your own pattern using flowers from the garden above.

Designing a Garden

Day 4

- Have students discuss the flower **patterns** shown on the top of page P6.
- Have students continue the pattern in Exercises 1-3 by drawing the flower that would come next.
- Tell students in Exercise 4 they need to use the flowers from the garden at the top of the page to create a pattern.
- Discuss with students the pattern they would like to create in their classroom garden.
- Have students work in small groups to create an indoor garden out of paper flowers or other creative play materials.
- Remind students to consider the size of the garden, the types of flowers they would like to plant, and the flower pattern they would like in their flower gardens.
- Have students draw a picture of their garden, including the pattern of flowers they have chosen.

Day 5

- Review with students the concepts covered this week while learning about plants and gardens.
- Discuss how a plant grows and what is needed for a plant to live.
- Have students choose which flowers to plant, keeping in mind the patterns discussed earlier in the week.
- Help students plant their flowers in the planter or container chosen earlier in the week. Discuss how the class will care for their garden.

Wrap-Up

- Use the Wrap-Up questions to assess students' work. Ask the following questions.
- **Which activities helped you plan your garden and how did they help?** Sample answers: Graphing our favorite flowers helped us know which type of flowers to plant, sorting flowers helped us know how much room to leave between flowers so they could grow, flower patterns helped us practice different ways the flowers could be planted, capacity helped us choose a planter for our garden.
- **How would you plan your garden differently if you were to do it again?** Sample answers: I would use a different container; I would plant the flowers in a different color pattern.
- **Which math concepts did you use to plan the classroom garden?** Sample answers: counting, patterning, sorting, graphing, comparing capacity
- **What did you learn about plants this week?** Sample answers: Plants have a life cycle; they need food, air, and water to live and grow.

Lesson Planner

Objective

Students participate in Olympic-style games in which they measure and compare distance, compare the capacity of containers, count by ones to 100, describe and compare the attributes of real-life objects, and name ordinal positions in a sequence.

Review Vocabulary

count, first, holds less, holds more, length, measure, second, third

Resources

Materials: paperclips, bean bags, baseball bat, construction paper rings (red, yellow, blue, black, green), hundreds chart, two bags, index cards showing three-dimensional figures, plastic baseball, paper plates, paper towel roll, paper, two large buckets, two small buckets, two large sponges, water, beans

Day 1

This project involves having students participate in indoor and outdoor Olympic-style games. At the end of each event, students will win a colored construction paper ring. When all events have been completed, students will construct their own Olympic symbol with their five rings.

- Discuss the picture on page P7. Have students use paper clips to measure the distance the bag was thrown. Have them record the distance.
- Compare and discuss the different **lengths** as a class.
- Tell them the first event they will participate in is the bean bag toss.
- Divide students into pairs. Have one partner throw a bean bag. Have the other partner **measure** the distance of the toss using a baseball bat. Record the distance on the board.
- Have partners switch roles and repeat. Reward students with their first colored ring.

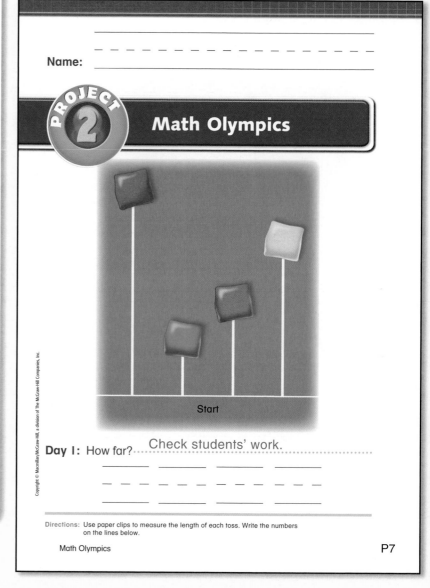

Name: _____

Math Olympics

Start

Day 1: How far? Check students' work.

Directions: Use paper clips to measure the length of each toss. Write the numbers on the lines below.

Math Olympics   P7

Extension: Have students throw straws (javelins) or paper plates (discuses) and measure using a paper clip chain.

Have a numbered target on the ground for students to throw the bean bags onto. Have them add their scores. Substitute pennies or other objects to toss into containers.

Day 2: Hop, hop, hop! Check students' work.

1	2	3	4	5	6	7	8	9	10
11	12	13	14	15	16	17	18	19	20
21	22	23	24	25	26	27	28	29	30
31	32	33	34	35	36	37	38	39	40
41	42	43	44	45	46	47	48	49	50
51	52	53	54	55	56	57	58	59	60
61	62	63	64	65	66	67	68	69	70
71	72	73	74	75	76	77	78	79	80
81	82	83	84	85	86	87	88	89	90
91	92	93	94	95	96	97	98	99	100

I hopped _____ times.

Directions: Point to each number on the chart and count by ones as each student in your class hops on one foot. Write how many times you hopped on one foot.

Math Olympics

Day 2

- Discuss the hundred chart on page P8 with students. Tell them they will be using the chart to **count** the number of times a student hops on one foot.
- Write students' names on the board. Call a student to the front of the room.
- Ask the student to hop on one foot while the class counts the hops by pointing to each number on the hundred chart. Record total hops on the board. Have each student record the number of times they hopped on one foot on the line.
- Continue until all students have hopped.
- Discuss results with the class.
- Reward students with their second colored ring.

Extension: Have students bounce a ball and record how many times they can bounce it in one minute. Have students count how many jumping jacks they can do in one minute.

Day 3

- Discuss page P9 with students. Have students match a three-dimensional figure to a real object.

- Divide the class into two even-numbered teams. If teams are odd-numbered, one student will go twice.

- Give each team a bag containing the same number of cards, with each card having a drawing of a three-dimensional figure.

- Have each team line up. Ask the first student in each line to pick a card from the bag.

- Have students find an object in the room that matches the figure on the card.

- When students return to line with the correct object, the next student in line takes a turn.

- End the game when all students have had a turn. Reward students with their third colored ring.

Extension: Add cards with numerals on them and have students find a set of objects that match the numeral.

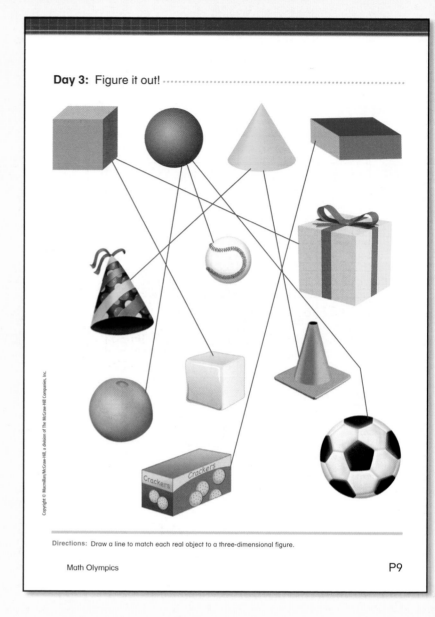

Day 3: Figure it out!

Directions: Draw a line to match each real object to a three-dimensional figure.

Math Olympics

P9

- Discuss capacity with students. Focus on objects that **hold more** and objects that **hold less**.

- Outdoor activity: Divide students into two teams. Put two large buckets filled with water at the starting line. Put two small containers a set distance away. Give the first students in line sponges. Have them soak the sponges in the large bucket of water, run to the small container, and squeeze the water into it. The first team to fill their small container wins.

- Extension/indoor activity: Have students carry dried beans on a spoon from larger bucket to smaller container.

- Reward the entire class with their last colored ring. Have students construct their own Olympic symbol.

Wrap-Up

- Use the Wrap-Up questions to assess students' work. Ask the following questions.

- **How did you use math to complete each event?**
  Sample answers: I measured a bean bag toss, counted hops, found matching figures, named *first*, *second*, and *third* as I ran across each base, and determined which objects hold more and which hold less.

- **What are some other Olympic Games that use math?**
  Sample answers: high jump measures distance, track events are measured by distance and time.

Day 4: Batter up! ·····································

5   4   3   2   1

Copyright © Macmillan/McGraw-Hill, a division of The McGraw-Hill Companies, Inc.

Directions: Name each batter's ordinal position. Write the number that tells each batter's position on the line below.

P10   Math Olympics

Day 4

- Discuss page P10 with students. Have students use ordinal numbers to name each batter's position in line.

- Have students write the number underneath each batter.

- Share with students the concept of the game of baseball and running around the bases. If possible, show pictures of baseball players or baseball cards.

- Outdoor activity: Divide the class into two teams. Have students play baseball using a plastic bat and ball or a beach ball. Have students yell "first," "second," and "third" when they cross each base.

- Indoor activity: Have students play baseball in the gym, using a paper towel roll as the bat and a soft sponge type ball.

- Reward the entire class with their fourth colored ring.

Lesson Planner

Objective

Students will construct a graph to answer questions, describe, identify, and compare figures and objects based on their attributes and weight, compare situations according to relative temperature, and count by ones.

Review Vocabulary

circle, heavy, light, numbers, rectangle, sort, square

Resources

Materials: empty packages of food from a grocery store, crayons, newspaper ads, grocery store ads, scissors, classroom objects, glue, poster board, book, pencil, variety of fruits and vegetables, pan scale

Day 1

Share with students that they will be creating their own grocery store in the classroom at the end of the week. Ask students to bring in empty packages of food from home to use in their grocery store.

- Discuss how math is found everywhere in our lives, and they can find math in places we often go, such as the grocery store.

- Show students many different packages of food from a grocery store, such as a square box of popcorn, a round orange, and a rectangular box of crackers.

- Ask students to share other items they see at the grocery store and identify their shapes.

- Have students find examples of a **rectangle**, **square**, and **circle** in the room.

- Direct students to page P11. Have them identify the food items in the picture.

- Discuss the different areas of a grocery store.

- Read the directions. Ask students to trace the squares in blue, circles in red, and rectangles in orange.

Name:

PROJECT 3 — Trip to the Grocery Store

Bakery

Fruit

Vegetables

Day 1: Figure Hunt

Check students' work.

Directions: Trace the squares in blue. Trace the circles in red. Trace the rectangles in orange.

Trip to the Grocery Store

P11

Day 2: Shelf Sort ···

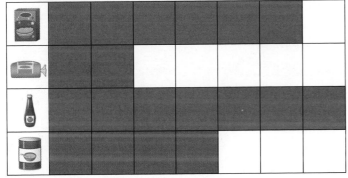

6   2   7   4

Directions: Count each item in the picture. Draw the items in the graph.
Write how many on the lines.

Trip to the Grocery Store

Day 2

- Have students recall the items they identified in the grocery on P11.
- Ask students where they might see **numbers** in a grocery store.
- Discuss price tags, shelf tags, and the numbers on food labels.
- Use packages from yesterday to look at the numbers on the nutritional value charts. Discuss the serving per package and other numbers that would be easy to explain.
- Bring in ads from the newspaper or grocery store that show prices with pictures of food.
- Have students cut out pictures of food they would want in their grocery store.
- Direct students to page P12. Identify the foods shown on the page and read the directions.
- Have students count how many of each item are in the picture and draw the items on the graph. Tell students to write the total number of each object on the line.

Day 3

- Discuss with students the different sections of a grocery store, such as the cold foods section, produce section, and canned/boxed food section, and that they are all located in different places in a grocery store.

- Have students work in groups to **sort** the pictures they cut out on Day 2. Ask students to sort them by sections in the grocery store.

- Have students glue the groups of items to a sheet of poster board that will be used as sections of their grocery store.

- Direct students to page P13. Identify the sections of the grocery store that are shown and the foods that are shown at the bottom of the page.

- Read the directions, have students draw a line from each item to the section where it belongs in the grocery store.

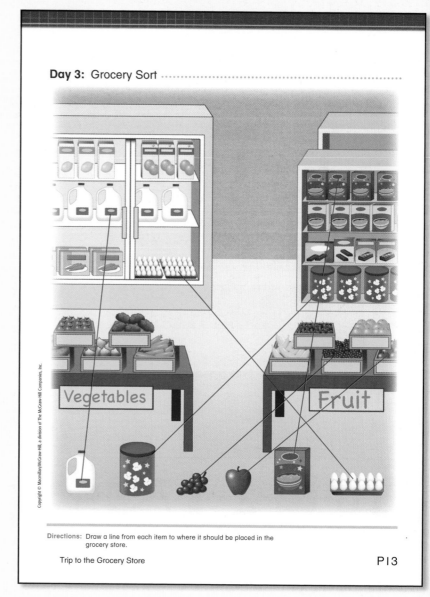

Day 3: Grocery Sort ·······························

Vegetables

Fruit

Directions: Draw a line from each item to where it should be placed in the grocery store.

Trip to the Grocery Store

P13

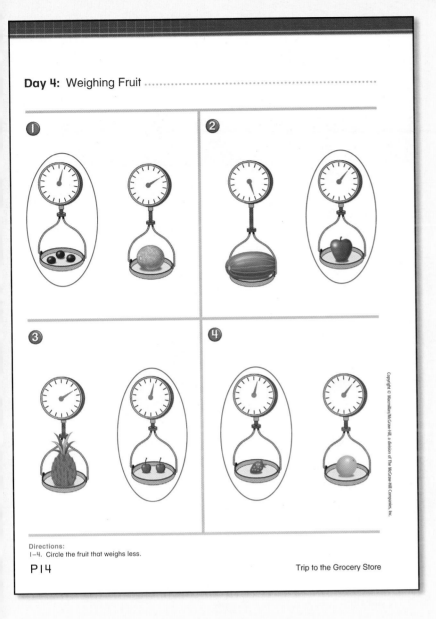

① ②

③ ④

Directions:
1–4. Circle the fruit that weighs less.

Trip to the Grocery Store

Day 5

Remind students they will be creating a grocery store in the room. Discuss the different areas of a grocery store and decide where each section should be set up in the room. Use poster boards with pictures of foods to help create the areas.

- Divide students into four groups.
- Have one group decide how the store will be set up. Have another group sort the pictures and food packages they brought in into the correct areas of the store.
- Have a third group price the food items. Have the last group set up a checkout area.
- Review with students the concepts they learned during the week.
- Give students time to explore the grocery store and take turns being customers and employees.

Extension: Take students on a field trip to an actual grocery store or to the school cafeteria and explore the pantry to find different shaped food containers. Challenge students to find figures, numbers, and a scale.

Wrap-Up

- Use the Wrap-Up questions to assess students' work. Ask the following questions.
- **How did you use math to create a grocery store?** Sample answers: weighed fruits and vegetables, sorted food items by figure and location, looked at prices of food items, looked at numbers on food labels
- **How did you sort food items in your grocery store?** Sample answer: We sorted them into fruits and vegetables, cereal and crackers, snacks, and juice and milk containers.

Day 4

- Remind students of how they can determine which item, out of two, is heavier or lighter.
- Ask a student to come to the front of the room and demonstrate holding a book in one hand and a pencil in the other to show **heavy** and **light** and to determine which is heavier.
- Allow students to use this method on a variety of items in the room. If possible, bring in fruits or vegetables for students to weigh.
- Describe to students how produce is weighed at a grocery store.
- Direct students to page P14. Identify each fruit on the page.
- Talk about the scales and how to tell which fruit is heaviest.
- Read the directions. Have students circle the fruit that weighs less.

Lesson Planner

Objective

Students measure length, compare and order objects according to length, identify and create patterns, compare containers by capacity, compare objects and figures based on their attributes, describe relative position in a sequence, and construct a graph to answer questions about animals.

Review Vocabulary

after, **before**, **different**, **first**, **longer**, **holds less**, **holds more**, **same**, **second**, **shorter**, **sort**, **third**

Resources

Materials: tape, pictures of safari animals: elephants, zebra, lions, snakes, tigers, giraffes, monkeys, lions; pencils, twisted pretzels, raisins, round dry cereal, triangular crackers, 2 sizes of measuring cups, large bowl, small bowls, foam or construction paper circles, triangles, rectangles, squares, yarn, glue, craft sticks, paper bags, crayons

Day 1

Share with students that they will be measuring length, sorting, graphing, identifying geometric figures, and using ordinal words as they learn about animals. Tell students they will be going on a teacher-created safari around the school or room at the end of the week. Explain to students that a safari is a trip people take to watch different types of animals.

- Before class, mark the length of some animals on the floor with tape: elephant 20 ft. long, zebra 6 ft. long, lion 10 ft. long, snake 8 ft. long. Label each measurement using a picture of the animal.

- Discuss patterns on animals, their habitats, and environments using pictures of animals they would see on a safari.

- Discuss the pictures on page P15 with students.

- Ask students what would they use to measure each type of animal? Would they always use the same unit of measure. no Why not? Sample answer: Animals are all different sizes so it would increase accuracy to use different units of measure.

- Have students choose an object to measure with and draw a picture of the object in the top box. Have students measure the length of the animals and record them on their pages.

- Ask students to choose two animals and compare their measurements. Discuss which animal is **longer** and which is **shorter**.

Day 2: Trail Mix Sort

Check students' work.

15			
14			
13			
12			
11			
10			
9			
8			
7			
6			
5			
4			
3			
2			
1			

_ _ _   _ _ _   _ _ _   _ _ _

Directions: Identify the shapes of the food in your bowl of trail mix. Sort your trail mix. Color one square for each piece of food to show how many of each. Write the total number below each piece of food.

P16   Safari

Day 2

- Introduce trail mix by explaining that it is a mixture of seeds, pretzels, cereal, nuts, and dried fruits that is usually eaten as a snack.

- Discuss the chart on page P16 with students. Tell students they will be using the chart to **sort** the different shapes in the trail mix.

- Have students observe as you mix the ingredients in a large bowl to make the trail mix. Discuss which measuring cup **holds more** and which **holds less**.

- Use the smaller measuring cup to scoop some trail mix into individual student bowls.

- Have students sort the trail mix by shapes into separate piles on their plate and color one square for each shape on their chart.

- Have students write the total number of each type of food below the corresponding picture.

- Discuss how the shapes are **alike** and **different**.

  CAUTION: Be aware of student food allergies.

Day 3

- Discuss page P17 with students. Have students count how many of each figure are in the picture and write the numbers.

- Provide templates or examples of masks for many different safari animals. Students could create masks of elephants, zebras, lions, snakes, tigers, giraffes, monkeys, or lions.

- Have students select an animal and create a mask using different foam or construction paper figures and colors.

- Help students glue a craft stick to the bottom of the mask so they can hold it up to their faces.

- Encourage students to discuss the animal they chose and the different figures they used to create their masks.

Day 3: Face Figures

◯	▢	△	▭
5	1	10	6

Directions: Count how many figures are used in the face. Write the numbers.

Safari

P17

Day 4: Safari Map

Directions: Circle the animal you saw second. Mark an X on the animal you saw fourth. Underline the animal you saw sixth.

P18

Safari

Day 5

Before class, place pictures of the safari animals throughout the school or room. The pictures could be of elephants, lions, tigers, zebras, snakes, monkeys, or giraffes. Review with students what they did to prepare for the safari earlier in the week.

Have the class walk together through the building or room searching for animals. When they get to an animal, remove the picture. After the walk, draw a large graph on the board and discuss what animals they found and how many of each.

Wrap-Up

- Use the Wrap-Up questions to assess students' work. Ask the following questions.
- **How did you use math to learn about safari animals?** Sample answer: We measured their length, found patterns on the animals, used figures to make animal masks, and graphed the animals we saw on our safari.
- **Which animal was the longest? Which animal was the shortest?** Sample answer: The elephant was the longest animal. The monkey was the shortest animal.

Day 4

- Discuss page P18 with students. Have them count the footprints to see how many steps it takes to get to the end of the map.
- Have students begin at the arrow at the top of the page.
- Discuss which animals they encountered **first, second**, and **third** as they "walked" through the map.
- Tell students to circle the animal they saw second. Have them mark an X on the animal they saw fourth. Then underline the sixth animal they had seen.
- Encourage students to use the words **before** and **after** when identifying when they saw each animal.
- Give each student a small paper bag. Help them tear the bags to make a flat map.
- Show students how to draw their own map around the classroom, with a start and finish line and a specific path.
- Allow students to trade maps with a partner and follow directions.

Student Handbook

Built-In Workbook

Reference

How to Use the Student Handbook

Use the Student Handbook:

- when you need more practice writing numbers

- when you need to know the meaning of a math word

- when you need to find number patterns, to order numbers, or to skip count

- when you need help writing the number names

Concepts and Skills Bank

Pennies

Objectives

Identify and count pennies to ten cents.

Vocabulary

penny, cent

Resources

Materials:
pennies, plastic container, chart paper, index cards, ten-frame

Activate Prior Knowledge

- Have a class discussion about money. **Why do we need money?** Sample answer: to buy things **How do people get money?** Sample answers: from the bank; from an ATM, working; grandparents

- Give each student a penny. Have students explore their coins. **What color is the coin?** copper or brown **What shape is the coin?** circle **What do you see on the coin?** Sample answer: a man's head, a building Ask students to relate experiences they have had using pennies.

- Draw a cent sign (¢) on chart paper and explain that it is another way to write the word *cents*, which tells how much money.

- Show a group of 10 pennies and explain that the more pennies you have, the more cents you have. Show students an empty container. Ask students to count out loud as you drop the 10 pennies one at a time into the container. **How many pennies do we have?** 10 pennies **How many cents do we have?** 10 cents

Using Student Page CS1

- Give each student 10 pennies. Have students identify the items on the shelves and their prices. Ask them to show how many pennies they would need to buy each item.

- **How do you show 3¢?** 3 pennies

- **How do you show 5¢?** 5 pennies

- Have students continue to show each amount of money. Then ask them to draw the pennies showing the number of cents they would need to buy each item.

Concepts and Skills Bank

Ⓙ Pennies

Vocabulary
penny
cent ¢

penny 1¢

Ⓙ

3 pennies — 3¢

5 pennies — 5¢

8 pennies — 8¢

10 pennies — GRANOLA — 10¢

Directions:
1. Use pennies to show the amount. Draw the pennies.

②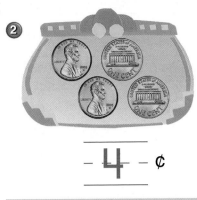

___4___ ¢

③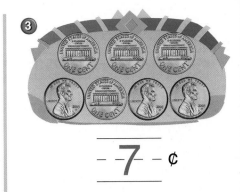

___7___ ¢

④

___6___ ¢

⑤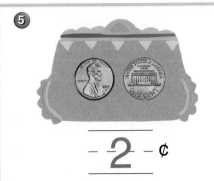

___2___ ¢

⑥

___8___ ¢

⑦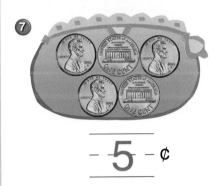

___5___ ¢

Directions:
2-7. Count the pennies. Write the amount.

Using Student Page CS2

- Have students work independently as they count the pennies and write the amount.
- If students are having trouble counting the pennies, reinforce one-to-one correspondence by having students use a ten-frame and count sets of up to ten pennies.

Assess and Close

Show students index cards with different amounts of money up to 10¢ written on them. Have students use pennies to represent the amount shown on each card.

Concepts and Skills Bank

Nickels

Objectives
Identify and count nickels to twenty-five cents.

Vocabulary
nickel

Resources
Materials:
pennies, nickels, chart paper

Activate Prior Knowledge

- Give each student a nickel. Have students examine their coins. Create a class chart titled "What We Notice About a Nickel" and record students observations. Sample answers: the coin is silver, the coin is round, the coin is worth 5 cents, the coin is larger than a penny

- Give students a collection of pennies and nickels. Say a number between 1 and 5. Have students show that number of nickels. Then have them represent each nickel with 5 pennies.

- Have students touch and count the nickels by 5s to find the amount. Then have them count the pennies to check their answers.

Using Student Page CS3

- **Circle the nickels. Write how many.** 4 nickels

- Show students how to skip count by 5s on the number line.

- **Use the number line and skip count by 5s to help you find how much the nickels are worth. Write the amount.** 20 cents

---

Concepts and Skills Bank

② Nickels

Vocabulary
nickel

nickel 5¢

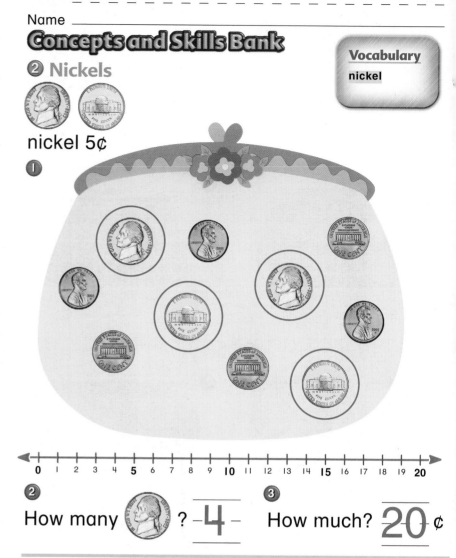

①

How many ? ─4─   How much? 20 ¢

Directions:
1. Circle the nickels in the purse. Count how many.
2. Write how many.
3. Use the number line to help you count by fives to find how much in nickels. Write how much.

Concepts and Skills Bank   CS3

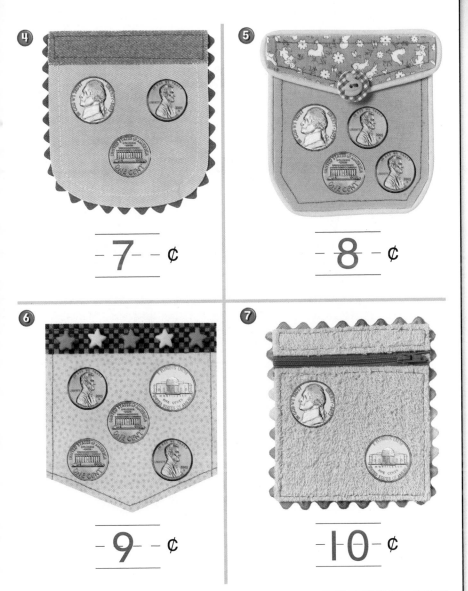

④

─ 7 ─ ¢

⑤

─ 8 ─ ¢

⑥

─ 9 ─ ¢

⑦

─ 10 ─ ¢

Directions:
4-6. Count up from 5 to find the amount. Write the amount.
7. Count by fives to find the amount. Write the amount.

Using Student Page CS4

- Display a nickel and a penny. **How much is a nickel worth?** 5 cents **How much is a penny worth?** 1 cent Demonstrate how to count up from 5 to find the amount of money, touching each coin as you count. Repeat using a nickel and 2 pennies, a nickel and 3 pennies, and a nickel and 4 pennies.

- Have students count the money in the first pocket. **How much money is in the first pocket?** 7 cents

- Have students work independently as they count and write the amount of money in each pocket.

Assess and Close

Which is worth more, 2 nickels or 2 pennies? 2 nickels **How do you know?** Sample answer: A penny is worth 1 cent and a nickel is worth 5 cents. Two pennies is worth 2 cents. Two nickels is worth 10 cents. Ten cents is more than two cents.

Concepts and Skills Bank

Dimes

Objectives

Identify and count dimes to fifty cents.

Vocabulary

dime

Resources

Materials:
pennies, nickels, dimes, hundred chart

Activate Prior Knowledge

- Have students sort pennies, nickels, and dimes into groups. As they sort, talk about the attributes that the coins have, such as shape, size, color, and design.

- **How much is 1 penny worth?** 1 cent **How much is 1 nickel worth?** 5 cents Show a dime as you explain that a dime is worth 10 cents, place 10 pennies under the dime.

- Display a hundred chart. **I have 5 nickels and I want to find how much they are worth by counting by 5s.** Have a volunteer point to the numbers on the hundred chart as the class skip-counts by 5s to 25. **How much are the 5 nickels worth?** 25 cents

- **I have 5 dimes and I want to find how much they are worth by counting by 10s.** Point to the hundred chart as the class skip-counts by 10s to 50. **How much are the 5 dimes worth?** 50 cents

Using Student Page CS5

- **Circle the dimes. Count. Write how many.** 5 dimes

- **Touch each dime and skip-count by 10s to find how much the dimes are worth. Write the amount.** 50 cents

---

Name _____

Concepts and Skills Bank

③ Dimes

dime 10¢

①

②
How many  🪙 ? __5__

③
How much? __50__ ¢

Directions:
1. Circle the dimes in the register drawer. Count how many.
2. Write how many.
3. Count by tens to find how much in dimes. Write how much.

Concepts and Skills Bank   **CS5**

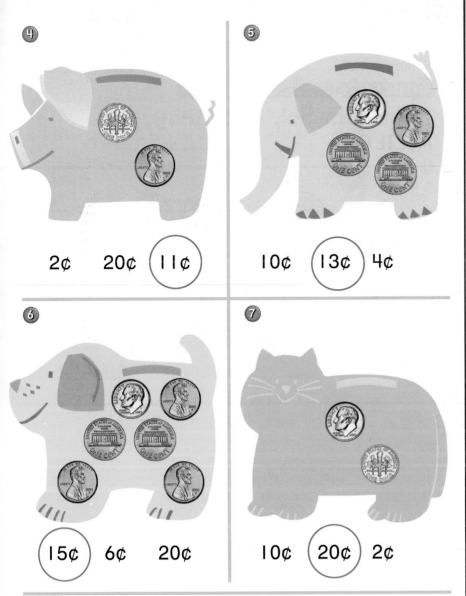

④ 2¢   20¢   (11¢)

⑤ 10¢   (13¢)   4¢

⑥ (15¢)   6¢   20¢

⑦ 10¢   (20¢)   2¢

Directions:
4-6. Count up from 10 to find the amount. Circle the amount.
7. Count by tens to find the amount. Circle the amount.

Using Student Page CS6

- Display a dime and a penny. **How much is a dime worth?** 10 cents **How much is a penny worth?** 1 cent Demonstrate how to count up from 10 to find the amount of money, touching each coin as you count. Repeat using a dime and 2 pennies, a dime and 3 pennies, a dime and 4 pennies, and a dime and 5 pennies.

- Have students count the money in the first bank. **How much money is in the first bank?** 11 cents

- Have students work independently as they count and write the amount of money in each bank.

Assess and Close
Have students use pennies and dimes to show amounts ranging from 11 cents to 50 cents.

Concepts and Skills Bank

Problem-Solving

Act It Out

Objectives

Use the act-it-out strategy to compare the values of a penny, a nickel, and a dime.

Vocabulary

Resources

Materials:
0–5 number cube, pennies, nickels, dimes

Activate Prior Knowledge

- Display a 0–5 number cube, a handful of pennies, a handful of nickels and dimes, and a ten-frame.

- Ask a student volunteer to toss the number cube and take that many pennies and place them on a ten-frame. Repeat until the ten-frame has 5 pennies on it.

- **Can we trade the pennies in the ten-frame for just one coin?** yes **What is that coin?** a nickel **How do you know?** A nickel is worth 5 cents. Five pennies is also worth 5 cents. Have a student trade the pennies for one nickel. Repeat the activity several times.

- **How many pennies are equal to 1 nickel?** 5 pennies **How many nickels are equal to 5 pennies?** 1 nickel

- Repeat activity using 10 pennies and a dime.

Using Student Page CS7

- **How many nickels can you get for the pennies in the bank?** 2 nickels
- **How many dimes?** 1 dime

Concepts and Skills Bank
④ Problem-Solving Strategy
Act It Out

①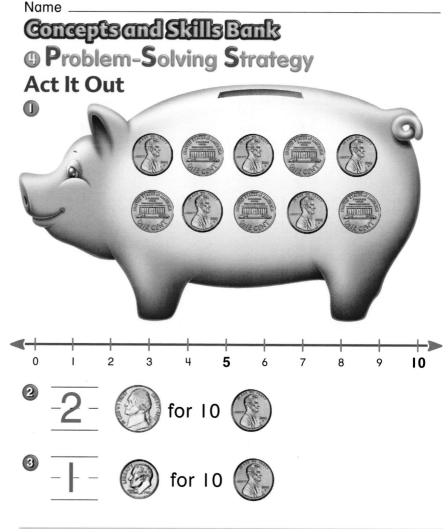

② $\underline{2}$ for 10

③ $\underline{1}$ for 10

Directions:
1. Count the pennies. Use coins and the number line to help you exchange the coins.
2. How many nickels can you get for the pennies? Write the number.
3. How many dimes can you get for the pennies? Write the number.

Concepts and Skills Bank   CS7

④

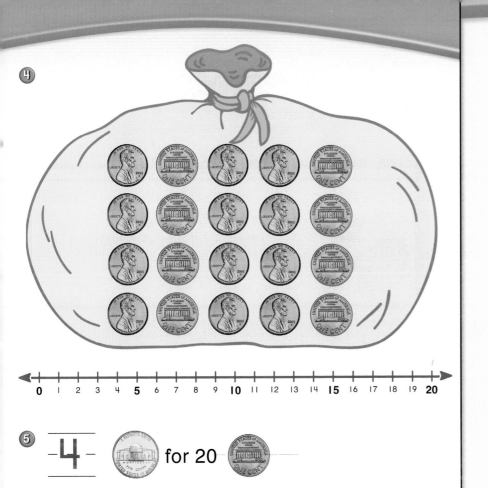

```
◄──┼──┼──┼──┼──┼──┼──┼──┼──┼──┼──┼──┼──┼──┼──┼──┼──┼──┼──┼──►
   0  1  2  3  4  5  6  7  8  9  10  11 12 13 14 15 16 17 18 19 20
```

⑤ -4- for 20

⑥ -2- (dime) for 20 (penny)

Directions:
4. Count the pennies. Use coins and the number line to help you exchange the coins.
5. How many nickels can you get for the pennies? Write the number.
6. How many dimes can you get for the pennies? Write the number.

Using Student Page CS8
- **How many nickels can you get for the pennies in the bag?** 4 nickels
- **How many dimes?** 2 dimes

Assess and Close
Give each student 1 nickel, 1 dime and ten pennies. **How many pennies can I get if I have 1 nickel?** 5 pennies **How many pennies can I get if I have 1 dime?** 10 pennies Have students act out their answers using coins. Check students' work.

Concepts and Skills Bank

Review Money

Objectives

Review identifying, counting, and exchanging coins.

Review Vocabulary

penny, cent, nickel, dime

Resources

pennies, nickels, dimes

Activate Prior Knowledge

- Tell simple riddles that ask students to guess which coin you are describing. Some examples are: **I am worth more than a penny and less than a dime. What am I?** a nickel **I am copper and larger than a dime. What am I?** a penny

- Invite students to think of their own coin riddles to share with the class.

Using Student Page CS9

- Have students draw the coins they would use to buy each toy.

---

①

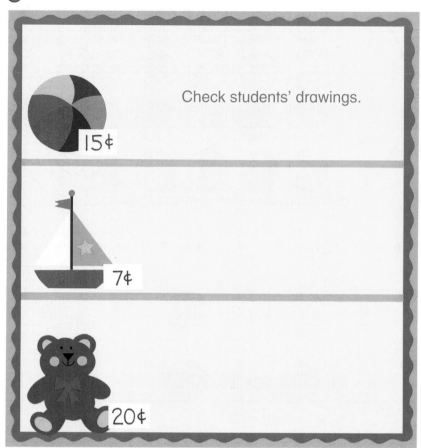

Check students' drawings.

15¢

7¢

20¢

Directions:
1. Use coins to show each price. Draw the coins you used.

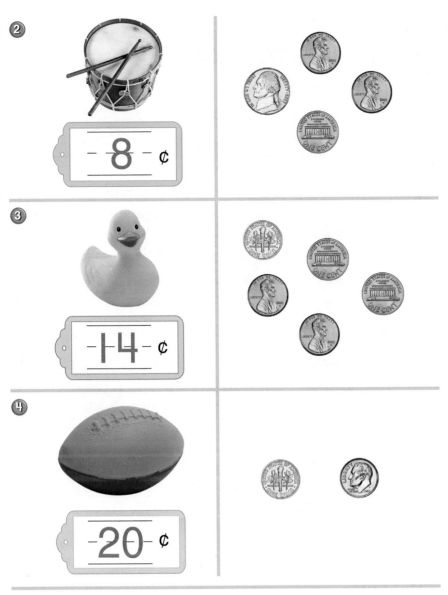

② 8 ¢

③ 14 ¢

④ 20 ¢

Directions:
2–4. Count the coins to find each price. Write the amount on the price tag.

CS10 Concepts and Skills Bank

Using Student Page CS10

- **How much does the drum cost?** 8¢
- **How much does the duck cost?** 14¢
- **How much does the football cost?** 20¢

Assess and Close

Using 10 pennies, 2 nickels, and 1 dime, have students tell different ways to make the following amounts of money: 8 cents, 15 cents, 20 cents, 11 cents. Sample answers: 8 cents—1 nickel and 3 pennies or 8 pennies; 15 cents—15 pennies or 3 nickels; 20 cents—20 pennies, 4 nickels, or 2 dimes; 11 cents—1 dime and 1 penny or 11 pennies.

Concepts and Skills Bank

Money

Objectives

- Identify a penny, nickel, dime, quarter, and dollar.

- Identify the value of a penny, nickel, dime, quarter, and dollar.

Vocabulary

penny, nickel, dime, quarter, dollar

Activate Prior Knowledge

Discuss situations in which students have used **money.** Sample answers: to pay for a toy, to buy lunch at school, to save in a piggy bank

Using student page CS11

- Hold up a play penny, nickel, dime, or dollar bill and identify its name and value. Repeat until all the money and the values have been identified. Give students play coins and dollar bills. Name different coin and dollar values and have the students hold up the coin or dollar bill.

- **What do you see in the box on this page?** a penny, nickel, dime, quarter, and dollar bill

- Point out a ¢ sign. Tell students that a ¢ sign is a symbol for cents. You may want to introduce a $ sign, a symbol for dollars, at this time.

- Have students identify the money at the bottom of the page before completing the exercises.

Concepts and Skills Bank

---

⑥ Money

 = 1¢ = 5¢ =10¢ = 25¢

 = 100¢

    blue

green

Directions:
1. Circle the pennies.
2. Put an X on the dimes.
3. Underline a nickel.
4. Color the quarter blue.
5. Color the dollar green.

Concepts and Skills Bank **CS11**

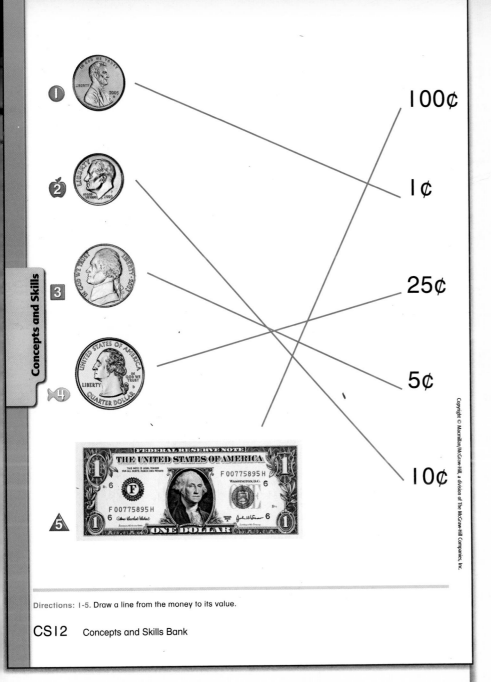

1 — 100¢

2 — 1¢

3 — 25¢

4 — 5¢

5 — 10¢

Directions: I–5. Draw a line from the money to its value.

CS12   Concepts and Skills Bank

Using student page CS12

Exercises 1–5 Have students work independently as they match coins and a dollar bill to the values.

Assess and Close

- Label items in the classroom with a picture of coins/dollar bill and the value. Have students use play money to purchase items. Discuss which coins/bills they used to purchase their items.

Concepts and Skills Bank

Measurement

Objectives

- Identify tools for measuring length, weight, and temperature.

- Choose the right type of measuring tool for a specific situation.

Vocabulary

ruler, yardstick, tape measure, scale, balance, thermometer

Activate Prior Knowledge

- **Have you ever gone to the doctor and been measured to find how tall you are?** yes

- **How did the doctor or nurse measure you?** Sample answer: against a chart on the wall

- **What did they use to measure your weight?** a scale

- **What did they use to take your temperature?** a thermometer

- Discuss other experiences students have had with measurement. Sample answers: measuring feet for shoes or weighing fruit and vegetables at the grocery store.

Using student page CS13

- Have students touch each measuring tool on the page as you identify and discuss it.

- To measure length you can use a ruler, a yard stick, or a tape measure.

- To find how heavy something is you can use a scale. You can also use a balance to measure weight.

- To measure temperature you can use a thermometer. There are different kinds of thermometers. A digital thermometer shows a number on a screen. Another kind of thermometer has a liquid in a glass tube. The liquid in the tube contracts and expands.

Concepts and Skills Bank

Name _____

Concepts and Skills Bank

⑦ Measurement

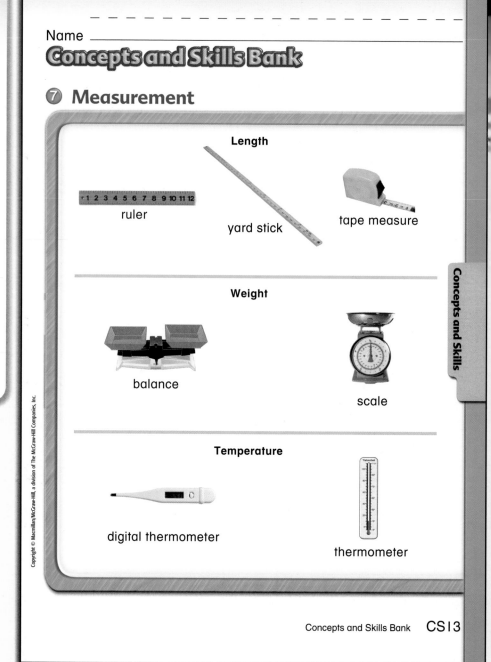

Length

ruler

yard stick

tape measure

Weight

balance

scale

Temperature

digital thermometer

thermometer

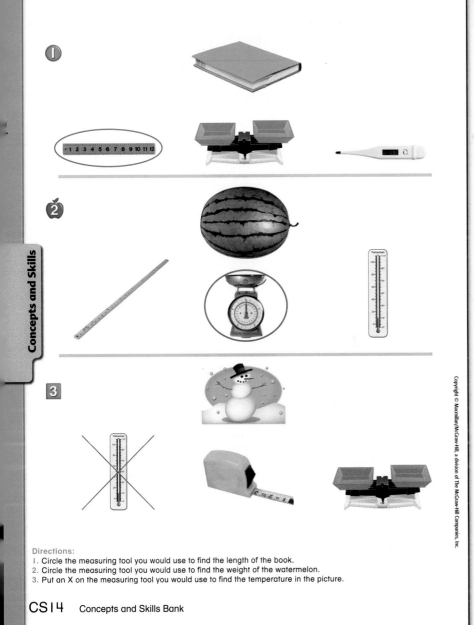

Directions:
1. Circle the measuring tool you would use to find the length of the book.
2. Circle the measuring tool you would use to find the weight of the watermelon.
3. Put an X on the measuring tool you would use to find the temperature in the picture.

Using student page CS14

- Go over all of the pictures in Exercise 1. Have students circle the measuring tool they would use to find the length of a book.

- Review all of the pictures in Exercise 2. Ask students to circle the measuring tool they would use to find the weight of a watermelon.

- Discuss the snowperson in Exercise 3. Ask students what temperature they think it is in the picture. Have students put an X on the measuring tool they would use to find the temperature.

Assess and Close

Measuring around the room Give each student a sheet of paper with three columns. Place a picture of a ruler in one column, a picture of a scale in the second column, and a picture of a thermometer in the third column. Have the students draw pictures in each column of objects that would be measured by the tool.

- Discuss results with the class.

Concepts and Skills Bank

Symmetry

Objective

Identify lines of symmetry.

Vocabulary

line of symmetry, symmetry

Materials: cut-out circles, hearts, and squares; one per student, crayons

Activate Prior Knowledge

- Display a circle and a square. Have the students identify each figure.

- Give each student a figure and have them fold the figure in half.

- Ask students what they notice about the figures? Sample answers: lines down the middle, both sides are the same shape and size, both sides match.

Using student page CS15

- Have students look at the rectangle in the box. Have them trace the line down the middle. Discuss how both sides of the rectangle are the same size and shape; they match. Explain that the rectangle has **symmetry**. The line in the center of the object is the **line of symmetry**.

- Have the students trace the line through each figure to show symmetry.

---

⑧ Symmetry

Directions: Draw a line through each object to show a line of symmetry.

Concepts and Skills Bank   CS15

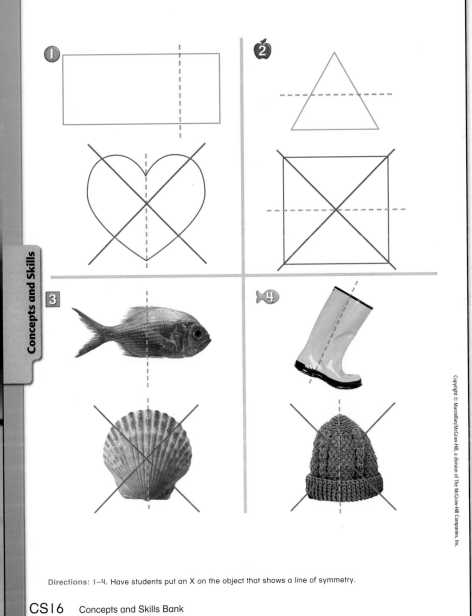

Directions: 1–4. Have students put an X on the object that shows a line of symmetry.

Using student page CS16

Exercises 1–4 Have students identify which object has a correct line of symmetry by placing an X on the correct object. Encourage the students to explain their choices.

Assess and Close

Give students two hearts, one with a correct line of symmetry and one with an incorrect line of symmetry.

- **Which figure shows symmetry? Explain your answer.** The heart with the two matching sides shows symmetry.

Glossary/Glosario

English	Español

about (page 218)

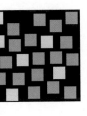

How many? about 20

aproximadamente

¿Cuántos? aproximadamente 20

above (page 71)

above

sobra

sobra

add (page 281)

3 ducks   2 more join   5 ducks in all

sumar

3 patos   2 más se unen   5 patos en total

after (page 75)

6 is just after 5

después

El 6 viene inmediatamente después del 5

Glossary/Glosario

English	Español

A tarde

afternoon (page 229)

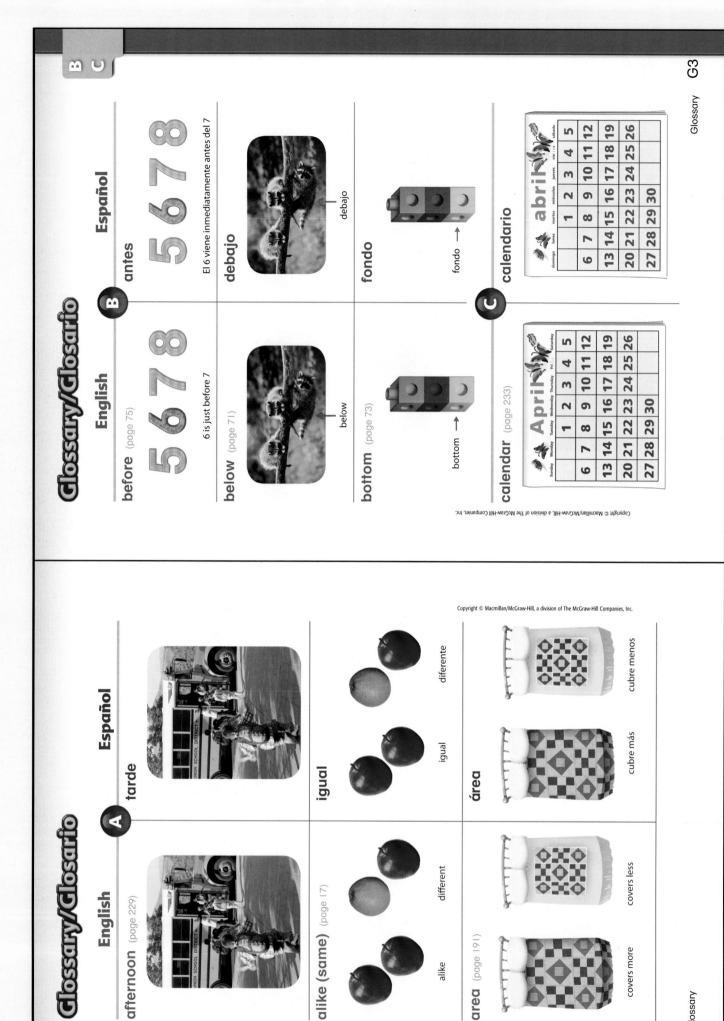

alike (same) (page 17)

alike   different   igual   diferente

area (page 191)

covers more   covers less   cubre más   cubre menos

área

Glossary/Glosario

English	Español

B antes

before (page 75)

5 6 7 8

6 is just before 7

El 6 viene inmediatamente antes del 7

below (page 71)

below   debajo

debajo

bottom (page 73)

bottom   fondo

fondo

C calendario

calendar (page 233)

April						
Sunday	Monday	Tuesday	Wednesday	Thursday	Fri	Saturday
		1	2	3	4	5
6	7	8	9	10	11	12
13	14	15	16	17	18	19
20	21	22	23	24	25	26
27	28	29	30			

abril						
domingo	lunes	martes	miércoles	jueves	vier.	sábado
		1	2	3	4	5
6	7	8	9	10	11	12
13	14	15	16	17	18	19
20	21	22	23	24	25	26
27	28	29	30			

Glossary/Glosario

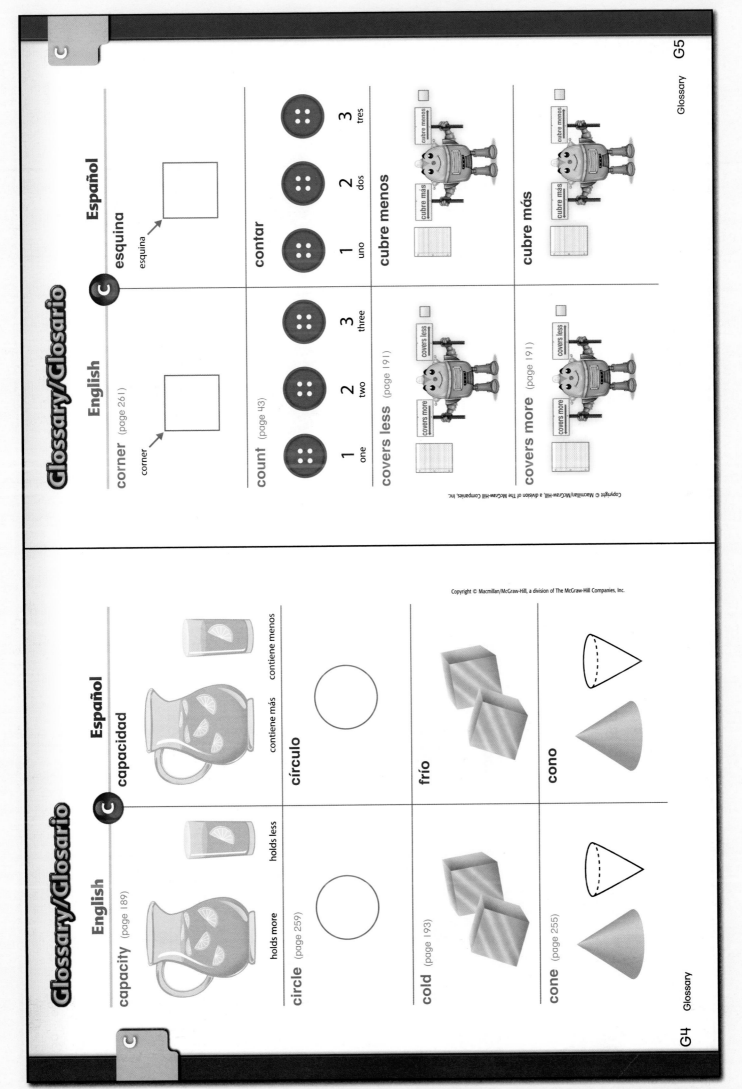

English / Español

capacity (page 189) / **capacidad**

holds more / holds less
contiene más / contiene menos

circle (page 259) / **círculo**

cold (page 193) / **frío**

cone (page 255) / **cono**

English / Español

corner (page 261) / **esquina**

corner / esquina

count (page 43) / **contar**

1 one / 2 two / 3 three
1 uno / 2 dos / 3 tres

covers less (page 191) / **cubre menos**

covers more / covers less
cubre más / cubre menos

covers more (page 191) / **cubre más**

covers more / covers less
cubre más / cubre menos

Glossary/Glosario

Glossary/Glosario

English	Español

D

different (page 17)

different — alike

diferente — iguales

E

equal to (page 183)

○○○ = ○○○

grupos iguales

○○○ = ○○○

3 en cada grupo

equal parts (page 269)

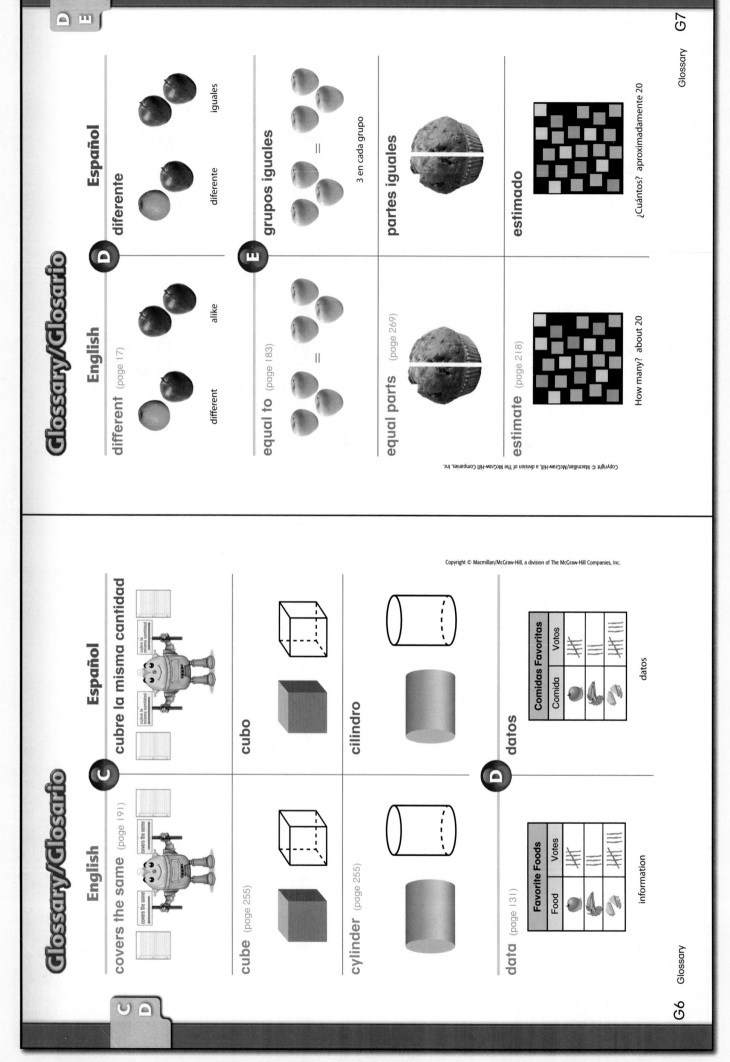

partes iguales

estimate (page 218)

How many? about 20

estimado

¿Cuántos? aproximadamente 20

Glossary/Glosario

English	Español

C

covers the same (page 191)

covers the same

cube (page 255)

cubre la misma cantidad

cubre la misma cantidad

cubo

cylinder (page 255)

cilindro

D

data (page 131)

Favorite Foods	
Food	Votes
🍎	

information

datos

Comidas Favoritas	
Comida	Votos
🍎	

datos

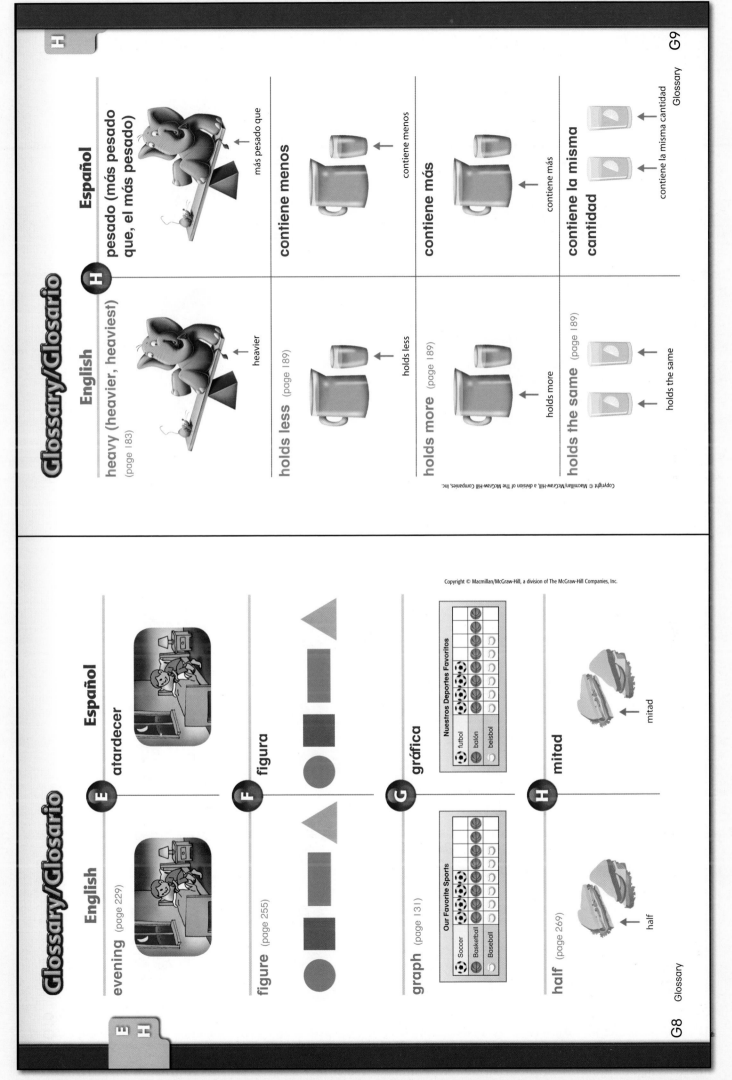

Glossary/Glosario

English | Español

H

heavy (heavier, heaviest) (page 183) — **pesado (más pesado que, el más pesado)**

- heavier — más pesado que

holds less (page 189) — **contiene menos**

- holds less — contiene menos

holds more (page 189) — **contiene más**

- holds more — contiene más

holds the same (page 189) — **contiene la misma cantidad**

- holds the same — contiene la misma cantidad

Copyright © Macmillan/McGraw-Hill, a division of The McGraw-Hill Companies, Inc.

Glossary/Glosario

English | Español

E

evening (page 229) — **atardecer**

F

figure (page 255) — **figura**

G

graph (page 131) — **gráfica**

Our Favorite Sports		Nuestros Deportes Favoritos	
Soccer		futbol	
Basketball		balón	
Baseball		beisbol	

H

half (page 269) — **mitad**

- half — mitad

Copyright © Macmillan/McGraw-Hill, a division of The McGraw-Hill Companies, Inc.

Glossary/Glosario

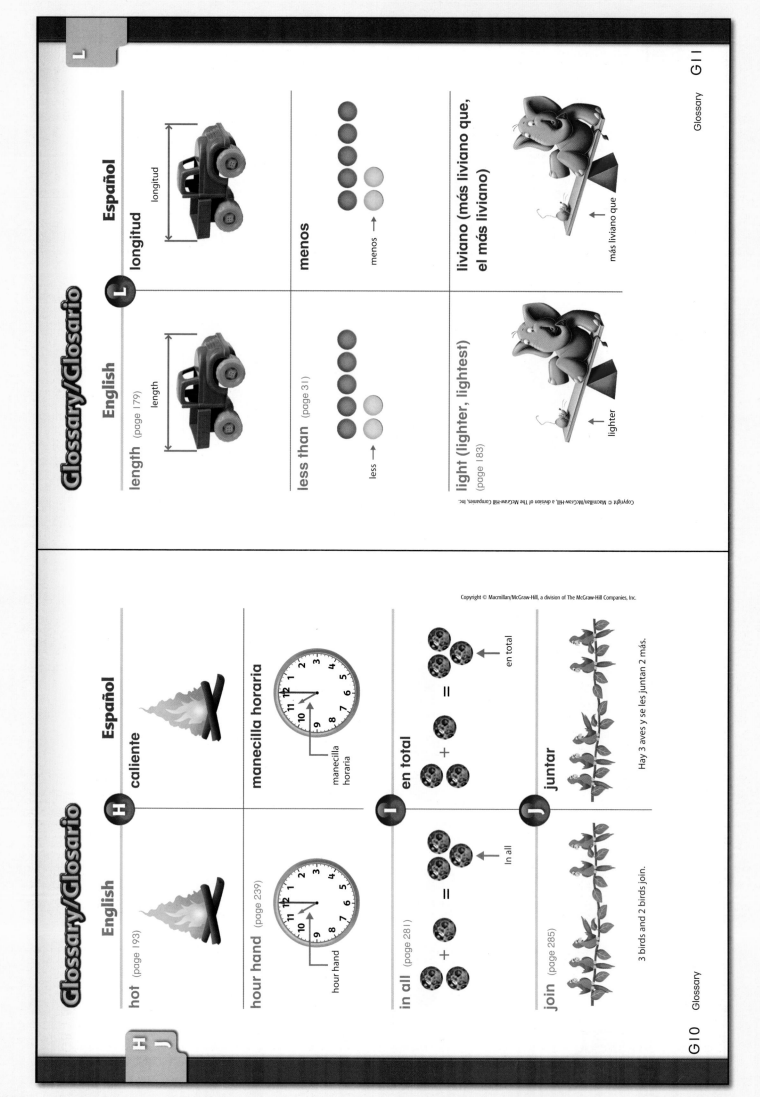

English	Español
length (page 179)	**longitud**
length	longitud
less than (page 31)	**menos**
less →	→ menos
light (lighter, lightest) (page 183)	**liviano (más liviano que, el más liviano)**
lighter	más liviano que

Copyright © Macmillan/McGraw-Hill, a division of The McGraw-Hill Companies, Inc.

English	Español
hot (page 193)	**caliente**
hour hand (page 239)	**manecilla horaria**
hour hand	manecilla horaria
in all (page 281)	**en total**
+ = in all →	+ = → en total
join (page 285)	**juntar**
3 birds and 2 birds join.	Hay 3 aves y se les juntan 2 más.

Copyright © Macmillan/McGraw-Hill, a division of The McGraw-Hill Companies, Inc.

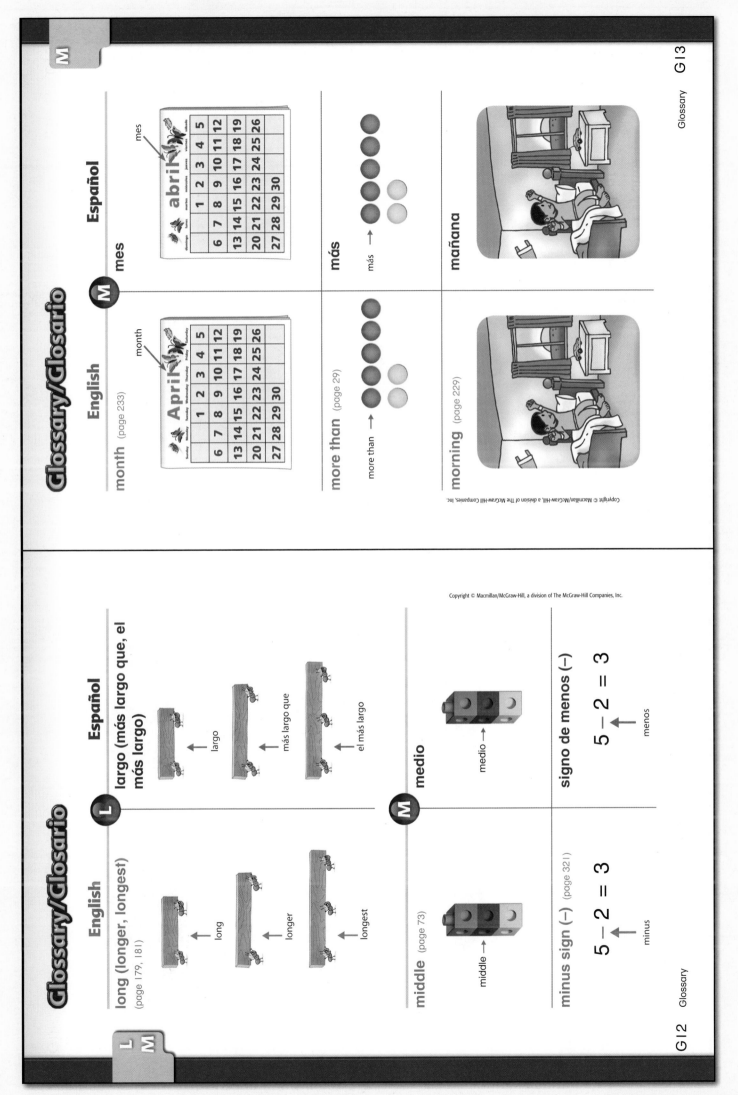

Glossary/Glosario

Glossary/Glosario

English	Español
month (page 233)	**mes**

April — month / abril — mes

English	Español
more than (page 29)	**más**

more than / más

English	Español
morning (page 229)	**mañana**

Glossary/Glosario

English	Español
long (longer, longest) (page 179, 181)	**largo (más largo que, el más largo)**

long / largo
longer / más largo que
longest / el más largo

English	Español
middle (page 73)	**medio**

middle / medio

English	Español
minus sign (–) (page 321)	**signo de menos (–)**

$5 - 2 = 3$ minus

$5 - 2 = 3$ menos

Glossary/Glosario

English	Español

N

number (page 45) / **número**

1, 2, 3, 4, 5, 6, 7, 8, 9
numbers 1–9 / numeros 1 al 9

O

o'clock (page 239) / **en punto**

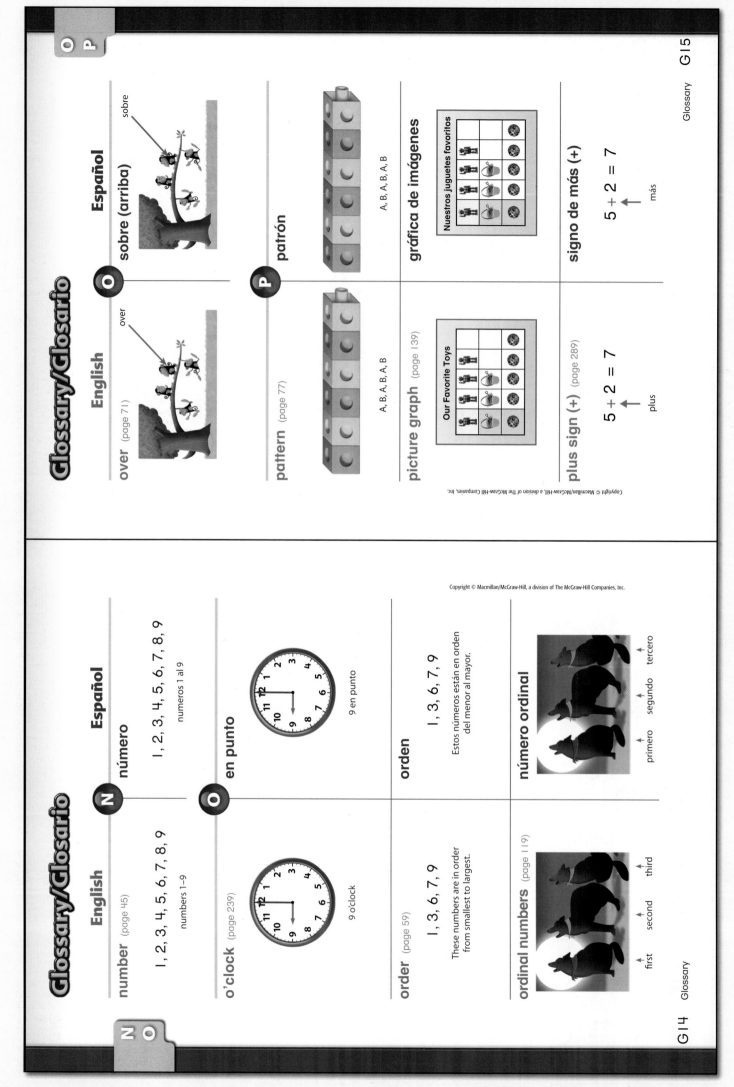

9 o'clock / 9 en punto

order (page 59) / **orden**

1, 3, 6, 7, 9

These numbers are in order from smallest to largest. / Estos numeros están en orden del menor al mayor.

ordinal numbers (page 119) / **número ordinal**

first, second, third / primero, segundo, tercero

Glossary/Glosario

English	Español

O

over (page 71) / **sobre (arriba)**

over / sobre

P

pattern (page 77) / **patrón**

A, B, A, B, A, B

picture graph (page 139) / **gráfica de imágenes**

Our Favorite Toys / Nuestros juguetes favoritos

plus sign (+) (page 289) / **signo de más (+)**

5 + 2 = 7
plus / más

Glossary/Glosario

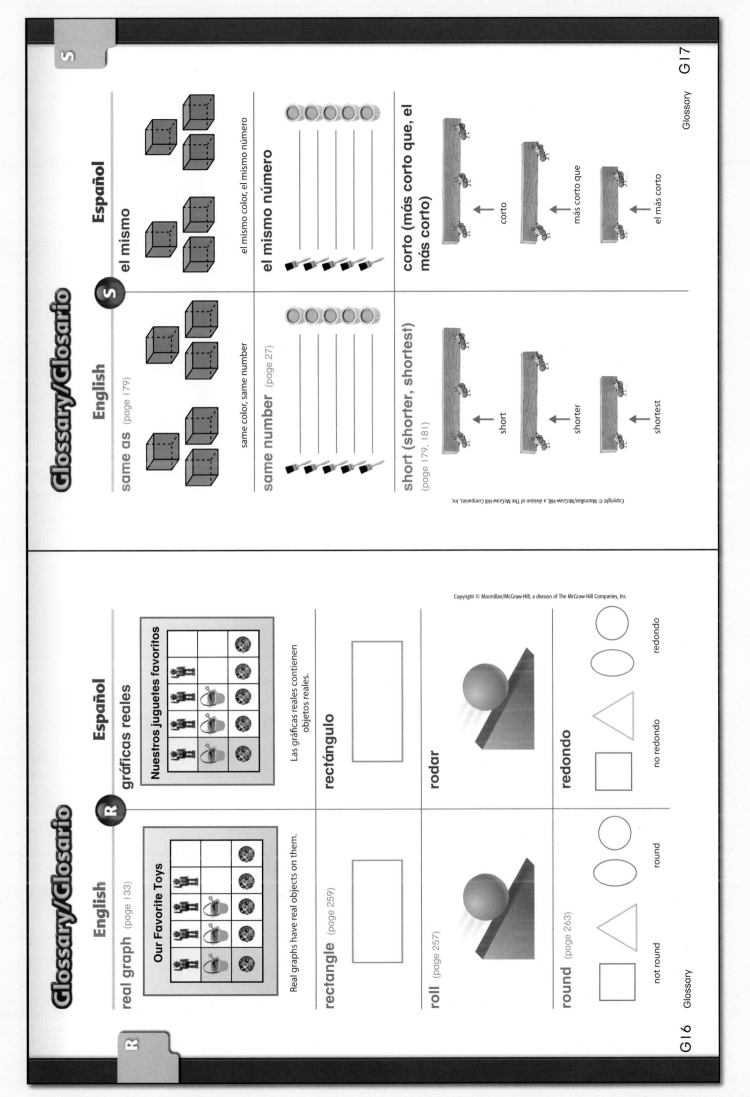

English | Español

S

same as (page 179) — **el mismo**

same number (page 27) — **el mismo número**

same color, same number — el mismo color, el mismo número

short (shorter, shortest) (page 179, 181) — **corto (más corto que, el más corto)**

short — corto
shorter — más corto que
shortest — el más corto

Copyright © Macmillan/McGraw-Hill, a division of The McGraw-Hill Companies, Inc.

English | Español

R

real graph (page 133) — **gráficas reales**

Our Favorite Toys — Nuestros juguetes favoritos

Real graphs have real objects on them. — Las gráficas reales contienen objetos reales.

rectangle (page 259) — **rectángulo**

roll (page 257) — **rodar**

round (page 263) — **redondo**

round — redondo
not round — no redondo

Copyright © Macmillan/McGraw-Hill, a division of The McGraw-Hill Companies, Inc.

Glossary/Glosario

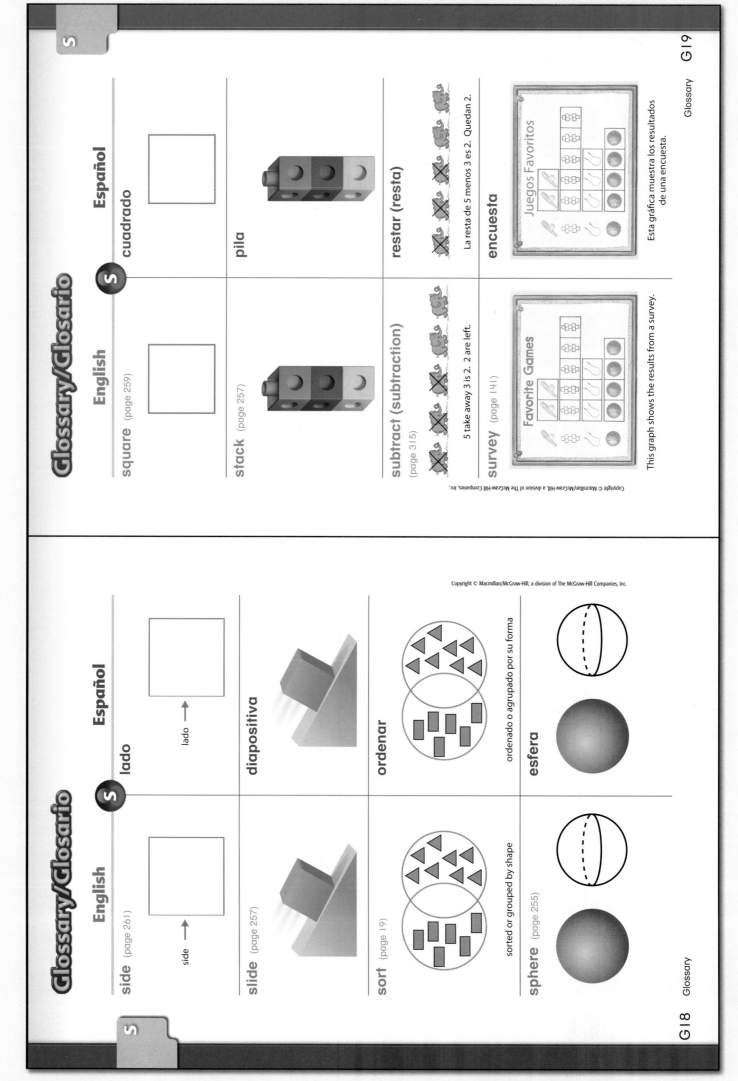

Glossary/Glosario

English — Español

side (page 261) / **lado**

side → / lado →

slide (page 257) / **diapositiva**

sort (page 19) / **ordenar**

sorted or grouped by shape / ordenado o agrupado por su forma

sphere (page 255) / **esfera**

Glossary/Glosario

English — Español

square (page 259) / **cuadrado**

stack (page 257) / **pila**

subtract (subtraction) (page 315) / **restar (resta)**

5 take away 3 is 2. 2 are left. / La resta de 5 menos 3 es 2. Quedan 2.

survey (page 141) / **encuesta**

Favorite Games / Juegos Favoritos

This graph shows the results from a survey. / Esta gráfica muestra los resultados de una encuesta.

Glossary/Glosario

G21

English	Español
tomorrow (page 235)	**mañana**
top (page 73)	**arriba**
triangle (page 259)	**triángulo**

Glossary **G21**

G20

English	Español
temperature (page 193)	**temperatura**
hot · cold	caliente · frío
three-dimensional figure (page 255)	**figura tridimensional**
cube · cone · sphere	cubo · cono · esfera
today (page 235)	**hoy**
yesterday · today	ayer · hoy

G20 Glossary

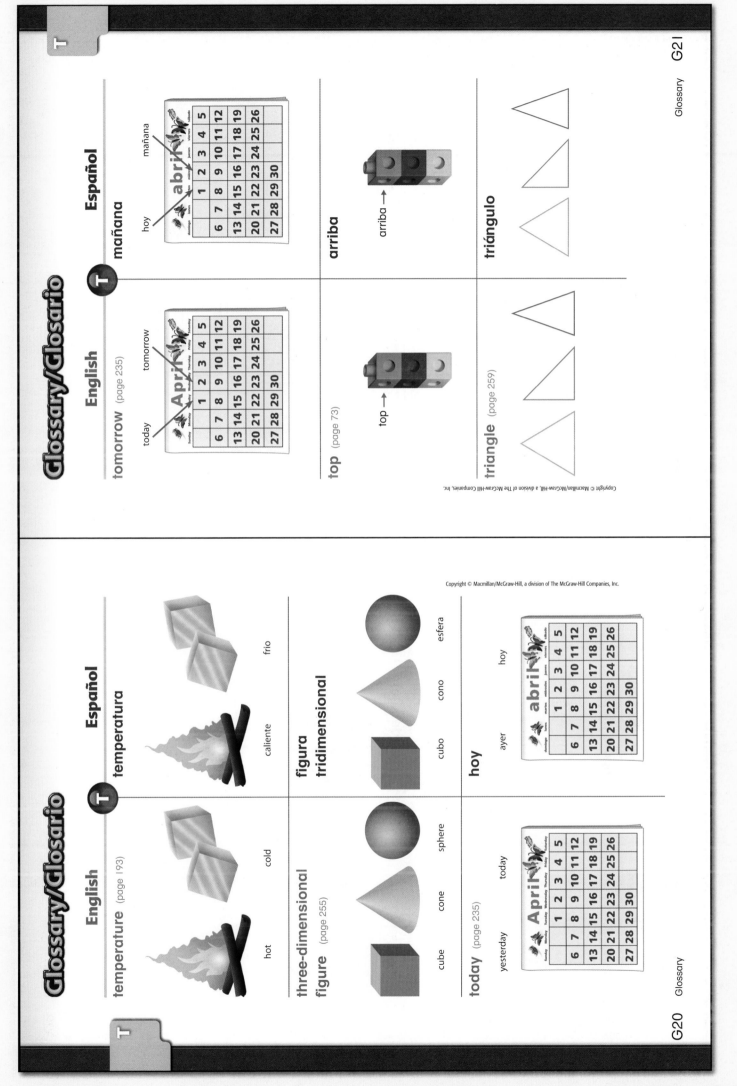

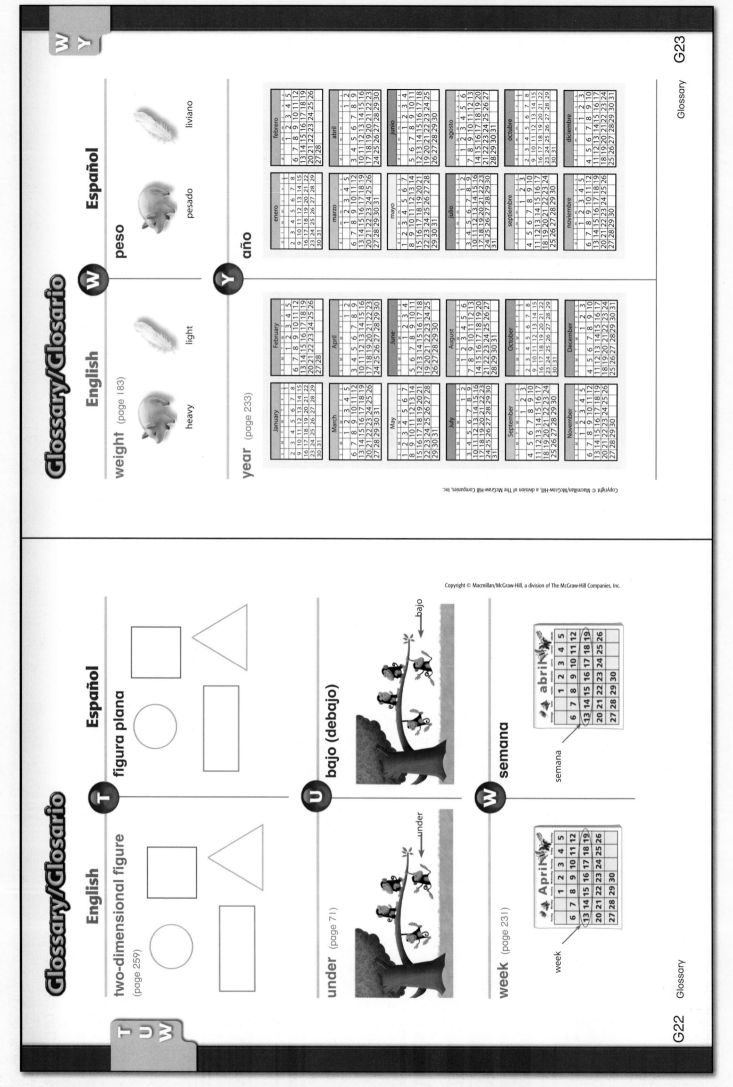

Glossary/Glosario

English — Español

weight (page 183) — **peso**

heavy — pesado

light — liviano

year (page 233) — **año**

February	April	June	August	October	December

January	March	May	July	September	November

Glossary/Glosario

English — Español

two-dimensional figure (page 259) — **figura plana**

under (page 71) — **bajo (debajo)**

under — bajo

week (page 231) — **semana**

April				
1	2	3	4	5
6	7	8	9	10	11	12
13	14	15	16	17	18	19
20	21	22	23	24	25	26
27	28	29	30

week

abril				
1	2	3	4	5
6	7	8	9	10	11	12
13	14	15	16	17	18	19
20	21	22	23	24	25	26
27	28	29	30

semana

Glossary/Glosario

English	Español
yesterday (page 235)	**ayer**

yesterday   today

April calendar with "yesterday" and "today" marked

ayer   hoy

abril calendar with "ayer" and "hoy" marked

PhotoCredits

vi-vii Doug Martin; 1(c)Ariel Skelley/CORBIS; 2 David M. Dennis/ Animals; 3 (tc)Goran Kapor/Alamy, (br)Pat O'Hara/CORBIS, (others)Stockbyte; 4 (tl)Siede Preis/Getty Images, (tr)JoSon/Getty Images, (cr)Getty Images, (br)Pat O'Hara/CORBIS; 5 (tc)FAN travelstock/Alamy, (others)Image Source/CORBIS; 6 Image Source/CORBIS; 7 John Henley/CORBIS; 9 Cory Morse/Getty Images; 11 Corbis Super RF/Alamy; 13 Randy Lincks/Masterfile; 15 (tl)Brand X Pictures/PunchStock, (others)Eclipse Studios; 16 (tl)Brand X Pictures/PunchStock; 17 (party hat rabbit cap)IndexOpen, (helmet)Ryan McVay, (fish)G.K. Vikki Hart/ Getty Images, (starfish)Jon Cartwright/Getty Images, (pineapple bear)Getty Images, (orange)Stockdisc/PunchStock; 18 (plane chair brush)Photos.com, (helicopter)CORBIS, (stool)Getty Images; 25 (tcr)Ryan McVay/Getty Images, (cr c)Getty Images, (b)CORBIS; 27 (l)Getty Images, (tc)IndexOpen, (c br)Masterfile, (bcl bcr)C Squared Studios/Getty Images, (bl)Chris Stock/Lebrecht/The Image Works; 32 (top to bottom) Stockdisc, CORBIS, Fielding Piepereit, Dove King/Getty Images, Photos.com, Masterfile, Masterfile; 33 (t)The Stock Asylum, LLC/Alamy, (b)Getty Images; 34 (tr)Photos To Go, (cr)The McGraw-Hill Companies, (cl)Getty Images, (br)Getty Images; 35 (top to bottom)Getty Images, PhotoLink/Getty Images, Getty Images; 39 F. Lukasseck/Masterfile; 41 (cr br)Eclipse Studios, (bl)Richard Hutchings/Digital Light Source, (tl)The McGraw-Hill Companies; 42 (bl)Richard Hutchings/Digital Light Source, (tl)The McGraw-Hill Companies 50 (tc)BL Productions/SuperStock, (l)artpartner-images.com/Alamy, (bc)super stock, (c b)Photos.com; 57 (wood)Ted Morrison/SuperStock, (saw)Photos.com, (hammer)IndexOpen, (nail)Masterfile, (paint)SuperStock, (screw)Leonard Lessin/Peter Arnold, Inc., (birdhouse)Peter Ardito/ Index Stock, (paint brush)Tony Hutchings/Getty Images, (screwdriver)photolibrary.com.pty.ltd/Index Stock, (bird)James Urbach/ Barnes Martin/IndexOpen, IndexOpen, Getty Images, G.K. Vikki Hart/ Getty Images, Ron Steiner/Alamy; 61 (t)CORBIS, (b)Tony Perrotte/ Alamy Images; 62 (t)Steve Niedorf Photography/Getty Images, (b)Jochen Sand/Getty Images; 64 (tcr c)G.K. & Vikki Hart/Getty Images, (tcl b)Getty Images, (t bo)McGraw-Hill Companies; 67 S Purdy Matthews/Getty Images; 69-70 Eclipse Studios; 80 (tc)Alamy, (tc)Punchstock, (cr)Getty Images, (cr)Punchstock, (bl)Punchstock, (b)Purestock/Getty Images; 81 (tl)Richard Hutchings/Digital Light Source, (others)The McGraw-Hill Companies; 85 (t)Richard Hutchings/Digital Light Source, (drum bell guitar)C Squared Studios/ Getty Images, (tambourine triangle)Getty Images, (maracas)George Doyle/Getty Images; 86 (cymbal)Lebrecht Music and Arts Photo Library/Alamy, (trumpet)Getty Images, (flute clarinet)C Squared Studios/Getty Images, (children)Richard Hutchings/Digital Light Source; 89 (glasses)Ingram Publishing/Alamy Images, (umbrello)Getty Images, (flipflops)Punchstock, (boots)Digital Vision/ Getty Images, (checkers)Jupiterimages, (playground)Andrea Rugg/ Beateworks/CORBIS; 90 (top to bottom)Getty Images, Jupiterimages, Ryan Mcvay/Getty Images, CORBIS, C Squared Studios/Getty Images; 91 (t)The McGraw-Hill Companies; (c)CORBIS; 92 (b)The McGraw-Hill Companies, (t)Richard Hutchings/Digital Light Source; 97 Image Source/SuperStock; 99-100 Eclipse Studios; 105 (tc)CSquared Studios/Getty Images, (others)Mazer; 115 (fish)Alamy Images, (birds guinea pigs)G.K. & Vikki Hart/Getty Images, (yam ball)Ken Cavanagh/The McGraw-Hill Companies, (cat post)Photospin/Imagestate, (bird seed bell)Mazer Corporation, (fish food)The McGraw-Hill Companies/Jacques Cornell; 116 (top to bottom)Comstock Images/Alamy Images, Mazer Corporation, Photospin/Alamy Images, Sergio Piumatti/Destinations, Getty Images, Kathleen Finlay/Masterfile, Getty Images; 123 (top to bottom)Getty Images, C Squared Studios/Getty Images, Brand X Pictures/Getty Images, C Squared Studios/Getty Images; 127 McGraw-Hill Companies; 129 (c)The McGraw-Hill Companies, (b bcr br)Eclipse Studios; 130 (c)The McGraw-Hill Companies, (b)Eclipse Studios; 143 (b)Ariel Skelley/CORBIS, (t)Artifacts Images; 144 (c)Paul Borton/CORBIS, (t)Bruce Hershey/Jupiterimages, (b)Richard Hutchings/Digital Light Source; 146 (dragonfly)Creatas/ PunchStock, (ladybug)D. Hurst/Alamy Images, (bell)C Squared Studios/Getty Images, (tambourine)Getty Images; 149 Raul Touzon/ Getty Images; 151-152 (br)Eclipse Studios; 155 Photos.com/ Jupiterimages; 156 (t)Masterfile, (c)Photos.com; 157 Ryan McVay/ Jupiterimages; 158 Getty Images; 159 Getty Images; 161 (l)Brand X Pictures/PunchStock, (cl r)Siede Preis/Getty Images, (cr)The McGraw-Hill Companies; 162 (t)D. Hurst/Alamy Images, (cl r)C Squared Studios/Getty Images, (c)Stockdisc/PunchStock; 165-166 Farrall/Getty Images; 163-164 Stockdisc/PunchStock; 169 StudiOhio; 169 (t)Brand X Pictures/PunchStock, (t)Borland/ PhotoLink/Getty Images, (tcl)Robert Glusic/Getty Images, (tcr)PhotoLink/Getty Images, (tr)MediaImages/Age Fotostock, (cl)CORBIS, (cr)BananaStock/PunchStock, (r)Creatas/Punchstock, (b)Richard Hutchings/Digital Light Source; 170 Beaconstox/Alamy Images; 172 (drum trumpet)Getty Images, (Photos To Go)Dove King/Getty Images, (boots)Digital Vision/Getty Images; 175 CORBIS; 177-178 Eclipse Studios; 183 (t)Richard Hutchings/Digital Light Source, (cl)The McGraw-Hill Companies, (cr br)StudiOhio, (bcl)Getty Images, (bl)Stockbyte/PictureQuest; 184 (tl)Getty Images, (tr)CORBIS, (cl)Stockbyte/Getty Images, (tcr)Comstock Images/ Alamy, (cr r)Don Brandenburg/iStockphoto., (t)Hemera Technologies/ Alamy; 189 StudiOhio; 195 (t)CORBIS, (b)Jacques Cornell/The McGraw-Hill Companies; 196 (t)G. I. Bernard/Photo Researchers, (b)Dove King/Getty Images; 197 (t)G.K. & Vikki Hart/Getty Images, (cl)Ingram Publishing; 198 Photos To Go; 201 Mark Tomalty/ Masterfile; 203-204 Eclipse Studios; 205 C Squared Studios/ Photodisc Green/Getty Images; 206 (t)Getty Images, (tc)The McGraw-Hill Companies, (bc)C Squared Studios/Getty Images, (b)Masterfile; 218 McGraw-Hill Companies; 219 (t)Comstock/ PunchStock, (b)David Buffington/Getty Images; 220 (tl)Michael Houghton/StudiOhio, (b)Cory Anderson/Eagle Eye Pictures/ Photographers Direct; 222 (t)Stockdisc/PunchStock, (tr (tcr)Jupiterimages, (cr)Getty Images, ., (tl)Karen Whylie/Masterfile; 225 Jose Luis Pelaez, Inc./CORBIS; 227-228 Eclipse Studios; 229 (b)Alamy Images, (t)Will & Deni McIntyre/CORBIS; 237 Bill Bachmann/Index Stock Imagery; 241 Richard Hutchings/Digital Light Source; 243 (bc)PunchStock/Getty Images, (tc)Punchstock, (b) CORBIS, (t)Digital Vision; 245 (t)Ariel Skelley/Getty Images, (b)Alamy Images; 246 Yvona momatiuk/Photo Researchers; 251 Katherine Fawssett/Getty Images; 252 The McGraw-Hill Companies; 253-254 Eclipse Studios; 255 (t)The McGraw-Hill Companies, (tl)Getty Images, (tcr)The McGraw-Hill Companies; 256 (tr)Stockbyte/PictureQuest, (cr)Mazer Corporation, (block)Alamy Images, (funnel)Mazer Corporation, (hot)Alamy Images, (marble)Ken Cavanagh/The McGraw-Hill Companies, (tennis balls cone cube cylinder cone)The McGraw-Hill Companies, (orange)Davies & Starr/Getty Images, (present)CORBIS; 256 (basketball)Ryan McVay/Getty Images, (beech ball)Punchstock, (top bead tissues com pencil box cheese beans)Mazer Corporation, (flashlight cereal cone)The McGraw-Hill Companies, (egg plum pylon)Getty Images 257 (cone cube cylinder sphere)The McGraw-Hill Companies; (b)CORBIS, (c)The McGraw-Hill Companies; Jacques Cornell, (bl)Mazer Corporation; 259 (yellow block)The McGraw-Hill Companies, (others)Mazer Corporation; 262 (sign switch)Getty Images, (towel button)The McGraw-Hill Companies, (cookie sheet)Mazer Corporation, (tire flag)Punchstock, (door)Nikreates/Alamy Images, (note pad)Greg Wright/Alamy

Name _____

Writing Numbers 0 to 5

0

1

2

3

4

5

Images, (pizza)Alamy Images, (refrigerator)C Squared Studios/Getty Images, (window)Dana Hoff/Beateworks/CORBIS; 264 (wheel cracker frame gift)The McGraw-Hill Companies, (flag sign)Getty Images, (orange clock)Punchstock, (domino)CORBIS, (toy boat)C Squared Studios/Getty Images; 265 (bl)CORBIS, (tl c)Getty Images, (tcl)Stefano Bianchetti/CORBIS, (tcr)Alamy Images, (tr)Mazer Corporation; 269 (tcl)Davies & Starr/Getty Images, (t c)Alamy Images, (tc)The McGraw-Hill Companies, (bl br)Mazer Corporation; 273 (b)Punchstock, (t)Ian Dagnall/Alamy Images; 274 c)Abode/Beateworks/CORBIS, (b)Punchstock; 275 (tcl)Davies & Starr/Getty Images, (cl)Mazer Corporation, (tcr)The McGraw-Hill Companies, (tr)Ken Cavanagh/The McGraw-Hill Companies; 279 Frans Lanting/Minden Pictures; 281-282 Eclipse Studios; 299 (t)Getty Images, (others)Jupiterimages; 300 Jupiterimages; 303-304 The McGraw-Hill Companies; 307 (tl)Julie Houck/Fotografica/CORBIS, (tr)CORBIS, (b)Paul Bricknell/Getty Images; 308 (tl)SW Productions/Getty Images, (tr)Purestock/Getty Images, (bl)Paul Hardy/CORBIS, (br)Bill Losh/Getty Images; 310 (c)The McGraw-Hill Companies, (t)Stefano Bianchetti/CORBIS, (b)Ingram Publishing/Superstock; 312 The McGraw-Hill Companies; 313 Steve Bloom; 315-316 Eclipse Studios; 341 (t)Jupiterimages, (bcl)Suzannah Skelton, (tc)Getty Images, (b)Mazer Corporations; 342 Mazer Corporation; 343 (b)AGE Fotostock, (t)Ed-Imaging; 344 (tl tc bo)Punchstock, (tr)National Resources Conservation Services, (bl)Getty Images, (br)Alamy Images; P1 (cl)Punchstock, (c)Jeff Greenberg/PhotoEdit, (cr)Punchstock; LA1-LA2 Tim Fuller; LA13 (tl tc)Alamy Images, (cl c)C Squared Studios/Getty Images, (bl)Burke/Triolo Productions/Getty Images, (bc)Getty Images, (br)Don Farrall/Getty Images; CS1-CS2 (c)Michael Houghton/StudiOhio CS3 (tl)The McGraw-Hill Companies Inc./Ken Lavanagh Photographer, (tc)Mark Steinmetz, (tr)Jupiterimages, (cr bl)Getty Images; CS4 (watermelon)Jupiterimages, (ruler)The McGraw-Hill Companies, (thermometer)Getty Images, (yard stick)Mark Steinmetz, (scale)Judith Collins/Alamy, (tape measure)Jupiterimages; CS5 (bl)Stockbyte, (br)Getty Images; CS6 (cr)Digital Vision/Getty Images, (br)David Tocose/Getty Images, (cl)C Squared Studios/Getty Images, (bl)Getty Images, (bc)Getty Images, (br)Don Farrall/Triolo Productions/Getty Images; G1 F. Lukasseck/Masterfile; G2 (apple orange)Stockdisc/PunchStock, (children)Siri Stafford/Getty Images; G7 (green apple)Getty Images, (muffin)Alamy, (others)Stockdisc/PunchStock; G17 Stockdisc/PunchStock; G22 Stockdisc/PunchStock; G23 (feather)The McGraw-Hill Companies, (pig)Getty Images.

Art Credits:

McGraw-Hill would like to acknowledge the artists and agencies who contributed to illustrating this program: Cover Jim Talbot represented by Mendola Artists; Don Bishop, Gary Ciccarelli, Garth Glazier, Hudaq, Barry Orkin, Tony Randazzo, Studio Liddell represented by AA Reps. Inc.; Garry Colby, Peter Grosshauser represented by Cliff Knecht, Artist Representative.

T3 (b)Stockbyte/Getty Images; T8 Bloom Works Inc./Alamy; T12 CORBIS; T13 Bananastock/PunchStock; T14-T15 Creosource/Corbis; 13H (br)Ed-Imaging, (cr)Eclipse Studios; 15 Eclipse Studios; 17B Jupiterimages; 19 Eclipse Studios; 21 (tl)Richard Hutchings/Digital Light Source, (tl)Eclipse Studios; 23 (tl)Eclipse Studios; 27 (b)Eclipse Studios, (bl)Richard Hutchings/Digital Light Source; 29 Eclipse Studios; 31 (b)Richard Hutchings/Digital Light Source, (tl)Eclipse Studios; 39B The McGraw-Hill Companies; 39G Getty Images; 41 Eclipse Studios; 43 (b)Richard Hutchings/Digital Light Source, (tl)Eclipse Studios; 45 (b)Richard Hutchings/Digital Light Source, (tl)Eclipse Studios, (tl)Eclipse Studios; 49 (b)Richard Hutchings/Digital Light Source, (tl)Eclipse Studios; 53 Eclipse Studios; 55 (b)Richard Hutchings/Digital Light Source; 57 (b)Richard Hutchings/Digital Light Source; 59 (b)Richard Hutchings/Digital Light

Source, (tl)Eclipse Studios; 67H (br)Richard Hutchings/Digital Light Source, (c)The McGraw-Hill Companies; 69 Eclipse Studios; 71 (t)Eclipse Studios, (t)Richard Hutchings/Digital Light Source; 73 (t)Richard Hutchings/Digital Light Source, (t)Eclipse Studios; 75 (t)Eclipse Studios, (t)Richard Hutchings/Digital Light Source; 77 (b)Richard Hutchings/Digital Light Source, (t)Eclipse Studios; 81 (b)Richard Hutchings/Digital Light Source, (t)Eclipse Studios; 81A (duck green apple)Getty Images, (red apple)Stockdisc/PunchStock; 83 (b)Richard Hutchings/Digital Light Source, (t)Eclipse Studios; 85B Getty Images; 85 (b)Richard Hutchings/Digital Light Source, (t)Eclipse Studios; 87A (bell drum) C Squared Studios/Getty Images, (baseball duck)Getty Images, (owl) Digital Vision/PunchStock, (soccer ball) Ryan McVay/Getty Images; 87 (t)Eclipse Studios, (b)Richard Hutchings/Digital Light Source; 89 Richard Hutchings/Digital Light Source; 97H Richard Hutchings/Digital Light Source; 99-101 Eclipse Studios; 103 (b)Richard Hutchings/Digital Light Source, (tl)Eclipse Studios; 105 Eclipse Studios; 109 (t)Richard Hutchings/Digital Light Source, (t)Eclipse Studios; 111 (t)Richard Hutchings/Digital Light Source, (t)Eclipse Studios; 113 115 (b)Richard Hutchings/Digital Light Source, (t)Eclipse Studios; 117 (b)Richard Hutchings/Digital Light Source, (t)Eclipse Studios; 119 (b)Richard Hutchings/Digital Light Source, (t)Eclipse Studios; 127G Eclipse Studios; 127H (c)Getty Images, (b)Ed-Imaging; 129-131 Eclipse Studios; 133 Richard Hutchings/Digital Light Source; 135-141 Eclipse Studios; 149H Ed-Imaging; 151 Eclipse Studios; 153 Richard Hutchings/Digital Light Source; 155-161 Richard Hutchings/Digital Light Source; 163 Eclipse Studios; 165-167 Richard Hutchings/Digital Light Source; 175G Eclipse Studios; 175H Ed-Imaging; 177 Eclipse Studios; 179 (b)Richard Hutchings/Digital Light Source, (t)Eclipse Studios; 183 (b)Richard Hutchings/Digital Light Source, (t)Eclipse Studios; 185 Richard Hutchings/Digital Light Source; 189 (bc)Richard Hutchings/Digital Light Source, (bl,)Richard Hutchings/Digital Light Source; 191 Richard Hutchings/Digital Light Source, (t)Eclipse Studios; 195 (bc)Richard Hutchings/Digital Light Source, (t, tcr)Eclipse Studios; 197 (t)Eclipse Studios, (t)Eclipse Studios; 199 Eclipse Studios; 203 Richard Hutchings/Digital Light Source, (t)Eclipse Studios; 205-219 Eclipse Studios; 225B (tc)Siri Stafford/Getty Images, (tr)Mike Powell/Getty Images; 225G Eclipse Studios; 225H Ed-Imaging; 227 Eclipse Studios; 229 Richard Hutchings/Digital Light Source; 231 (bc)Eclipse Studios, (bc)Richard Hutchings/Digital Light Source; 233 (bc)Richard Hutchings/Digital Light Source; 235 (bc)Richard Hutchings/Digital Light Source, (tc)Eclipse Studios; 239 Ed-Imaging; 239 (t)Eclipse Studios, (tc)Eclipse Studios; 239B Ed-Imaging; 241 (bc)Richard Hutchings/Digital Light Source, (tc)Eclipse Studios; 243 (bc)Richard Hutchings/Digital Light Source, (tc)Eclipse Studios; 251B Alamy Images; 251G The McGraw-Hill Companies; 251H-251 Ed-Imaging; 253-257 Eclipse Studios; 259 (bc)Richard Hutchings/Digital Light Source, (tc)Eclipse Studios; 261-263 Eclipse Studios; 267 Richard Hutchings/Digital Light Source; 267-271 Eclipse Studios; 278 Richard Hutchings/Digital Light Source; 279G-279H Ed-Imaging; 283B Ed-Imaging; 283 Eclipse Studios; 287B Ed-Imaging; 287 Eclipse Studios; 291 (b)Richard Hutchings/Digital Light Source, (t) Eclipse Studios; 293 Eclipse Studios; 297 (b)Richard Hutchings/Digital Light Source, (t)Eclipse Studios; 299 (b)Richard Hutchings/Digital Light Source, (t)Eclipse Studios; 301 (t)Eclipse Studios; 303 (t)Eclipse Studios; 305 Richard Hutchings/Digital Light Source; 305 Eclipse Studios; 313 Ed-Imaging; 315 Eclipse Studios; 317 (b)Richard Hutchings/Digital Light Source, (tc)Eclipse Studios; 321 (bl)Richard Hutchings/Digital Light Source, (tc)Eclipse Studios; 323 Eclipse Studios; 325 (b)Richard Hutchings/Digital Light Source, (t)Eclipse Studios; 331 Eclipse Studios; 333 Richard Hutchings/Digital Light Source; 335 Eclipse Studios; 337 Eclipse Studios; 339-341 Richard Hutchings/Digital Light Source; 341 Eclipse Studios.

Name

Writing Numbers 11 to 15

11
12
13
14
15

Writing Numbers

Name

Writing Numbers 6 to 10

6
7
8
9
10

Facts Practice

Name

Writing Numbers 21 to 25

21 21
22 22
23 23
24 24
25 25

Name

Writing Numbers 16 to 20

16 16
17 17
18 18
19 19
20 20

Facts Practice

WorkMat I

Name

Writing Numbers 26 to 30

26 | 26

27 | 27

28 | 28

29 | 29

30 | 30

WN6   Writing Numbers

Writing Numbers

Facts Practice

Writing Numbers   **WN6**

WorkMat 3: Graphing Mat

WorkMat 3

Copyright © Macmillan/McGraw-Hill, a division of The McGraw-Hill Companies, Inc.

WorkMat 2

WorkMat 2: Two-Part Mat

WorkMat 5

WorkMat 4

WorkMats

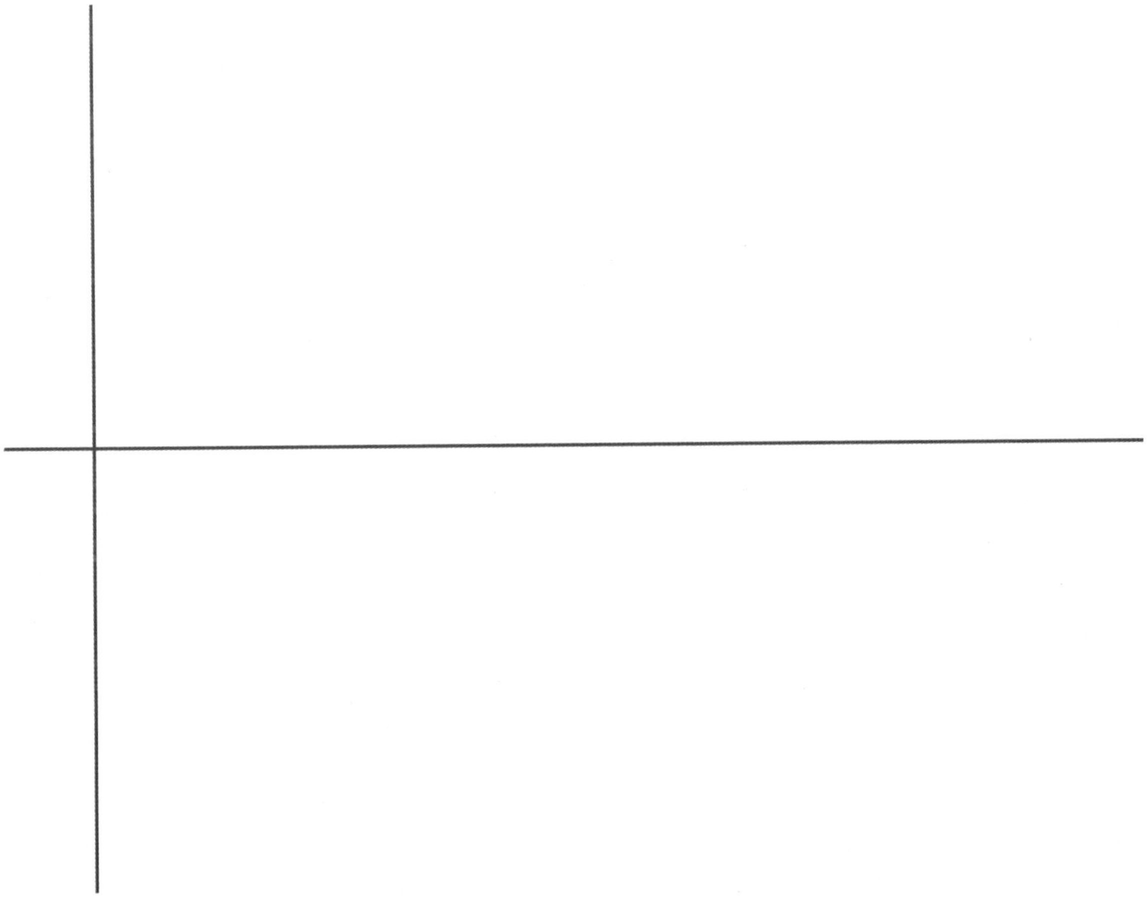

WorkMat 7: Part-Part-Whole

Whole	
Part	Part

WorkMat 7

Copyright © Macmillan/McGraw-Hill, a division of The McGraw-Hill Companies, Inc.

WorkMat 6

WorkMat 6: Ten-Frames

WorkMats

WorkMat 8

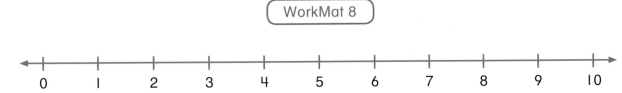

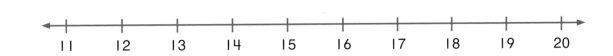

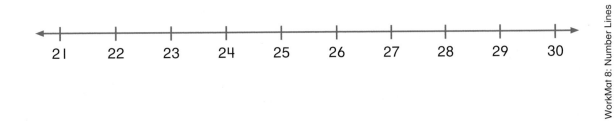

WorkMat 8: Number Lines

WorkMats

Index

Problem Solving
A three-pronged approach helps students apply skills to problem situations. Problem-Solving Strategy lessons teach strategies; Problem-Solving Investigations afford students diverse opportunities to select these strategies; Real-World Problem Solving exercises strengthen students' abilities to apply and solve problems outside the mathematics classroom.

Index